Temperature & Exercise

ANIMAL PHYSIOLOGY BOOK 2   EDITED BY DAVID ROBINSON

THE S324 COURSE TEAM

COURSE TEAM CHAIR

David Robinson

COURSE MANAGER

Colin Walker

AUTHORS FOR BOOK 2

Bob Cordell
Richard Holmes
Caroline Pond
Stewart Richards (Wye College)
David Robinson
Ted Taylor and Nina Whiteley
(The University of Birmingham)
Alison Tedstone (London School of Hygiene and
Tropical Medicine)

OTHER CONTRIBUTORS

Anthony Cassidy
Bob Cordell
Marion Hall
Robin Harding
Tim Halliday
Jean Holley
Colin Jones (University of Oxford)
Jonathan Rosewell
Jennie Simmons
Jeff Thomas

EDITOR

Joanna Munnelly

DESIGN

Debbie Crouch

ILLUSTRATION

Janis Gilbert
Mike Gilkes

BBC

Hendrik Ball
Sandra Budin
Andrew Crilly
Mike Gunton
David Jackson
Aileen Llewellyn
Barrie Whatley

COURSE SECRETARY

Yvonne Royals

ASSESSORS FOR BOOK 2

Dr Roger Avery (University of Bristol)
Professor Pat Butler (The University of Birmingham)
Dr Mike Jakobsen (University of East London)
Dr Ros Le Feuvre (University of Manchester)
Dr Stewart Petersen (University of Leicester)
Professor Paul Racey (University of Aberdeen)
Dr Malcolm Ramsey (University of Saskatchewan)

The Open University, Walton Hall, Milton Keynes MK7 6AA

First published 1994. Revised edition 1997. Reprinted 2000.

Edited, designed and typeset by The Open University

Printed in the United Kingdom by Henry Ling Ltd, at the Dorset Press, Dorchester, Dorset

ISBN 0 7492 5119 0

This text forms part of an Open University Third Level Course. If you would like a copy of *Studying with the Open University*, please write to the Course Reservations and Sales Centre, PO Box 724, The Open University, Walton Hall, Milton Keynes, MK7 6ZS. If you have not already enrolled on the Course and would like to buy this or other Open University material, please write to Open University Educational Enterprises Ltd, 12 Cofferidge Close, Stony Stratford, Milton Keynes, MK11 1BY, United Kingdom.

S324book2i2.2

CONTENTS

CHAPTER 1 THERMOBIOLOGY

Prepared for the Course Team by David Robinson

1.1 Introduction

This book is primarily about temperature and oxygen — about the physiological adaptations of animals to their external thermal environment. However, it is also concerned with the developing links between three subject areas of biology. Partly as a result of emergent technologies, but also the result of an increasing interest in whole animal biology, ecologists, physiologists and evolutionary biologists have converged in their interests and are asking very similar questions. How a particular reptile survives high desert temperatures close to its lethal temperature is, physiologically, a very interesting question. An ecologist would see the answer to that question as of significance in the habitat selection and distribution of the animal. The evolutionary biologist would ask what process of selection acted on that animal so that it came to live in such very high temperatures. So, all three areas of biology are interested in the adaptations of that reptile to its thermal environment.

Laboratory experiments can provide a great deal of physiological information, but eventually all the deductions made from laboratory work need to be validated under natural conditions. It is here that emergent technologies have made their contribution. Electronic instruments have become more sophisticated and much smaller, and require far less power. As a consequence, experiments that formerly could only be carried out in the laboratory can now be carried out under field conditions. Of greater consequence is the development of radio and satellite telemetry, allowing the experimenter to obtain data from free-living animals that can carry instrument packages and transmitters around with them. The physiologist can now plan on collecting data from animals on the other side of the world, via a satellite.

In understanding the physiological mechanisms of gas exchange and thermo-regulation, we are very much concerned with interactions between the animal and its environment. A certain amount of basic physics is required and this emphasizes the multi-disciplinary nature of whole animal physiology — a theme that runs through all the books in this series.

The physiology of animals in extreme conditions has always been of interest because studying extremes is probing the limits of adaptation. The major pioneers in this field were Knut Schmidt-Nielsen from Duke University and Per Scholander of the Scripps Institute. Both started working in the early 1950s and you will meet some of their classic studies later in this book. Extremes are still of great interest and so in this book the biology of polar and desert animals features prominently, as well as those animals that hibernate through periods of extreme cold. We shall also consider the problems faced by animals at low oxygen levels, including humans at high altitude. Exercise represents a challenge to homeostasis and is, if really strenuous, another opportunity to study the extremes of adaptation. In the final chapter of the book, the physiology of exercise and training is discussed, primarily with reference to humans since so much more data has been collected in human studies. The chapter also deals briefly with the physiological problems faced by humans in an entirely artificial situation — breathing at depth in the sea.

1.1.1 Effects of temperature on cells

Why do animals need thermal adaptations to their environment? To answer this, we need to consider both the diversity of habitats that animals can occupy and the physical characteristics of those habitats. However, the key to the question lies in the internal environment of an animal. What is it about the temperature requirements of the internal environment that have led to the evolution of physiological adaptations to the external world?

The answer concerns the problem of stability. The rates of all metabolic processes are temperature-dependent, and mechanisms that might minimize or mitigate the effects of temperature fluctuations have evolved. An example of the problem of stability is shown in Figure 1.1, where the effect of temperature (T) on the activity of succinate:cytochrome c reductase in heart mitochondria has been studied in the laboratory. The activity of the enzyme is highly temperature dependent (note that activity is plotted on a $\log_{10}$ scale) so the rate of energy supply to heart cells would vary substantially if the internal temperature was to change. This degree of variation might well not be tolerable for the heart. The marked change in slope of the curve in Figure 1.1 at about 20 °C shows another facet of the temperature dependence of cellular processes, due to a change in the fluid properties of the mitochondrial membrane. A lot of the enzymes involved in the electron transport chain, and hence in the production of energy, are membrane-bound, and a change in the membrane fluidity changes their activities.

There is an interesting correlation between the change-over temperature observed in the mitochondrial enzyme and a physiological feature of the whole animal. The heart mitochondria in the experiment were taken from a marsupial mouse (*Sminthopsis crassicaudata*). Under certain circumstances, this mouse

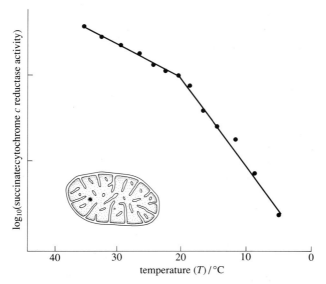

Figure 1.1 The effect of temperature (T) on the activity of succinate:cytochrome c reductase in heart mitochondria from a marsupial mouse (*Sminthopsis crassicaudata*). The abrupt change in slope at about 20 °C is due to a change in both the membrane and the membrane-bound enzymes of the mitochondria.

enters torpor, i.e. the animal becomes inactive and the mechanisms of body temperature control allow the body temperature to drop. The minimum body temperature recorded during torpor is about 16 °C, so it is possible that there is a direct link between the temperature requirements of the heart mitochondria and the minimum body temperature that the control mechanisms will permit.

The internal temperature of an animal is, of course, influenced by the external temperature. It is also influenced by the metabolic activity of the cells of the animal. None of the reactions are anywhere near 100% efficient, and the energy lost through inefficiency is liberated as heat. The conversion of glucose molecules to ATP is around 30% efficient, so there is a substantial amount of heat energy produced by catabolism. This heat energy contributes to the maintenance of a body temperature that is largely independent of the external environment in mammals and birds. This contrasts with animals that rely on the environment as a source of heat energy. In this chapter we shall consider the development of physiological adaptations to changing external temperatures, in an evolutionary context, and the two principal types of thermal strategy adopted by animals. We shall also discuss the physical characteristics of the types of external environment that animals occupy. As you will appreciate as you read this book, a great deal of the heat flux between animal and environment is a consequence of purely physical processes with no active contribution from the animal. This next section describes the terrestrial, aquatic and aerial environments, and the thermal challenges that they pose to animals.

1.2 Thermal characteristics of the external environment

The Sun is the major source of heat energy for the Earth. The surface temperature of the Earth is the result of the balance between the incoming short-wave radiation from the Sun and the re-radiation of heat energy to space, at a longer wavelength.

■   Why is energy re-radiated by the Earth at a longer wavelength than that of the short wavelength radiation that is absorbed from the Sun?

The wavelength of radiated energy from any body is related to its temperature, and the temperature of the Earth is less than that of the Sun. If sunlight is converted into a spectrum and the energy at different wavelengths is plotted on a graph (Figure 1.2), a peak occurs at a wavelength of around 500 nm. The temperature of the Sun is 6 000 K. For an object at a temperature of 300 K, the peak in emitted energy occurs at a very much longer wavelength. (The Earth has a temperature of 255 K.)

Roughly 19% of the energy from the Sun reaching the atmosphere actually arrives at the ground directly. Of the other 81%, 28% is reflected back into space from the cloud layer, 16% is re-radiated into space by the atmosphere as long wavelength radiation, and 37% is scattered by the atmosphere. Some of the scattered radiation reaches the ground, some is reflected back into space. These energy fluxes are illustrated in Figure 1.3 (*overleaf*).

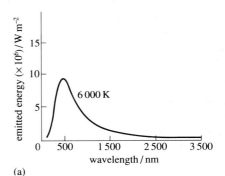

(a)

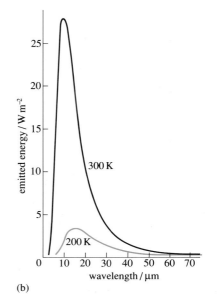

(b)

Figure 1.2   Emission curves for (a) the Sun at 6 000 K, and (b) a body at temperatures of 200 K and 300 K.

7

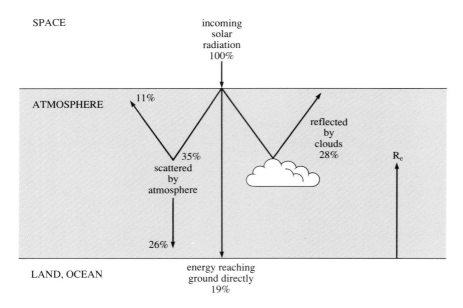

Figure 1.3 The distribution of heat energy reaching the atmosphere from the Sun. There is long wavelength radiation back from the Earth and atmosphere to space, which has a number of components but is represented here as R_e (radiation back from the Earth).

Air has a low specific heat, and so a small amount of heat will bring about a relatively large change in temperature. In addition, it has a low thermal conductivity, which means that heat will not be conducted rapidly, and so it is possible for large thermal gradients to build up. These properties of air make the terrestrial environment a complex and diverse one, in thermal terms. The vegetation adds to the complexity and most terrestrial environments are far from uniform, containing a large number of thermal niches that animals can occupy. Climatological data for a particular environment will obviously give an indication of the type of habitat that it represents, but figures such as air temperature only give a general guide. So steep are the gradients within terrestrial environments that biologists cannot use just climatological data. They are concerned with the microclimates that animals occupy. Microclimates may be more greatly influenced by, for example, shading, wind speed, and reflected heat from the ground than general data would indicate. So, measurements of the detailed ways in which variables like temperature affect animals can be very difficult.

Air temperature not only varies geographically and seasonally, but there is also quite a marked effect with altitude. There is not a standard relation of temperature to altitude, as local conditions can affect temperature so much, but roughly speaking, a rise of 1 000 m in altitude will give a decrease in temperature of 5–10 °C. This is significant, particularly to those animals that move over large vertical distances, e.g. birds normally living near sea-level that migrate over mountain ranges.

Water is a very different medium from air, and so the aquatic environment poses other problems for animals. Water, unlike air, has a high specific heat. This means that a large amount of heat can be absorbed by water with only a very small change in temperature. Water is also a better conductor of heat than air, so the steep temperature gradients that are characteristic of terrestrial environments are not generally as pronounced in aquatic ones. Aquatic environments are much more uniform than terrestrial ones and the concept of microclimates is not really applicable to most of them. However, the changes of density with temperature can produce layering effects in water. The compression by the air and water above has an effect as well which can be ignored here. Figure 1.4 shows the changes of density (a) and temperature (b) with depth in the ocean. The temperature curve has a marked change in gradient in the first 1 000 m. This steep temperature gradient is called a **thermocline**, and there is a permanent thermocline in the oceans that is deep enough to be unaffected by the seasons. A temporary thermocline may appear in some seasons in the oceans. Associated with the temperature gradient are steep density and salinity gradients; it is the combined effect of salinity, density and temperature

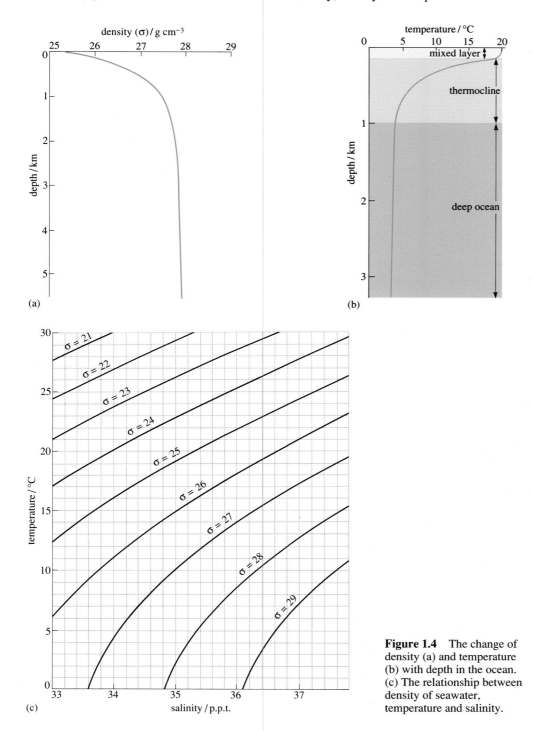

(a)

(b)

(c)

Figure 1.4   The change of density (a) and temperature (b) with depth in the ocean. (c) The relationship between density of seawater, temperature and salinity.

(Figure 1.4c) that produces the layering in the water and hence the thermocline. (At a set salinity, water is more dense at lower temperatures than at high temperatures.) Seasonal thermoclines may also occur in lakes, but being fresh water, the stratification is a function of temperature and density only.

In both water and air there are other variables that have physiological significance to animals, notably pressure. This will be discussed further in Chapter 7. In this next section we discuss the ways in which thermobiology is studied, and the impact on the subject of both new techniques and perspectives borrowed from other disciplines.

1.3 Approaches to the study of temperature

A fundamental problem with earlier work on temperature was that the very act of measuring the body temperature (T_b) of an animal induced stress that altered the body temperature. The act of picking up small animals could alter their temperature, with heat being conducted from the experimenter. A lot of measurements on reptiles, for example, have been made with a Schultheis thermometer, which is a mercury thermometer with a very fine bulb. When the bulb is inserted into the cloaca of the reptile a value for the deep body temperature can be obtained. However, unless the animal is large, it is certainly not in an unstressed and natural state during this operation. Furthermore, measurements during activity are impossible. Some ingenious methods were devised to try and get accurate temperature measurements. The American biologist Robert K. Josephson, from the University of California (1973), wanted to get body temperature measurements of bush crickets that were singing, to compare them with individuals that were not singing. He punched a small thermistor (a device whose electrical characteristics vary predictably with temperature) through the cuticle into the flight muscle and got an instantaneous body temperature reading. These measurements were very accurate, but were only snap-shots: continuous monitoring was not possible.

1.3.1 Infrared thermography

The development of infrared television cameras has made remote temperature measurements possible by a technique called **infrared thermography**. The camera is sensitive to infrared radiation and, since the amount of heat radiated is proportional to temperature, it is possible to relate the brightness of each area of the animal's image to the temperature of that area. Professor Heiner Römer of the University of Graz in Austria has recently repeated Josephson's experiment, using an infrared camera, and has shown that when a bush cricket is singing, the flight muscle area of the body is 10 °C warmer than the rest of the body. The importance of this technique is that instead of a single measurement that interferes with the animal, infrared thermography can give a whole range of simultaneous measurements.

■ Does infrared thermography give temperature measurements that are exactly comparable to the Schulthess thermometer or the thermistor punched into the flight muscle?

Infrared thermography gives information about the surface temperature rather than the deep body temperature, although of course the surface temperature does reflect what is going on beneath. To get information about the deep body temperature still requires a thermistor to be inserted into the body.

1.3.2   Radiotelethermometry

The development of very small radiotransmitters has made continuous monitoring possible, using attached or implanted temperature detectors. This has enabled researchers to build up long term pictures of body temperature fluctuation in animals, without the animals being stressed. This technique, **radiotelethermometry**, was initially used in the laboratory, but it is now being applied to free-ranging animals. However, attaching a radio to an animal presents a number of problems. The radio needs an aerial, but anything that projects from the radio may get caught on obstructions and be damaged or, more seriously, harm the animal. Using modern electronic components, very small radios can be built, but the battery pack still presents a major limitation both in terms of size and mass. Of course the animal may not appreciate being encumbered with a radio and may try to remove it, so it has to be positioned out of reach.

Small mammals, such as field mice, are fitted with a collar that contains a small radiotransmitter and a battery pack, with the collar acting as an aerial. The signal from the transmitter does not travel very far, perhaps 50–100 m in good conditions, but this is sufficient for the researcher to track the animal using a directional aerial. The temperature is encoded in the radio signal as a series of pulses, with the repetition rate being proportional to temperature, and the identity of the individual being indicated by the frequency on which the signal is transmitted. Mice fitted with a transmitter and external temperature probe can transmit the burrow temperature, and results show that the burrow temperature is influenced by the number of individuals in the burrow. If experiments with an implanted thermistor were carried out, the signals could show whether or not the mice go into torpor when they are resting in their burrows. There is good reason to believe that they do, based on laboratory experiments, but no evidence as yet from field observations.

Larger animals are easier to work with, and hedgehogs have been studied over a 3-year period using implanted transmitters. In this case, the animals were not totally free-ranging but were maintained in an outside pen. An example of the type of data that radiotelemetry can provide is shown in Figure 1.5 (*overleaf*). The curves are plotted from body temperature measurements made at 30-minute intervals. The measurements were made in late summer, when the hedgehogs would be approaching the start of their period of hibernation. The differences in body temperature between the lactating and the non-breeding animals show up clearly; the steep, transient drops in body temperature of the non-breeding hedgehog are characteristic of an animal that will shortly enter hibernation. They are called 'test drops' in body temperature. Thus, the lactating females enter hibernation later than the non-breeding females. You will read more about this in Chapter 6.

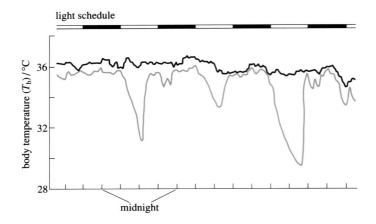

Figure 1.5   Daily body temperature changes in two female hedgehogs. The black line shows data from a lactating hedgehog, the blue line data from a non-breeding animal.

1.4 Temperature and energy budgets

The experiments with mice are not just looking at temperature on its own. The tracking data give information about the activity of the tagged animal and this, together with other physiological measurements, provides data for calculating the overall energy budget. In a small mammal, the proportion of food energy used to maintain body temperature can be very high. As heat energy is a by-product of catabolism, the measurement of metabolic rate gives a clear indication of the rate of conversion of food energy to heat energy. Metabolic rate can be calculated by measuring oxygen uptake or carbon dioxide production. This is relatively easy to do if the animal can be enclosed in a container, but cannot be applied to a free-ranging animal. So, the study of the field mice lacks a basic measurement, that of metabolic rate. What is needed is a non-invasive method of measuring the energy usage of free-ranging animals.

1.4.1 Doubly-labelled water

Physiologists regularly make use of isotopes as tracers. Both oxygen and carbon exist in different isotopes. Oxygen has an atomic weight of 16, but there is a heavier isotope with an atomic weight of 18. Similarly, carbon is normally found with an atomic weight of 12 but a much rarer, heavier isotope, ^{14}C, also occurs. The movement of oxygen and carbon atoms from atmospheric carbon dioxide can be followed using tracers when studying the photosynthetic system of plants.

During catabolism in animal cells, substrates such as glucose are broken down to acetyl CoA which then enters the TCA cycle (Figure 1.6). For every molecule of acetyl CoA that enters the cycle to be broken down, two molecules of water are required and two molecules of carbon dioxide are produced. Half of the oxygen atoms in the CO_2 come from water. In addition, protons (H^+) are passed via the cytochrome system, through the mitochondrial membrane to return via the ATPase, generating ATP and forming water with atmospheric oxygen. So, oxygen atoms are lost from the animal in either CO_2 or H_2O, whereas hydrogen is only lost via water evaporation or excretion.

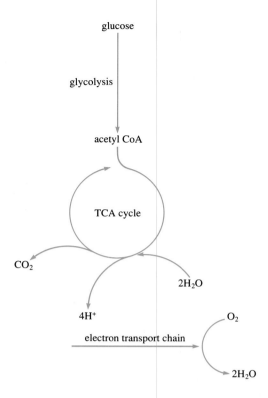

glucose

glycolysis

acetyl CoA

TCA cycle

CO_2

$2H_2O$

$4H^+$

O_2

electron transport chain

$2H_2O$

Figure 1.6   Movement of oxygen and hydrogen atoms during catabolism.

If an animal breathes in labelled oxygen, or is given water containing oxygen labelled with ^{18}O, then after a period of time for equilibration, labelled oxygen will appear in expired carbon dioxide. What is interesting about such measurements is that the amount of label in the carbon dioxide is roughly the same as the amount in the body water and is independent of the source of the original oxygen (gas or water). Why is this so?

When carbon dioxide dissolves in blood it reacts with water to form bicarbonate ions and carbonic acid.

$$CO_2 + H_2O \rightleftharpoons H^+ + HCO_3^-$$

The enzyme carbonic anhydrase catalyses the formation of H^+ and HCO_3^- and the reaction is virtually instantaneous. So, oxygen in the dissolved carbon dioxide and oxygen in body water rapidly come into equilibrium. Now this is a very important point, for it means that if ^{18}O is introduced into an animal it rapidly appears in the pool of internal water. Thereafter, the amount of label present will decline as metabolism proceeds, with label being lost in water and carbon dioxide. Obviously the rate of loss will depend on the rate of metabolism, and to measure the rate of loss it is not necessary to analyse expired gas: successive blood samples, when analysed, will show the rate of decline. However, the rate is influenced by both water loss and carbon dioxide loss, and it is the carbon dioxide loss that is measured in order to obtain the metabolic rate.

■   How do you think that the decline in ^{18}O due to carbon dioxide loss can be separated from the decline due to water loss?

If the labelled oxygen is introduced into the animal in the form of water, and the water is also labelled with hydrogen, then the decline in labelled hydrogen in the blood can also be measured.

■   What causes the decline in hydrogen label in the blood?

Hydrogen is lost in water, so the difference in turnover between the two labels depends upon the rate at which carbon dioxide is produced and expired. This is illustrated in Figure 1.7. The technique of using water with both labelled hydrogen and labelled oxygen is known as the **doubly-labelled water** technique.

A number of assumptions are made in this technique, but the results it gives are still estimated to be accurate to around 5%, compared with about 2% for other methods. Although less accurate, this method gives data that could not be collected in another way since the animals can be free-ranging, at least between blood samples.

The technique has been applied to a range of animals, in studies of energetics. One of the most striking examples comes from the work of Professor Paul Racey at Aberdeen University. In studying the energetics of bats he has been able to estimate how much energy the bat uses in echo location as it is flying. Using doubly-labelled water, he compared flight energy expenditure in echo locating bats with that in non-echo locating bats and birds. He found no significant difference between the groups and hence concluded that there was little cost of echo location in flying bats.

The relative ease with which metabolism can be assessed with this technique has great significance for thermobiologists, since the generation of heat by metabolism is such an important strategy in birds and mammals. The next section considers the differences in metabolic rate between animals.

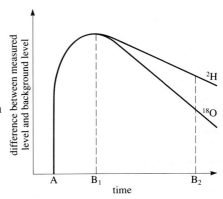

Figure 1.7   An experiment to measure carbon dioxide production, and hence metabolic rate, in an animal. Water labelled with ^{18}O and ^{2}H was injected into the animal at time A. At time B_1, the first blood sample was taken, corresponding to the point at which the labelled and unlabelled atoms had come into equilibrium. A second blood sample was taken at time B_2, 24 hours later. The difference in turnover of the two isotopes gives a measure of carbon dioxide production.

1.5 Tachymetabolism and bradymetabolism

In Section 1.1 the effect of varying temperature on chemical reactions within the cell was discussed. From this discussion it was clear that there was an advantage in maintaining body temperature within limits. The physiological processes by which body temperature is controlled are termed **thermoregulation**. It is possible to get a measure of the ability of an animal to thermoregulate by comparing the body temperature (T_b) with the ambient temperature (T_a). Figure 1.8 shows a plot of T_b against T_a for two hypothetical animals, one that does not thermoregulate (a thermoconformer) and one that does (a thermoregulator). The equation of the line is:

$$T_b = a + bT_a \qquad (1)$$

where a is the intercept of the line with the x-axis and b is the slope. For the thermoregulator, a has a value between 20 and 40 °C and b is zero. For the thermoconformer a is zero and b is 1. Table 1.1 gives values of a and b for a range of animals. The aquatic salamander, for example, is a perfect thermoconformer, having values for a and b of 0 and 1, respectively. The least weasel, on the other hand, is a perfect regulator, with values for a and b of 39.5 and 0, respectively.

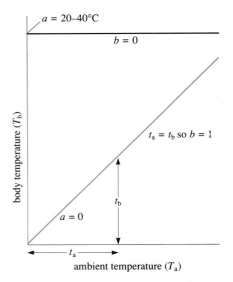

Figure 1.8   Two hypothetical animals, a perfect regulator (black line) and a thermoconformer (blue line).

The table divides into two groups, those above and those below the line. Animals above the line make little use of metabolic heat and rely on external heat sources (ectotherms); those below the line in the table make use of metabolic heat to regulate body temperature (endotherms). This distinction between ectotherms and endotherms is considered further in Chapter 2. For the present you just need to be aware of these two thermoregulatory strategies. Animals that make use of metabolic heat have a relatively high metabolic rate with a consequently large demand for food energy. This strategy is called **tachymetabolism**, meaning high metabolism. The opposite strategy, which makes little use of metabolic heat, is **bradymetabolism**. Animals that are tachymetabolic have, in energetic terms, a high cost solution to maintaining body temperature. However, as you will see in Chapter 2, bradymetabolic animals may nevertheless be very good at thermoregulating. So, how did tachymetabolism evolve?

Table 1.1   Coefficients for the relationship between T_a and T_b in a range of animals.

	a	b
forest anole lizard	−3.8	1.17
Tenebrionid beetle	1.3	1.01
aquatic salamander	0	1.0
Asian honeybee	18.3	0.81
male diamond python	9.6	0.67
bullfrog	12.0	0.60
non-brooding diamond python	14.5	0.48
desert cicada	24.8	0.44
open habitat anole lizard	16.4	0.43
dragonfly	26.3	0.43
sphinx moth caterpillar	23.7	0.40
naked mole rat	20.6	0.41
Cuculinid moth	30.8	0.28
bluefin tuna	25.5	0.24
dragonfly	35.1	0.21
poor-will	33.6	0.17
brooding diamond python	28.0	0.12
pocket mouse	35.4	0.081
honey possum	35.1	0.07
queen bumblebee (brooding)	35.0	0.07
cactus mouse	35.8	0.059
Chilean tinamou (related to the partridge)	35.4	0.05
house finch	40.0	0.05
rosy finch	41.0	0.02
Amazonian parrot	40.9	0.01
least weasel	39.5	0
mallee fowl	40.3	−0.04

1.5.1 The evolution of homeothermy

The term **homeothermy** is often used to describe animals with a stable body temperature. (The opposite is **poikilothermy**, where the animal's body temperature tracks the ambient temperature, and large changes in T_b may occur.) As you will read in Chapter 2, neither term is a precise one, but both continue to be used in thermobiology. Here, homeothermy will be used to mean 'stable body temperature maintained by tachymetabolism'. The evolution of tachymetabolism appears to have occurred in animals where the preferred body temperature could not be maintained by the heat produced as a by-product of metabolic activity such as normal locomotion. It is possible that the development of thermoregulation was preceded by increasing use of locomotion purely to generate heat. Shivering, which is muscle movement without locomotion, would have evolved later on. In some mammals, heat is produced by non-shivering thermogenesis, a biochemical process occurring in specialized cells called brown adipocytes. Energy from catabolism is stored as ATP in other cells, but in the brown adipocyte ATP generation can be switched off and the energy from catabolism liberated as heat. However, it is not clear how an increase in heat generation by muscular movement could have been a stage in the evolution of heat generation by non-muscular means. So, on the route to tachymetabolic regulation, there could have been independent evolution of shivering and non-shivering means of generating heat.

An alternative hypothesis was put forward by A. W. Crompton and others in the late 1970s. They suggested that there were two steps in the evolution of homeothermy. Initially, small mammals became active at night with a body temperature only slightly above T_a, perhaps about 25 °C, but nevertheless requiring a slightly elevated metabolic rate. This was the first evolutionary step. After a period of evolution and radiation of these nocturnal animals, some then became active in the day as well as at night. The consequence of maintaining a body temperature of 25 °C in a *higher* ambient temperature would be increased water loss due to cooling by evaporation (see Chapter 3). The second evolutionary step was the decrease of this unfavourable temperature gradient with the environment by an increase in body temperature. The only way to achieve this rise was tachymetabolism. The problem with this theory is that all the mammals that have been looked at, even those with low body temperatures, have essentially the same metabolic capacity: the difference lies in their T_b. So, there is no actual evidence of a low T_b having preceded tachymetabolism.

A completely different approach has been suggested by B. K. McNab in 1978. The ancestors of the mammals were reptiles, but the first mammals were substantially smaller than the dinosaurs or their relatives. It is thought that dinosaurs might well have been essentially homeothermic as a consequence of their size, though they needed to be bradymetabolic in order to avoid overheating. Consequently, the ancestors of the mammals were homeothermic, but being so small they could only remain homeothermic by becoming tachymetabolic. This theory suggests, plausibly, that increased insulation and metabolism evolved gradually as the size of animal declined on the evolutionary route from reptile to mammal. At the end of Chapter 2, we shall return to the question of the thermal strategies of dinosaurs.

At the time that the mammals were evolving from a reptilian stock, and developing into homeotherms, the birds were evolving independently as homeotherms. Whatever the stages in the evolutionary route taken by these two groups might have been, it is interesting that both took the path of high-cost thermoregulation.

1.6 Elevated body temperatures

Much of the study of body temperature has focused on the mechanisms that are involved in maintaining it close to an optimum value. However, as personal experience reminds us, there are occasions when the body temperature of mammals rises above the optimum, usually refered to as fever. In humans, the onset of fever is accompanied by a feeling of cold. Shivering and additional clothes help to raise the body temperature until the sufferer feels comfortable and shivering stops. At this point, the body temperature has reached a new, elevated level. The implication of this is that the normal setting for the thermostat in the hypothalamus has been changed, and the set point of 37.5 °C, above which sweating and other mechanisms for cooling come into play, has been raised. The temperature changes associated with a fever in a human are illustrated in Figure 1.9. The change of set-point that occurs during fever indicates that fever is not an uncontrolled rise in temperature and that the normal homeostatic mechanisms continue to operate. However, the physiological purpose of fever in humans is not clear.

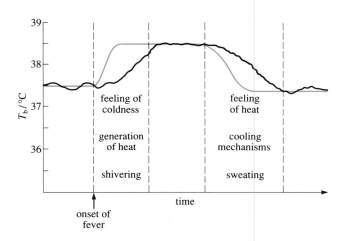

Figure 1.9   Body temperature in a human subject during a fever. The blue line shows the set point, the black line the deep body temperature.

Fever is not restricted to mammals. A series of experiments with lizards suggested that there was an advantage in having an elevated body temperature during an infection. Lizards infected with a pathogen were divided into five groups kept at temperatures between 34 °C and 42 °C. The lizards at the higher temperatures had a significantly greater chance of surviving the infection. In another series of experiments, grasshoppers given infected food selected a higher ambient temperature than uninfected individuals and thus had a higher body temperature. This group appeared to resist the infection better than a group denied access to the higher temperature.

Thus, it would appear that an elevated body temperature has an advantage to animals under certain conditions, but a full physiological explanation for that advantage has still to be made.

1.7 The study of body temperature

In this chapter you have read about a number of physiological processes that are part of temperature regulation. Central to this consideration of temperature has been body temperature. In fact, body temperature can be placed in the pivotal position of a whole range of subjects. Figure 1.10 is a map of the study of body temperature. In the map, the body temperature that is measured is shown as being the product of an interaction between the thermal environment, the 'laws' of physics, and the phenotype. To study the thermal environment the biologist is concerned with the thermal profile, topography, competition, etc. — consideration of the 'laws' of physics leads to study of heating and cooling effects, etc. In the smaller black circles are subjects that arise as the result of interactions. At the edges of the map are three major disciplines. In the next five chapters you will explore areas of this map and, hopefully, appreciate why the study of body temperature is so central to a study of whole animal physiology.

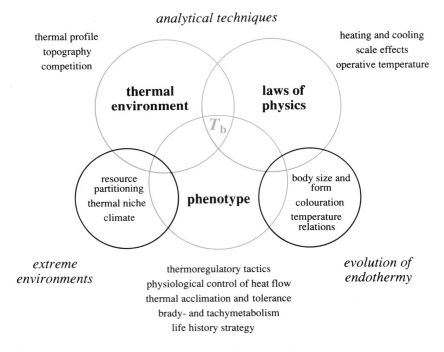

Figure 1.10   The relationship between the influences on body temperature and the study of subjects in thermobiology.

1.8 Conclusion

The study of thermoregulation in free-ranging animals has been aided by the development of new techniques. Handling and stressing of animals can alter body temperature but the development of implanted radio transmitters has provided much more accurate information and allowed monitoring of body temperature over long periods of time. Information about metabolism in free-ranging animals has been difficult to get, but the technique of measuring carbon dioxide production rates using isotopically labelled water has enabled fairly accurate measurements to be conducted, even on flying mammals. Tachymetabolism, a high cost thermoregulatory strategy, has evolved separately in birds and mammals, but the mechanism by which it has evolved is obscure.

Objectives for Chapter 1

When you have completed this chapter you should be able to:

1.1   Define and use, or recognize definitions and applications of, each of the **bold** terms.

1.2   Explain the advantages to an animal of a stable body temperature.

1.3   Describe the advantages and limitations of the technique of radiotelethermometry.

1.4   Outline the basic principles of the doubly-labelled water technique for measuring metabolic rate.

1.5   Compare and contrast bradymetabolism and tachymetabolism.

1.6   Describe the range of body temperatures found in mammals.

1.7   Discuss and criticize the theories for the evolution of homeothermy in mammals.

1.8   Define the major subject interests of thermobiology.

Questions for Chapter 1

(Answers to questions are at the end of the book.)

Question 1.1 (Objective 1.3)

In preparing an experiment in which a seal was fitted with a radiotransmitter, what design points would you have to consider for the radio?

Question 1.2 (Objective 1.4)

Why are two isotopes used for the measurement of metabolic rate using the doubly-labelled water technique?

Question 1.3 (Objective 1.5)

Figure 1.11 shows the results from an experiment in which (a) mitochondrial density (measured as membrane surface area), and (b) cytochrome oxidase activity were measured in two animals, A and B. The results from one animal (B) have been normalized to 100%. What deductions can be made from the data about the type of animals that the data were derived from?

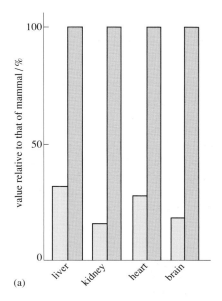

(a)

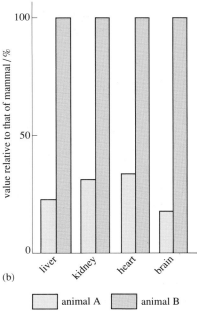

(b)

| animal A | animal B |

Figure 1.11   An experiment in which (a) mitochondrial density, and (b) cytochrome oxidase activity were measured in two different animal species, A and B. The results from one animal (B) have been normalized, and then the values from the other animal (A) are shown as percentages of the normalized ones.

Look at the graph in Figure 1.12, which shows the rectal temperature of five mammals at different ambient temperatures, under experimental rather than natural conditions. Which of lines A–E would you expect to correspond to:

(a) a cat, (b) a platypus, (c) an opossum, and (d) a lizard.

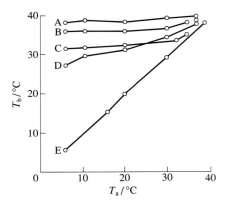

Figure 1.12   Body temperatures of five different animals at a range of ambient temperatures.

CHAPTER 2 THERMOREGULATORY STRATEGIES

Prepared for the Course Team by David Robinson

2.1 Introduction

We are all familiar with the importance of being at the right temperature. Short exposure to extremes of heat or cold induces discomfort and eventually torpor: long exposure causes death. Between the extremes, changes in temperature are tolerable. Animals are not found over the whole range of environmental temperatures: they normally live at temperatures between 0 and 50 °C, although few survive in habitats where the external temperature varies by as much as 50 °C. Some animals, such as mammals, have a body temperature that is almost constant and is decoupled from changes in environmental temperature. Other animals, such as some amphibians, most fish and invertebrates, have a body temperature that often conforms to the environmental temperature.

For most physiological processes, as you read in the previous chapter, a change in temperature alters the rate of the process, and there is usually an optimum temperature. Such optima have been demonstrated for a variety of biochemical and physiological phenomena, such as growth rates, enzyme activity and digestive efficiency. Some behavioural activities also have optimum temperatures, for example prey capture or running endurance. These processes and activities operate efficiently if the change in temperature is small, and therefore smaller than the changes normally found in any terrestrial environment. In this chapter, and the two that follow, we shall be considering the mechanisms by which animals avoid temperature extremes being imposed upon their bodies by their environments.

2.2 The 'cold-blooded' and 'warm-blooded' distinction

It is almost a part of folklore that mammals are warm-blooded and that reptiles, amphibians and fish are cold-blooded. However, the desert iguana (*Dipsosaurus dorsalis*, Plate 2.1) can have a body temperature of around 40 °C, which would be a high temperature for a 'warm-blooded' mammal, and a hibernating mammal may have a body temperature less than 10 °C, cold even for a 'cold-blooded animal'. The distinction between cold-blooded and warm-blooded is intended to convey the impression that reptiles are conformers to environmental temperature, whereas birds and mammals are independent of it. This generalization is not always supported by observation, as the data in the next section show.

If you measure the body temperature of a mammal and a lizard at a series of different ambient temperatures, with each animal in a container where the temperature can be accurately controlled, you obtain the type of relationship between body temperature (T_b) and ambient temperature (T_a) illustrated in Figure 2.1. Broadly, the body temperature of the lizard is linearly related to

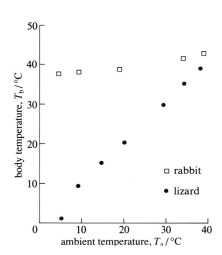

Figure 2.1 The relationship between body temperature (T_b) and ambient temperature (T_a) for two animals, a typical lizard and a mammal.

ambient temperature, whereas that of the mammal is constant. The mammal can clearly regulate body temperature; the lizard presumably cannot. Since both animals are in a controlled environment, there is only one source of additional heat that the mammal could be using: an internal one. We have already hinted that reptiles utilize *external* heat sources, so comparing the performance of mammals and reptiles in the type of situation just described tells us more about the mammal than the reptile.

2.3 Temperature and metabolic rate

The metabolic processes that take place in cells generate heat as a by-product. This heat can be measured either directly by using calorimetry, or indirectly by measuring the rate of production of carbon dioxide or consumption of oxygen. In an early experiment (*c.* 1780), a small mammal was placed in a container along with a known mass of ice. The expired carbon dioxide was collected and its mass was shown to be related to the mass of ice that had melted. The amount of ice that melted was, of course, related to the heat output of the mammal. This experiment neatly linked the production of gas and heat, and showed that one could be used as a measure of the other. We distinguish, therefore, between **direct calorimetry**, in which heat flux is measured, and **indirect calorimetry**, in which gas production or utilization is measured.

Figure 2.2 shows some methods used for studying heat production in human neonates. Of these, the closed circuit system is the most widely used, but much of the work has been done on newborn rabbits rather than on humans. Apart from obvious ethical considerations, the rabbit is a better subject as it feeds only once a day (often taking in milk equivalent to 10% of its body weight) and then rests for the remainder of the day. It has a high metabolic rate, and responds rapidly to changed environmental conditions. In addition, since the animal is inside a container, it is easy to monitor the changing concentrations of oxygen and carbon dioxide that result from its activities. This type of experiment enables the metabolic rate to be calculated.

Metabolic rates fall within a range of values between a minimal value, the **basal metabolic rate (BMR)**, and the **summit metabolic rate**.

■   Under what conditions would you expect to measure summit metabolic rate?

The summit metabolic rate would be measured when the animal was under the greatest physiological stress, such as intensive exercise or extreme cold stress for a mammal or bird. It is difficult to show that the measured rate actually *is* the maximum, of course, so there is a small measure of uncertainty in figures for summit metabolic rate.

■   Under what conditions would you expect to measure basal metabolic rate?

The animal must be at rest, and not feeding or digesting food. However, the metabolic rate measured when an animal is at rest is not necessarily the BMR.

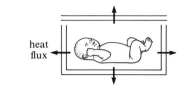

DIRECT CALORIMETRY

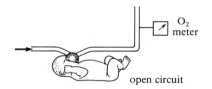

open circuit

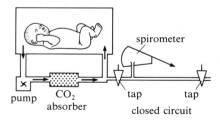

INDIRECT CALORIMETRY

Figure 2.2   Different methods that could be used to measure the rate of heat production in human infants. To measure heat flux directly, the calorimeter containing the baby could be completely immersed in water, and the heat gained by the water estimated from the rise in water temperature. The methods of indirect calorimetry all involve measuring either oxygen consumption or carbon dioxide production, or both.

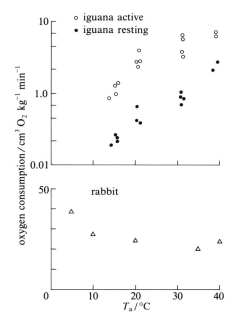

Figure 2.3 The metabolic rates, determined by oxygen consumption, of an active iguana, a resting iguana, and a rabbit at different ambient temperatures.

Metabolic rates are temperature-dependent, so BMR is measured when the animal is making no thermoregulatory effort.

The metabolic rate of a resting lizard at different temperatures is compared with that of a mammal in Figure 2.3. As the temperature falls, the metabolic rate of the lizard also falls, but that of the mammal actually rises. The mammal must be sensing a fall in temperature and the oxygen consumption is then rising as extra metabolic heat is produced in compensation. The lizard has a higher metabolic rate when it is active than when it is resting, but the rate still declines in the same manner as the temperature falls. Incidentally, measuring the metabolic rate of an active animal requires a rather special technique. In Figure 2.4, an iguana is shown walking on an endless belt, wearing a face mask which has a constant flow of air through it. The mask can be attached to a system for analysing oxygen consumption, such as those illustrated in Figure 2.2.

Measurements such as those shown in Figure 2.3 provide a basis for distinguishing between reptiles and mammals in terms of their pattern of thermoregulation, a distinction with which you should be familiar (see Section 1.5.1). Poikilothermy describes a pattern in which large changes in body temperature occur. Homeothermy has been defined as the maintenance of body temperature within $\pm 2\,°C$ of an optimum. This distinction, though widely used, is an arbitrary one that does not stand up to close examination. Field measurements have shown that many reptiles and fish actually have very stable body temperatures even though their environment is not thermally homogeneous or stable. Figure 2.5 (*overleaf*) shows how the body temperature of a Spanish wall lizard (*Podarcis hispanica*) changes on a sunny day in April. The bold line shows the behaviour of a perfect conformer. The actual measurements plotted on this graph yield a regression line close to the line of the perfect regulator.

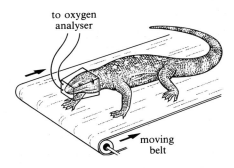

Figure 2.4 A method for measuring the oxygen consumption of an iguana travelling at speed. For small animals it is possible to dispense with the mask and just enclose the animal and drive belt in a container whose oxygen content can be monitored.

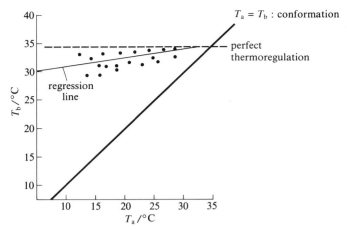

Figure 2.5   The body temperature of a group of Spanish wall lizards (*Podarcis hispanica*) on a sunny day in April. The regression line through the points is produced by a calculation that makes an estimate of the position of the mean values for the whole population, from which the measured points are assumed to be a representative sample.

The significance of these field measurements is that an animal classified as poikilothermic turns out to be capable of regulation during the day, and the body temperature is far more constant than the observations illustrated in Figure 2.1 would suggest. At night, however, the body temperature of the lizard inevitably follows that of the environment, and the lizard behaves like a poikilotherm. So, the distinction between homeotherms and poikilotherms is not an absolute one; it depends upon the prevailing conditions. These terms remain in use, but their limitations are such that a more precise terminology is needed. This topic is discussed further in Section 2.7.

2.4 Metabolic rates of mammals

In Figure 2.3 you saw how the metabolic rate of a rabbit increased as ambient temperature fell. However, the relationship was not linear, and it is not easy to draw an accurate curve with only five data points.

Table 2.1 gives a series of measurements of ambient temperature, colonic temperature and metabolic rate derived from an observations on a cat. Plot the data in the table as follows, on Figure 2.6. Use the horizontal axis to express ambient temperature between 10 and 40 °C. Plot oxygen consumption as the vertical axis, drawn on the left-hand side of the graph (0–30), and above it draw a second vertical scale for body temperature (38–40 °C).

Now answer the following questions:

(1)   On the basis of the evidence from your graph, is the cat a homeotherm or a poikilotherm?

(2)   Is the curve for metabolic rate against ambient temperature smooth or discontinuous?

Table 2.1   Data obtained from an experiment on a cat.

T_a/°C	15.0	17.5	20.0	22.5	25.0	27.5	30.0	32.5	35.0	37.5	40.0
T_b/°C	38.10	38.10	38.15	38.25	38.30	38.35	38.40	38.65	38.90	39.25	39.50
oxygen consumption/cm³ O$_2$ min⁻¹	25.0	22.7	20.8	18.0	16.2	13.0	11.2	11.0	11.0	11.1	12.3

Plate 2.1 The desert iguana (*Dipsosaurus dorsalis*, length 60 cm).

Plate 2.2 (a) The Spanish wall lizard (*Podarcis hispanica*, length 20 cm), (b), (c) Bedriagai's skink (*Chalcides bedriagai*, length 13 cm), and (d) the Moorish gecko (*Tarentola mauretanica*, length 20 cm).

(a)

(b)

(c)

(d)

Plate 5.1 Svalbard reindeer (*Rangifer tarandus platyrhynchus*) on Svalbard. This picture was taken in July, when the vegetation is at its maximum height and the adults are growing antlers for the rut in September.

Plate 5.2 The arctic fox (*Alopex lagopus*) in northern Canada in late autumn; the brown summer coat is almost completely replaced by the white winter coat.

Plate 5.3 The willow ptarmigan (*Lagopus lagopus lagopus*) in winter plumage, with the arctic willow bushes on which they feed. This photograph was taken near Churchill, Manitoba, on the western shore of Hudson Bay, Canada, in late October.

Plate 6.1 The American goldfinch (*Carduelis tristis*, length 13 cm).

Plate 6.2 The redpoll (*Carduelis flammea*, length 13 cm).

Plate 6.3 The rufous humming-bird (*Selasphorus rufus*, length 9 cm).

Plate 6.4 Gould's manakin (*Manacus vitellinus*, length 9 cm).

Plate 6.5 The purple carib, a West Indian humming-bird (*Eulampis jugularis*, length 12.5 cm).

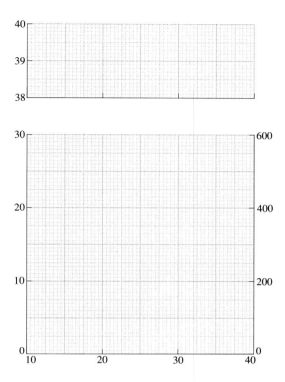

Figure 2.6   A blank graph on which to plot the data from Table 2.1.

(3)   What is the slope of the curve for metabolic rate against ambient temperature? If it is a discontinuous curve, you will need to derive the slope of each part.

(4)   Note that there is a relationship between the amount of heat generated internally and oxygen consumption. To show this relationship, draw a second vertical axis to the right of your graph, in units of heat (J), assuming that the breakdown of metabolic substrates yields approximately 20 J for every cm^3 of oxygen consumed (plot a scale between 0 and 600 J). The lower curve on your diagram is now a measure of both oxygen consumption and the total amount of heat generated internally.

The graph you draw should resemble Figure 2.19 in the Answers to Questions section at the end of the book, with only the plotted lines drawn in at this stage. From your graph you should be able to answer as follows:

(1)   the cat is a homeotherm (despite the severe cold, T_b drops by less than 1.5 °C),

(2)   the curve is discontinuous, and

(3)   above the critical temperature the slope of the line is −0.1/7.5 = −0.01. Below 30 °C the slope is −13.8/15 = −0.92.

From your graph it is evident that between 30 °C and 37 °C the metabolic rate is steady at the lowest or basal level. This region of steady metabolic rate is the **thermoneutral zone**, which is the range of ambient temperatures over which the metabolic rate is at a basal level. Below 30 °C the slope of the curve of oxygen consumption changes to −0.92. The point at which the curve changes is the lower **critical temperature** (T_{lc}). When T_a falls to a point within the thermoneutral zone, T_b may fall, but once the critical temperature is reached, extra energy is expended to generate extra heat and T_b levels out. Because T_b does not increase, the rate of heat generation by the animal must equal the rate of heat loss to the environment. As T_b is almost independent of T_a and the metabolic rate is inversely related to T_a below the critical temperature, the cat is demonstrating a typical homeothermic response and remains in **heat balance** for most values of T_a. Thus, if you were to plot a curve of total heat loss from the cat to the environment at various environmental temperatures below 30 °C, your new curve would conform to the one you have plotted. At the end of this chapter you will return to this graph and, in Question 2.3, try to divide the total heat loss into separate components.

Processes or reactions vary with temperature, and a measure of the effect of temperature is the Q_{10}. **Q_{10}** is the increase in the velocity of a chemical or physical reaction produced by a 10 °C rise in temperature. Q_{10} values for physical processes such as diffusion are usually less than 1.5. For thermochemical reactions values for Q_{10} lie between 2 and 3. High values are obtained for whole metabolic pathways that are very heat-sensitive, e.g. the death of unicellular animals, for which an increase of 10 °C can increase mortality by 1 000 times (i.e. $Q_{10} = 1\,000$).

However, a Q_{10} value for a particular process is not constant. Q_{10} itself varies with temperature, as is illustrated in Table 2.2, which shows values for the Q_{10} for the heart rate of a freshwater crustacean.

For some biochemical reactions there is no change of Q_{10} over a wide temperature range. In some intertidal invertebrates, despite living in habitats where they experience the large swings in ambient temperature of 20 °C or more that are a consequence of tidal flow, the metabolic rate has a consistent value, around 1.0. A possible explanation for this pattern is that the enzymes involved in chains of reactions have different temperature characteristics. A decrease in the rate of one reaction as the temperature moves away from the optimum for it is compensated for by an increase in the rate of another as the temperature is moving towards the optimum for that reaction. This phenomenon of staggered temperature optima for reactions is known as **temperature compensation**. You will read more about temperature compensation in Section 2.8.

Table 2.2   The Q_{10} for the heart rate of a freshwater crayfish (*Austropotamobius pallipes*) at different temperatures.

Temperature / °C	Q_{10}
5	2.4
10	1.9
15	1.6
20	1.4
25	0.8
30	0.5

2.5   Heat flow

Reptiles that maintain a relatively stable body temperature during the day are in heat balance during that period; the total amount of heat gained is equal to the sum of the heat losses. The body temperature acts as a controlling factor on the rate and efficiency of the physiological and biochemical processes going on inside the animal, so T_b exerts a feedback effect on the attainment of heat balance. If T_b rises and the metabolic rate rises, then more internal heat is produced, which will tend to raise T_b even more. On the other hand, increasing internal temperature alters the rate of heat transfer through the skin, and perhaps increases the flow of blood (and hence of heat) towards the skin. This type of inter-relationship makes it difficult to produce an accurate description of heat balance, with real figures. However, it is profitable to apply the physical principles we have discussed to produce an energy budget, although an inevitable degree of simplification is required.

First, let us take as an example an animal that does not generate a large amount of heat internally. We do not then have to consider the physiological control of heat production as an important component of the overall heat energy budget. A reptile is a suitable subject. Second, to simplify the calculations of surface area, let us select an animal that approximates to a simple geometric shape, such as a snake. Finally, let us assume a desert environment with level ground and a cloudless sky. If the snake is in heat balance:

$$\text{energy gain} = \text{energy loss} \tag{1}$$

We shall consider each side of the equation in turn.

2.5.1   Sources of energy gain

The most obvious source of heat energy is the Sun. The radiation from the Sun itself can be regarded as constant, but the amount of radiation reaching the ground varies with latitude, season, time of day and atmospheric conditions. On a clear day in the tropics, an average figure of $850\,\text{W m}^{-2}$ for a flat surface is reasonable. A snake is not a flat surface, however, so the energy absorbed by the animal per unit of surface area is smaller. If we assume a snake to be cylindrical (not unreasonable), with the long axis of the body at right angles to the Sun's rays, then the radiant energy reaching the snake would be less than half the radiation reaching the ground. For a cylinder, the average energy reaching it would be:

$$\frac{850}{\pi} = 270\,\text{W m}^{-2} \tag{2}$$

There are two complicating factors. First, there is some reflection of radiation from the ground to the snake, and this increases the amount of energy absorbed. Second, the snake's skin reflects some radiation; experiments with lizards suggest that up to 25% of incoming radiation is reflected. So, the first component of the energy budget is:

$$\text{energy gain from solar radiation} \sim 200\,\text{W m}^{-2} \tag{3}$$

Metabolic processes within an animal produce heat, and oxygen is consumed. As you know, the metabolic rate of an animal can be calculated by measuring oxygen consumption. For a typical snake at $30\,°\text{C}$, oxygen consumption was measured as $1.7\,\text{cm}^3$ per kg body weight per minute. The heat produced when $1\,\text{cm}^3\,O_2$ is used for metabolism (irrespective of food source) is $20\,\text{J}$. Therefore,

heat production of this typical snake is $1.7 \times 20\,\text{J kg}^{-1}\,\text{min}^{-1}$

or (since $1\,\text{J s}^{-1}$ is equivalent to $1\,\text{W}$)

$$1.7 \times \frac{20}{60} = 0.57\,\text{W kg}^{-1} \tag{4}$$

To fit this figure into the budget, it needs to be converted to W m^{-2}. The snake has a surface area of approximately $0.02\,\text{m}^2$ and weighs $0.15\,\text{kg}$. Therefore,

heat production by metabolism is $0.57 \times \dfrac{0.15}{0.02} = 4.28\,\text{W m}^{-2} \tag{5}$

So the heat produced by metabolism is very small compared with the heat gained from solar radiation (Equation 3).

2.5.2 Routes of energy loss

Animals emit radiation as well as absorb it. The mean wavelength of radiation from any body varies with body temperature: the higher the temperature, the shorter the wavelength radiated. The emitted radiation from our snake is of a longer wavelength than solar radiation, since animals are cooler than the Sun. Although we assumed earlier that the cylindrical snake reflected up to 25% of the visible radiation from the Sun, this is not true for long wavelengths such as infrared radiation. At long wavelengths, an animal approximates to a **black body**, i.e. absorbing almost all of the radiation of that wavelength and reflecting very little. A black body is also a near perfect emitter of radiation, with the rate of emission depending upon the absolute temperature (kelvin or K) of the surface. For a black body at a temperature k,

$$\text{emission equals } 5.7 \times 10^{-8}\, k^4 \, \text{W m}^{-2} \tag{6}$$

where 5.7×10^{-8} is the Stefan constant.

For the snake at 30 °C, with the properties of a black body,

$$\text{the emission is } 5.7 \times 10^{-8} \times (30 + 273)^4 = 480 \, \text{W m}^{-2} \tag{7}$$

However, this emission rate is counterbalanced by absorption from two other sources that should be readily apparent to you — atmospheric long-wave radiation and energy gained from the ground.

When the air temperature is 30 °C, atmospheric long-wave radiation has been measured as 400 W m^{-2}. Ground radiation is calculated by assuming the ground to be a black-body radiator (and thus a good absorber) at a temperature of 40 °C. Ground temperature exceeds air temperature because the ground is a better absorber of heat than the air. So, the infrared section of the energy budget is:

$$\text{loss to atmosphere} = 480 \, \text{W m}^{-2} \tag{8}$$

$$\text{gain from atmosphere} = 400 \, \text{W m}^{-2} \text{ over half the surface area} \tag{9}$$

Since the snake is a cylinder the gain is over half the surface area — the upper half. There is also a gain from the warm ground. Using the same black-body formula for the ground at 40 °C,

$$\text{gain from the ground} = 5.7 \times 10^{-8} \times (40 + 273)^4 \, \text{W m}^{-2}$$
$$= 547 \, \text{W m}^{-2} \tag{10}$$

Remember that only half, at most, of the surface of the snake is in contact with the ground, so:

$$\text{mean energy gain} = \frac{400 + 547}{2} = 473.5 \, \text{W m}^{-2} \tag{11}$$

net infrared radiation loss to the atmosphere
$$= 480 - 473.5 = 6.5 \, \text{W m}^{-2} \tag{12}$$

Animals in the open lose heat by convection caused by warm air rising from their bodies but almost all the loss is really by forced convection due to wind. The rate of loss is proportional to the difference in temperature between the surface of the animal and the air. If the cylindrical snake (diameter 0.05 m) is resting with its long axis *at a right angle* to a wind of 1 m s⁻¹,

$$\text{rate of heat loss per degree difference} = 6.6\ \text{W m}^{-2}\,\text{K}^{-1} \tag{13}$$

(This value is calculated from the relationship 0.9 (wind velocity/snake diameter)^3.)

Some water is also lost by evaporation. When water evaporates, energy is needed to bring about the change of state from fluid to gas. This energy, which is in addition to the energy required to bring the water to its boiling point, is the **latent heat of vaporization**. Water loss from a snake at 30 °C has been measured as 0.92 mg g⁻¹ body mass h⁻¹. Given this figure, and knowing the latent heat of vaporization of water to be 2.5 J mg⁻¹, it is possible to estimate heat loss by evaporation. For the snake it is 2.0 W m⁻², so evaporation is not a major contributor to heat loss in snakes.

2.5.3 Balancing the energy budget

The figures from Sections 2.5.1 and 2.5.2 can now be assembled in a table to show the energy budget of the snake (Table 2.3).

You can now see that these calculations allow us to explain why, on a sunny day, snakes and lizards heat up rapidly. A significant route for heat loss is convection, providing that there is air movement, but only a howling gale under a clear blue sky would allow the reptile to be out in the open and remain in thermal balance. So, under normal conditions, a reptile would spend some time basking, then move into the shade and then back again, maintaining an appropriate body temperature by moving between sun and shade. The length of time spent in the Sun is dictated by the rise of body temperature. The larger the animal, the longer it takes to heat up. A 1.5 m alligator was found to bask for 7.5 minutes raising its T_b by 2 °C. Small lizards heat up much more rapidly. The relationship between size and rates of heating and cooling is considered further in Section 2.7.

In these calculations we specified a warm day, but as snakes and lizards are such good absorbers of heat, it is possible for the body temperature of a high-altitude lizard such as *Liolaemus* to rise to 30–35 °C even though the ambient temperature is 2.5–10 °C. This ability to absorb heat as a result of the *physical* properties of the body is an important factor that has to be considered in analysing the thermal strategies of animals. In the next section we consider experiments designed to separate the metabolic and physical components of heat gain in poikilotherms.

Table 2.3 Calculated energy budget for a snake.

(a) Losses		(b) Gains	
infrared radiation	6.5 W m⁻² (Equation 12)	solar radiation 200 W m⁻² (Equation 3)	
convection	6.6 W m⁻² K⁻¹ (Equation 13) at 1 m s⁻¹ wind velocity	metabolism 4.28 W m⁻² (Equation 5)	
evaporation	2.0 W m⁻²		

Summary of Section 2.5

It is possible to calculate approximate energy budgets for ectotherms and show that an animal can achieve a high body temperature relatively easily on a sunny day. The heat gained by radiation from the Sun and by metabolism is in excess of the heat lost by radiation, convection and evaporation.

2.6 Operative environmental temperature

The thermal environment of animals is very complex, as the calculations of heat gain and loss for a snake have revealed. That complexity can be appreciated by studying Figure 2.7. In calculating gains and losses in the snake a range of assumptions were necessary. Can these assumptions be tested by measurement in the field?

The two principal variables that have been discussed so far are ambient temperature and body temperature: obviously both of these can be measured in the field, giving a snapshot of the thermal state of the animal. Although not a subject that can be covered here, it is worth bearing in mind that measuring body

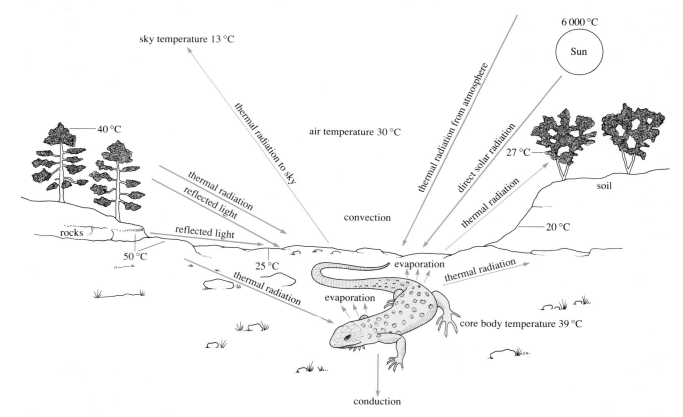

Figure 2.7 Heat exchange with the environment in a terrestrial reptile on a hot sunny day.

temperature has to be done in such a way that the act of measuring does not itself alter T_b. Such snapshot measurements reveal a relationship between T_a and T_b, but if T_b is higher than T_a, they do not show how the animal is reaching that higher temperature. The effective temperature of the environment is dependant upon the effects of conduction, convection, radiation and air temperature. Air temperature may be below the effective environmental temperature if there is a substantial amount of radiated heat.

There is a third key temperature, the **operative environmental temperature** **(T_e)**. T_e is the temperature that an animal would reach in the environment if it was biologically inactive, i.e. only the physical characteristics of the animal are taken into account. It is defined, in physical terms, as the temperature of a black body of uniform temperature, in an identical situation to that which the animal occupies, with the same values for conduction, convection and radiation. Since the definition is a purely physical one it is possible to make models of animals and use them to measure T_e experimentally.

2.6.1   Thermal modelling of ectotherms

A number of people have experimented with models of animals in this context. A recent study was carried out in 1990 by Dr Keith Vanning of Nottingham University who made models of adders (*Viperus berus berus*). His technique was to make a cast of an adder using a quick-setting dental compound (Figure 2.8) and then fill it with plaster to produce a positive cast. From this positive cast he made a rubber mould which could be used many times to produce metal positives. Each positive was electroplated with copper. The metal used for the positive had a low melting point so that after copper plating it could be melted out in boiling water, leaving the thin copper model of the adder. This model was then painted to match the natural colours of an adder, but additionally the painted surface was checked with a spectrophotometer to ensure that it had the same reflective properties as adder skin.

The performance of model adders was then compared with that of a real adder, in a cage in the open air. The model adders were fitted with thermistors that monitored their internal temperature, and gave an instantaneous reading of T_e. The live adder was fitted with a thermistor in the cloaca, which provided a reading of internal body temperature, and a radio transmitter. So, measurements made with the models could be compared with measurements of T_b for a living adder in the same environment (shown in Figure 2.9, *overleaf*). The real snake has a considerable thermal inertia, compared with the model snake, and a period of 30 minutes was required to reach equilibrium. Once equilibrium was reached, T_b and T_e stayed within 1 °C of each other, suggesting that, at least under experimental conditions, there was little difference between the thermal characteristics of the model and the real snake.

When comparable measurements were made in the field, it became clear that there were only small differences between T_e and T_b. Typical values obtained by Keith Vanning are shown in Table 2.4 (for adders A–H), and suggest that T_e is a very good estimate of actual T_b.

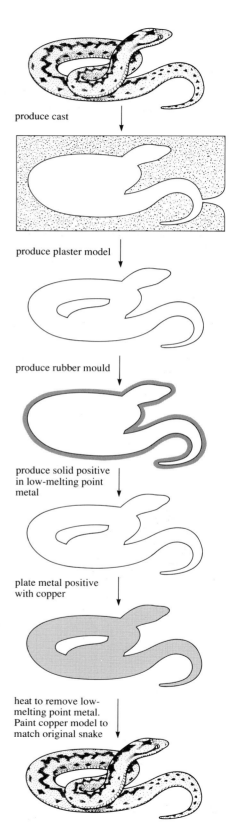

produce cast

produce plaster model

produce rubber mould

produce solid positive in low-melting point metal

plate metal positive with copper

heat to remove low-melting point metal. Paint copper model to match original snake

Figure 2.8   Making models of adders to measure T_e.

Table 2.4 The maximum differences measured between T_e (measured from models) and T_b (measured by radiotelethermometry).

Length of equilibrium period / min	Maximum difference between T_e and T_b							
	A	B	C	D	E	F	G	H
30	+0.2	+0.2	+1.2	+1.2	+0.8	–	–	–
60	+0.8	−1.5	−0.2	−0.8	−1.8	−1.4	−3.2	−1.8

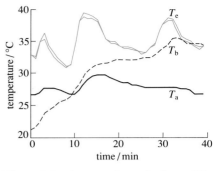

Figure 2.9 A comparison of values of T_b, measured from a female adder (dashed black line), T_e, measured from two models of female adders under the same conditions (blue lines), and T_a (black line). The measurements were made in August.

The combination of models and radiotelethermometry (Section 1.3.2) enabled Keith Vanning to plot daily thermal profiles for adders at different seasons of the year. These data show how free-living adders make use of the thermal resources available in the environment (Figure 2.10). The difference between the shade air temperature (T_a) and the operative environmental temperature (T_e) is largest in April: T_a does not rise above 15 °C and yet T_e reaches 36 °C and T_b reaches

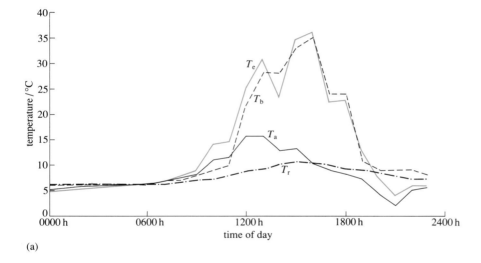

(a)

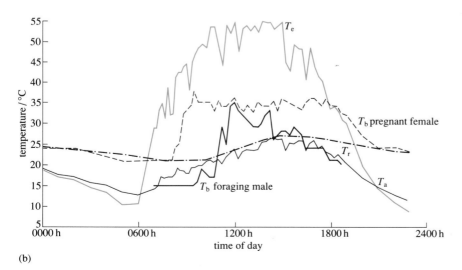

(b)

Figure 2.10 Two examples of a daily thermal profile for an adder with a radiotelemetry device attached. The field site is in Northamptonshire. (a) 20 April 1986. T_b follows T_e closely, showing that on this day the environment was providing a constraint on body temperature. (b) 17 July 1986. There are data from two adders, one a foraging male (solid black line) and the other a pregnant female (dotted black line). For most of the day T_e is so high that the animals are not constrained and can freely select T_b. Notice that in both graphs when T_e falls later in the day T_b does not fall as fast, due to the thermal inertia of the adder. T_r is the temperature of the adder's resting place.

34 °C. These figures demonstrate the ability of the animal to maintain a body temperature well above ambient, with behavioural patterns that maximise the use of available heat resources.

2.6.2 Behaviour and operative environmental temperature

In the experiments with the adders the operative environmental temperature was not affected by the behaviour of the individual animals. However, an animal's behaviour *can* alter T_e. The Cape ground squirrel (*Xerus inauris*) has a long tail (Figure 2.11a) that it uses as a parasol, shading its body from direct sunlight. This behaviour reduces the operative environmental temperature by as much as 5 °C, which is very important for the thermoregulatory behaviour of the squirrel (Figure 2.11b).

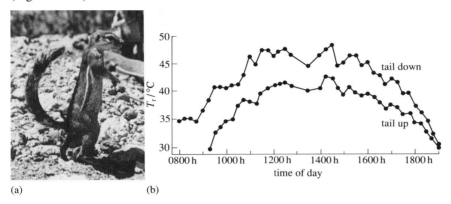

(a)   (b)

) The Cape ground
nauris). (b) The effect
tail on T_e.

Summary of Section 2.6

The temperature that an animal can reach in the environment by physical means alone is called the operative environmental temperature (T_e). Measurements that compared the thermal characteristics of model snakes with the thermal behaviour of their real counterparts showed that a body temperature well above the ambient temperature could be maintained by the snake, and that the pattern of variation in body temperature of the model was similar to that of the live animal.

2.7 The scaling factor

A division of thermoregulatory strategies more realistic than poikilotherms and homeotherms would be between **ectotherms,** which mostly utilize external sources of heat, such as radiant heat from the Sun and from warm surfaces, and **endotherms**, which rely on the heat generated by metabolism. (Very few reptiles can achieve any daytime regulation by using additional metabolic heat, and the majority of reptiles therefore exploit heat available from other sources.) You would expect that endotherms would have a higher BMR than ectotherms because they generate the heat required for a stable body temperature, and generally speaking, the rate of oxygen consumption of lizards is only 0.1–0.3 times that of a mammal of the same mass. However, lizards with body temperatures of 35 °C can, for a short time, equal or slightly exceed the rate of metabolic heat production of a resting mammal of the same mass. Two facts suggest that the physiological role of this heat generation is likely to be small. First, the high metabolic rate cannot normally be sustained, so any resultant increase in body temperature is likely to be transient. Second, the **peripheral thermal conductivity** of lizards is so high that heat is lost very rapidly, almost as fast as it is produced. Compared with the skin of reptiles, the fur of mammals is a good insulator, and therefore conducts heat to the exterior slowly. The insulating properties of mammalian fur will be discussed further in Chapter 3.

An example of this metabolic heat production in reptiles can be seen in the Indian python (*Python molurus*) which, when incubating eggs, maintains a body tempera-ture 7 °C higher than normal as a conseqence of periodic muscle contractions. The increase in oxygen consumption as a consequence of the muscular movement is nearly ninefold.

The thermal conductivity of the skin is dependent upon the physical characteristics of the skin itself which, together with the temperature gradient across the skin, determine the rate of heat loss. For a lizard with a body temperature higher than the air temperature the rate at which the internal temperature falls depends upon the amount of heat stored internally — the thermal inertia — which is a function of mass. So, under identical conditions the body temperature of a large lizard falls more slowly than that of a small one. However, this difference in cooling rates is not just a function of mass; the area of skin over which heat loss takes place clearly influences the total loss. A large lizard has a larger surface area than a small one, but if we compare the effects of size on mass, volume and surface area separately we find that as animals get bigger, these three measures of body size increase by different proportions.

2.7.1 Surface area, mass, volume and size

If you were to take a small animal, and produce a larger-scale model of it, say twice natural size, the linear dimensions of the model would be twice as large. However, the surface area of the model would not be increased by a factor of 2, nor would the volume, as can be seen for a cubic animal in Figure 2.12. If the linear dimensions double, the surface area increases by a factor of 4 (2^2) and the volume by a factor of 8 (2^3). So, the ratio of the surface area to the volume has actually fallen. In general terms, the larger the animal the smaller the surface area:volume ratio. A small animal not only stores less heat than a larger one, but has a greater potential for losing heat because of the relatively larger surface area. In this context it is reasonable to equate volume with mass when comparing animals of similar shape but different sizes, since we can make the assumption that the mean density of the tissue is the same for both.

Everything that we have said about the rate of heat loss through the skin is equally applicable to rates of heat gain. Once fully grown, an animal is unable to change the total surface area of the body except by getting fatter. However, it is able to change the proportion of the body surface that is exposed to high or low temperatures, and thus vary the rate of heat exchange with the environment. Lizards and snakes often flatten themselves against the ground at 90° to the rays of the Sun in the early morning, which maximizes the surface area exposed to the solar radiation. As T_b rises, they change their posture, reducing the rate of heat gain by reducing the surface area exposed to the Sun.

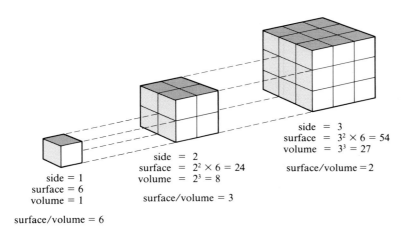

side = 1
surface = 6
volume = 1

surface/volume = 6

side = 2
surface = $2^2 \times 6 = 24$
volume = $2^3 = 8$

surface/volume = 3

side = 3
surface = $3^2 \times 6 = 54$
volume = $3^3 = 27$

surface/volume = 2

Figure 2.12   The linear dimensions, surface areas and volumes of three different-sized cubes are compared here to show how the surface area:volume ratio decreases as linear dimensions increase.

2.7.2 Thermoregulatory strategies

We have seen that once external heat sources are available, reptiles can maintain high and relatively stable body temperatures. Reptiles occupy a wide variety of ecological niches, and precise thermoregulation of this kind is only cost-effective in those niches where incident radiation levels are high. If a reptile were to attempt to maintain a high and stable body temperature in a temperate climate with variable weather conditions, much of the day might be spent in basking, without reaching a particularly high or stable T_b. Of course the reptile can move around to keep in the warmest areas of the environment, moving away from heat when T_b starts to rise too high. This movement between warm and cool areas, thus maintaining T_b, is called **shuttling**.

Shuttling has an energetic cost, and has some risk associated with it. In areas where sunny patches are relatively few, reptiles do not incur the high energetic costs of regular shuttling, and tolerate fluctuating body temperatures. Those reptiles that burrow, or that are secretive in nature also tolerate fluctuating body temperatures even though the energy resources of the environment are such that they could keep a stable high T_b. We call these animals **thermal generalists** in contradistinction to those that maintain a high stable T_b, the **thermal specialists**. The Spanish wall lizard (*Podarcis hispanica*, Plate 2.2a) is a thermal specialist (recall Figure 2.5), whereas Bedriagai's skink (*Chalcides bedriagai,* Plate 2.2b), which spends a lot of time underneath rocks, is a thermal generalist.

Nocturnal reptiles also have the problem of the high cost of thermal specialization. The Moorish gecko (*Tarentola mauretanica*, Plate 2.2c) is nocturnal and is most active for a few hours after sunset. It cannot, of course, bask at night, but if it is given a source of radiant heat in the laboratory, it acts as a thermal specialist with a T_b of 30 °C and a variation of less than 5 °C. In the wild at night, T_b is much lower (as low as 18 °C) and variations of up to 11 °C may occur. So in the wild the gecko is a thermal generalist at night. During the early morning it basks, and its skin darkens until it is almost black; at night, the gecko is very pale.

■   What advantages does the change in skin colour give?

Dark colours absorb and radiate heat better than light colours. So at night a light colour should reduce radiation (though measurements on the actual animals have not yet been made), and there is not much heat to absorb. By day, the dark skin aids heat absorption; the fact that radiation to the atmosphere from such a dark surface is greater is of small consequence compared to the energy available from the Sun that is available.

The reason why the gecko raises T_b during the early morning is not clear. Presumably some physiological process, perhaps digestion or reproduction, requires a higher T_b than the gecko can maintain at night.

The ability of the gecko to change its skin colour reminds us that many of the reptiles that maintain relatively stable body temperatures have a suite of physiological mechanisms for enhancing heat gain or loss. When ambient temperature is altered, the temperature of dead lizards changes more slowly than live ones, because the circulatory system plays an important role in the transport of heat from the core to the surface. For example, as an iguana heats up, cardiac output increases, but the difference in oxygen content of arterial and venous blood actually decreases, which suggests that the blood is circulating more rapidly than we would expect if its function were oxygen transport alone. This observation emphasizes the importance of the circulatory system in dissipating heat. The increased cardiac output is achieved in part by a short-circuit that allows venous blood to go direct into the systemic arch (arterial system) without passing through the pulmonary circulation. You should remember that the mammalian heart (and that of birds and crocodiles) has four separate chambers, but the heart of squamate reptiles (lizards and snakes) has an incomplete division between the ventricles, which allows some mixing of oxygenated and deoxygenated blood, as in this example.

It has been shown that a rise in temperature of a reptile causes expansion of the blood capillaries in the skin. By applying localized heat to a portion of the skin of an iguana, it can be shown that the rate of loss of a radioactive tracer (^{133}xenon) from the skin increases, whereas local cooling decreases the loss. So, vasoconstriction and vasodilation (constriction and dilation of the blood vessels) change the amount of blood flowing through the skin, and thus slow down or speed up heat loss. Some reptiles increase respiratory heat loss by panting when heat stressed. All these examples remind us that although reptiles rely extensively on behavioural thermoregulation, many of them possess sophisticated physiological mechanisms: however, such a ready distinction may be a false dichotomy.

2.7.3 Temperature regulation in large reptiles

In the earlier sections you read how energy budgets could be calculated for an animal, both in theory and practice. It is obviously of interest to investigate thermal strategies, but how far can we go in using such studies to make predictions?

In 1972 Robert T. Bakker at Harvard opened up a great debate amongst both thermobiologists, and biologists generally, about the thermal strategies adopted by dinosaurs. He suggested that some dinosaurs were endotherms, rather than ectotherms like present-day reptiles. Since dinosaurs are extinct, it is not possible to use all the analytical techniques available to the researcher studying living animals. However, the theoretical approach that was outlined earlier, based on physical parameters, can provide some insights into the problem.

Consider first the consequences of assuming that dinosaurs were endothermic. To be regarded as endotherms they would have to provide sufficient heat from metabolism to support a body temperature well above the ambient temperature. As calculated in Section 2.5.3, a snake can generate only 4.3 W m^{-2} by metabolism, not a significant proportion of its total heat budget. The rest comes from external sources, so the snake is ectothermic. However, really large dinosaurs, if endothermic, might have generated more heat internally than could be readily dissipated at the surface. Recall from Section 2.7.1 the relationship between surface area and mass. Large dinosaurs would have had a relatively small surface area, in relation to their volume.

The key question we need to ask is:

'Does the rate of heat loss through dinosaur skin allow a body temperature well above ambient?'

Professor R. McNeill Alexander at the University of Leeds has used data from modern reptiles to predict the possible body temperatures that dinosaurs would have had if they were ectothermic, and if they were endothermic.

Data on heating and cooling under experimental conditions has been collected for a range of reptile species. Figure 2.13 shows the time constant for cooling in air for reptiles of different mass. The time constant (t) is the time at which the body temperature would have fallen to ambient temperature, had it cooled at the initial cooling rate. How was the time constant measured?

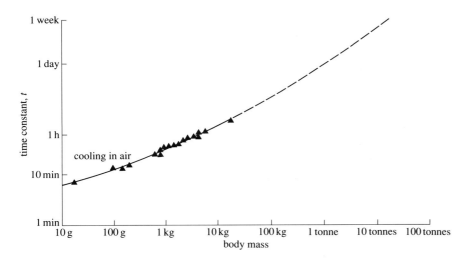

Figure 2.13   The time constant for cooling plotted against the body mass of a group of living reptiles.

Living reptiles were placed in a warm environment until they had come into thermal equilibrium with it, and their body temperature was monitored using an implanted thermistor. They were then transferred to a much cooler environment and the difference between the body temperature and ambient temperature was measured at regular intervals. As metabolic rate contributed little to body temperature in the experimental animals, the body temperature declined exponentially, as it would do for an inanimate object. A typical curve of $T_b - T_a$ is illustrated in Figure 2.14 (*overleaf*). The initial temperature difference is d °C, with the actual cooling curve plotted in blue. Projecting the initial rate down to the x-axis gives the time constant (t). However, since the curve is an exponential one, the time constant can be obtained by finding the time at which the temperature difference has reached 0.37d, equivalent to d × 1/e.

The rate of fall of temperature is thus $\dfrac{d}{t}$ (12)

The rate of loss of heat is then calculated from the heat capacity of the tissues, which is approximately 3.5 kJ kg^{-1}.

So rate of heat loss $= \dfrac{3.5d}{t}$ (13)

If a stable body temperature is maintained without absorbing external heat, then

heat loss = heat gain from metabolism.

An estimate of heat provided by metabolism can be made by extrapolation from data for living animals (Figure 2.15).

Thus heat produced by metabolism $M = \dfrac{3.5d}{t}$ (14)

By rearranging this equation we can find for a dinosaur of particular mass the temperature difference that could be maintained.

$d = \dfrac{Mt}{3.5}$ (15)

Professor McNeill Alexander did these calculations for four different sized dinosaurs and his figures are shown in Table 2.5. They suggest that only dinosaurs with masses around 5 tonnes or greater could reasonably be endothermic with a reptilian metabolism, i.e. an equivalent metabolic rate to that of a smaller, modern-day reptile. On the other hand, such large animals would overheat substantially with a mammalian metabolic rate.

■ What assumptions did McNeill Alexander have to make about the metabolic rate in preparing Table 2.5?

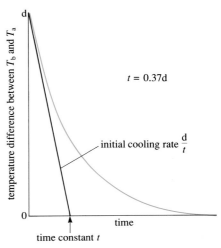

Figure 2.14 A theoretical cooling curve for a reptile showing how the time constant is measured. The temperature difference between the body (T_b) and the environment (T_a) is plotted against time. The initial temperature difference is d °C. The time constant (t) is the time that would be taken for the difference between T_b and T_a to fall to zero, if the reptile cooled at the initial rate.

Table 2.5 Calculated temperature differences between dinosaurs and their environments.

	body mass			
	50 kg	500 kg	5 tonnes	50 tonnes
metabolic rate (W) for				
reptile-like metabolism	17	110	730	4 900
mammal-like metabolism	75	430	2 500	14 000
time constant (days) from				
cooling experiments	0.13	0.69	3.7	20
warming experiments	0.07	0.34	1.6	8
heat capacity (MJ per 1 °C)	0.18	1.8	18	180
temperature difference (°C) for				
reptile-like metabolism	0.2–0.4	0.7–1.4	2–4	6–13
mammal-like metabolism	3–5	7–15	20–50	60–140

The calculated temperature difference (°C) is $\dfrac{\text{metabolic rate (W)} \times \text{time constant (s)}}{\text{heat capacity (J per 1 °C)}}$

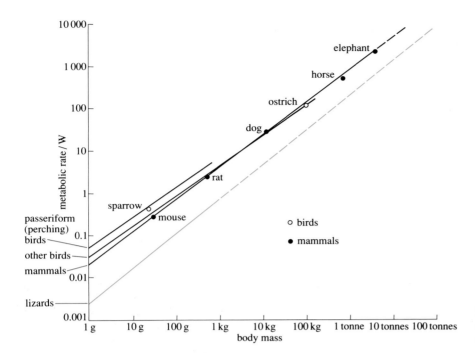

Figure 2.15 Graph of metabolic rate against body mass for a range of animals.

The figures in Table 2.5 assume that the animals are not exercising, so the metabolic rate is the basal rate. A second assumption is that all heat loss is via the skin.

■   What other routes of heat loss are there?

The most important one is evaporative water loss. Heat lost by this method would be quite significant, but would depend upon the humidity of the environment that the animal occupied. Animals living in arid conditions would not be expected to tolerate large evaporative losses of water.

Sadly, these calculations do not provide an answer to the question of whether the dinosaurs were ectotherms or endotherms. What the figures *do* show, however, is that *if* they had a mammal-like metabolism, as Bakker contended, then the larger ones would have to have had cooling strategies and, at present, we can only speculate on what these mechanisms might have been. The figures also show that the larger dinosaurs could have been endothermic with a reptile-like metabolism, purely as a consequence of their size.

Summary of Section 2.7

The fundamental difference between reptiles and mammals, as far as thermoregulation is concerned, is that reptiles rely principally on external sources of heat whereas mammals rely principally on internal sources. The rate of heat loss through the skin of a mature reptile is generally greater than through the skin of a mature mammal because the fur of the mammal reduces the peripheral thermal conductivity. Rates of heat loss and gain are also a function of the exposed surface area. Larger animals have a smaller surface area relative to their volume than small animals; as a consequence, large animals heat up and cool down more slowly.

2.8 Temperature compensation

Section 2.3 described a range of physiological processes that have an optimum temperature. In homeothermic mammals, for example the rabbit and cat that we considered in Section 2.3, the physiological and biochemical processes proceed at rates that are independent of environmental temperatures.

In animals in which the body temperature fluctuates, the rate of any temperature-sensitive process also fluctuates. If there is any process that is acutely sensitive to temperature it is possible that a temperature drop of a few degrees might stop that process altogether. In fact, if we measure cardiac rate in some non-mammalian vertebrates over a range of summer temperatures, and extrapolate the velocity–temperature curve so obtained to winter temperatures, we would predict that the heart would cease to beat in the winter. For animals that overwinter this conclusion is clearly absurd. The form of compensation that actually occurs is illustrated in Figure 2.16, which shows the difference in metabolic rate between two groups of newts (*Triturus viridescens*) and two groups of frogs (*Rana pipiens*). Both genera overwinter in a cold climate in the wild. One group of each species has been kept at a low ambient temperature, and the other group has been kept at a high ambient temperature. The oxygen consumption of individuals is then measured at a range of different ambient temperatures. The results for *Triturus* show that the metabolic rate–temperature curve for the low-temperature group has been shifted up the *y*-axis. At an ambient temperature of 15 °C, the metabolic rate of the low-temperature group is almost twice that of the high-temperature group. Such temperature compensation enables the animal to live at lower environmental temperatures, but the straight shift of the curve means that, when exposed to a high temperature, the metabolic rate would be very high. A high BMR might not matter, but if the curve for the cardiac rate was shifted in a similar manner, the heart might malfunction at high temperatures. The curves for *Rana* show a different pattern of temperature compensation, with the curve for the low-temperature group shifted more at low ambient temperatures (where such a shift is most useful) and less at higher temperatures, where a large shift might be detrimental. We are very uncertain of the biochemical basis of these types of changes.

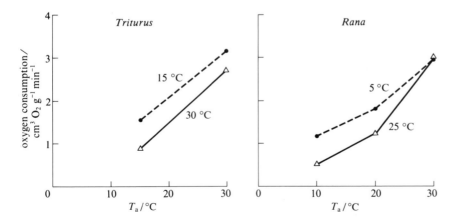

Figure 2.16 The total oxygen consumption of the amphibians *Triturus viridescens* and *Rana pipiens* at varying ambient temperatures. Mean data for two populations of each species are shown, and the acclimation temperature of each group is indicated above each curve.

The physiological basis for a wide variety of responses to ambient temperature changes in homeotherms will be considered in more detail in Chapters 3–5, but at this stage it will be useful to distinguish three levels at which these types of compensation (and indeed many other physiological changes) might occur: (a) evolutionary (obviously long-term), (b) **acclimatization**, and (c) **acclimation**.

Acclimation is the term applied to changes that occur in response to one variable, often in controlled experiments. An example of acclimation is the change in metabolic rate in the amphibians maintained at different temperatures in the experiment shown in Figure 2.16. There is only one variable that differs between the two experimental groups. Acclimatization in this context is applied to compensatory changes in nature where changes in seasonal temperature cycle are associated with other variables, such as photoperiod changes, and other environmental changes, and where the situation is much more complex. For example, European (human) climbers high in the Himalayas have to acclimatize to temperature changes, pressure changes, and possibly daylength changes simultaneously.

2.9 Conclusion

A useful distinction can be made between ectotherms, which rely on external sources of heat to raise their body temperature, and endotherms, which can generate substantial amounts of metabolic heat internally. The great majority of reptiles are ectothermic, but by relying on solar radiation, their body temperature is frequently above that of the surrounding atmosphere. Of course, reptiles do generate some metabolic heat but the absence of effective insulation means that this heat is rapidly dissipated to the outside. For a few large reptiles, in which the low ratio of surface area to volume favours the retention of metabolic heat, body temperature is raised significantly by internal heat. However, the energetic cost of internal heating is very high. For instance, when the Indian python incubates its eggs, it raises its body temperature by 7 °C with periodic muscular contractions; oxygen consumption is increased nearly ninefold. There are energetic advantages therefore in utilizing external sources of heat because a higher proportion of the available metabolic energy can be diverted to other functions, e.g. growth and reproduction. However, as you will see from Chapter 3, despite its high cost there are significant benefits from endothermy because it enables animals to maintain their normal activity in extremes of temperature.

In full sunlight, reptiles heat up fairly rapidly, especially if they are small. To avoid overheating, reptiles can 'shuttle' to and from cover, and adjust body posture or skin colour. They are therefore able to thermoregulate by behavioural methods. In addition, some reptiles have sophisticated physiological responses that contribute to thermoregulation. For instance, heat stress can cause changes in the flow of blood to the skin, which, because it alters peripheral thermal conductivity, can increase the rate of heat loss from the body. Thus although reptiles are more dependent upon climatic conditions for successful behavioural thermoregulation, there is evidence for physiological control of body temperature, which enables them to exploit the advantages of ectothermy to the full.

Objectives for Chapter 2

When you have completed this chapter you should be able to:

2.1   Define and use, or recognize definitions and applications of, each of the **bold** terms.

2.2   Explain the term 'heat balance', and describe the physical factors that determine heat loss and gain.

2.3   Explain how the concept of a 'black body' is useful in analysing thermoregulation, and how it relates to colour change in reptiles.

2.4   Calculate heat energy budgets for animals.

2.5   Define the relationship between surface area, mass, volume and linear dimensions of animals. Discuss, giving examples, the relationship between these dimensions and the rate of heat loss.

2.6   Interpret simple temperature data for species of reptiles and identify the thermoregulatory strategies adopted under different conditions.

Questions for Chapter 2

(Answers to questions are at the end of the book.)

Question 2.1 (Objective 2.1)

Which of the following are examples of acclimation, acclimatization, temperature compensation, ectothermy, endothermy or a combination of several?

(a) An explorer plans to walk to the North Pole across the Arctic ice. He trains by spending the last few days before departure in a frozen meat store.

(b) Two groups of lizard of the genus *Sceloporus* were maintained at different temperatures for 5 weeks. The oxygen consumption of each group was then measured at 34 °C. Those maintained at 16 °C had a mean metabolic rate of 5.1 cm^3 of oxygen per unit weight per hour, compared with 7.2 cm^3 for the group maintained at 33 °C.

Question 2.2 (Objectives 2.3 and 2.4)

The marine iguana (*Amblyrhynchus*) is found in the Galapagos. It eats seaweed and it has to dive into the cold sea in order to feed.

(a) Describe the effect this action might have on the iguana's T_b. Would you classify this animal as a thermogeneralist or a thermoregulator?

(b) Researchers have shown that the marine iguana warms up more rapidly than it cools. Can you provide an explanation for this phenomenon in terms of: (i) the advantage to the iguana; (ii) the physiological mechanisms that could be involved?

Question 2.3 (Objectives 2.2 and 2.4)

In Section 2.4 you plotted a graph of metabolic rate and body temperature of a cat at different ambient temperatures. Consider first the line for total heat loss (which is identical to that for heat production and metabolic rate). You now know that there are several routes for heat loss, one of which is heat loss due to the evaporation of water (this figure was very low in the reptile example we considered). Mammals use evaporative cooling (i.e. sweating) to reduce T_b at high temperatures. Given that evaporative heat loss (H_{ev}) at 10 °C is equivalent to 80 J, draw an estimated curve for H_{ev} at different ambient temperatures. Now subtract the values for H_{ev} from the curve for total heat loss and produce a new curve, H_{cr}, which represents the loss due to conduction and radiation. At what point does the curve for H_{cr} cross the x-axis?

Question 2.4 (Objective 2.6)

Figure 2.17 shows the measured values of T_b at different ambient temperatures for two populations of lizard, P (○) and Q (●). Plot the best straight line through each set of points and describe the probable thermoregulatory strategy of the members of each population. Calculate the slope of each line. Plot the line that you would obtain if T_b and T_a were always equal. Would you expect the two populations to be found in different habitats? If so, suggest what these might be.

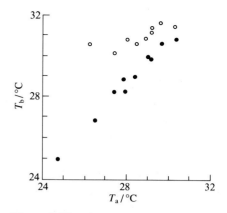

Figure 2.17   The measured values of T_b for two populations of lizard, P (○) and Q (●).

CHAPTER 3 RESPONSES TO HEAT AND COLD IN HOMEOTHERMS

Prepared for the Course Team by David Robinson and Stuart Richards

3.1 Introduction

Adult homeotherms maintain the constancy of their deep-body temperatures by means of elaborate sensory and effector mechanisms integrated by the nervous system. Receptors sensitive to thermal changes are located both peripherally in the skin, and centrally in the brain and spinal cord, as well as in other organs throughout the body. Information from these receptors passes to the hypothalamus. Appropriate reactions that counter any threat to thermal stability are believed to be initiated by a complex process of integration still little understood. The limits of thermoregulation are set at low ambient temperatures by the heat-generating capacity of the organism's body, and at high temperatures by its heat-dissipating abilities. Within these extremes, there is a balance between the rate of heat production and the rate of heat loss, so that the set level of deep-body temperature is maintained.

Whether any given combination of climatic factors results in 'thermal comfort' or in heat or cold stress depends on the species, the individual's state of acclimatization, its social and developmental status, and a host of behavioural characteristics, notably habitat selection. Thus, for much of their time many species occupy a relatively protected micro-environment — perhaps a nest or burrow — or one achieved by huddling with their fellows within a seemingly hostile macroenvironment that could not be tolerated for long.

In the previous chapter you produced a graph of thermal data for the cat. The graph is similar to the theoretical one illustrated in Figure 3.1 (*overleaf*). However, it is important to be clear that idealized diagrams like Figure 3.1 present relationships that are far simpler than those of the real world. They illustrate general principles, but can describe the responses of individual animals only if a great deal more detail is provided. In particular, an animal's lower critical temperature (T_{lc}) is influenced by the nature of its present diet or recent thermal history, so that even within a single species certain individuals respond to a given temperature as if it were 'cool', and others as if it were 'warm'. For example, as animals acclimatize to a sudden temperature change, the T_{lc} falls. This variability of response raises the whole question of long-term adaptation to heat and cold: there is a semantic problem concerning the traditional distinction between physiological and behavioural thermoregulation. As the thermobiologist John Bligh has pointed out, this distinction cannot be satisfactory.

'… since none would argue that the complex behavioural patterns by which an organism selects a suitable environment, changes its thermal insulation or modifies its surface area relative to its mass, are non-physiological'.

Of course, all such behavioural patterns are part of the body's homeostatic mechanism. An important functional distinction here is that, whereas the performance of complex behavioural patterns is dependent (at least in mammals) upon the integrity of the cerebral hemispheres, the other responses are not, although they generally do require an intact hypothalamus. For this reason, Bligh suggested that a distinction be made, not between physiological and behavioural thermoregulation, but rather between *behavioural* and *autonomic thermoregulation*, as both are physiological. This distinction has been widely accepted, and is adopted in what follows.

In the broadest sense, this chapter considers how mammals and birds respond to thermal changes in the environment — both by long-term adaptation and, more especially, short-term reactions. It begins by examining the autonomic and behavioural means by which mammals and birds maintain thermal homeostasis under cold stress (the physiology of animals that live in the polar regions will be considered in Chapter 5). Sections 3.3 and 3.4 provide an explanation of the importance of evaporative water loss in hot conditions, with a description of sweating, panting and the associated circulatory responses. Section 3.5 discusses the means by which specially adapted mammals and birds cope with the hazards of prolonged, arid heat.

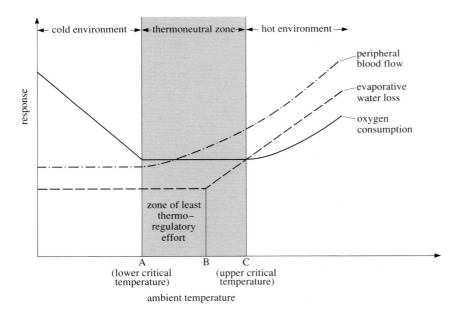

Figure 3.1   A physiological distinction between hot and cold environments. The lower critical temperature A (T_{lc}) marks the boundary between cold and hot. The zone from A to C (from the lower critical temperature to the upper critical temperature) defines the zone of thermoneutrality. Within that zone, there may be evaporative cooling, which is an active process. Within the thermoneutral zone, the range of T_a over which no evaporative water loss occurs is called the zone of least thermoregulatory effort: A to B.

3.2 Terrestrial homeotherms in the cold

For present purposes, we shall accept the simple physiological distinction made in Figure 3.1 and consider that an environment cooler than the lower critical temperature of a given animal constitutes a cold stress for that individual; the metabolic rate of the animal must be raised to maintain thermal homeostasis. This definition implies that, for the great majority of mammals and birds, some degree of cold stress could be experienced in almost any natural climate on earth, at some time of the day or year. Whereas the T_{lc} for the 'typical' homeotherm might lie between 20 °C and 30 °C, it can be as low as −30 °C in animals acclimatized to extreme cold such as the arctic fox. A cold tolerance of this magnitude obviously reflects the fox's immensely effective insulation: the peripheral thermal conductivity of its fur, and hence its rate of loss of body heat, is very low indeed.

For the arctic fox, 10 °C would constitute a 'hot' environment. However, for most homeotherms, which lack such an effective protective coat, such a temperature would elicit cold-defence reactions to raise heat production and minimize heat loss. In theory it is possible for an animal not to respond in this way but to be, to some extent, compliant, partially abandoning its homeothermy. This course is adopted by hibernating adult mammals, which may allow their core temperatures to fall to a few degrees above freezing, close to the ambient temperature. Under these conditions the basal metabolic rate (BMR) may fall to 1 or 2% of the rate when the animal is awake. In several orders of birds, notably humming-birds, there are species that become torpid through reduced metabolism and lowered body temperature at night when insect or nectar feeding is impossible, or when ambient conditions are hostile (more on which in Chapter 6). However, most adult homeotherms do not normally respond to cold in this way. The core temperatures of species acclimatized to cold conditions are not significantly lower than those of related species living in the tropics.

■   How would a typical mammal or bird fully acclimatized to a temperate climate respond if moved directly to an environment with an ambient temperature of −30 °C?

In the short term there would be a reduction of heat loss by postural and behavioural means, together with the erection of fur or feathers, and a reduction in peripheral blood flow. If these responses were insufficient to prevent a fall in core temperature, there would follow an increased rate of thermogenesis, typically by shivering.

In the medium and longer term we should expect genuine acclimatization to cold. The level of heat production would be raised by means that are more economical than those of the initial response, so shivering might decline with the onset of non-shivering thermogenesis (NST, discussed in detail in Chapter 4). There would be a gradual fall in T_{lc} as surface insulation was improved by the growth of fur and plumage, although these responses might take a full annual cycle to reach a maximum. These responses would be fuelled by an increased food intake and made more efficient by an enhanced oxygen carrying-capacity of the blood.

3.2.1 The metabolic response: non-shivering thermogenesis

Although acclimatization to cold stress is usually associated with a decrease in peripheral thermal conductivity, an essential element underlying the stable core temperature of the homeotherm is thermoregulatory heat production. The animal's metabolism increases over and above that produced by the intake of food, exercise, or the tissues generally, when under resting or basal conditions. You already know from Section 2.3 that, in homeotherms, this response typically results in a rate of metabolic heat production that is related inversely to ambient temperature. The highest level that can be induced by cold in a resting animal is termed the summit or peak metabolic rate (Section 2.3); if the heat produced proves insufficient to cope with the stress of cold, then the animal enters a state of hypothermia from which (except in hibernators) spontaneous recovery is unlikely.

An increase in metabolic rate is achieved either by shivering (considered in Section 3.2.2), or NST (considered in Chapter 4). In many species, as mentioned in the previous section, an initial, and energy-exhausting, burst of shivering is gradually replaced by a more economical form of heat production. Such is the case with the rat which, when warm-acclimated and exposed to severe cold, finds it impossible to avoid hypothermia despite shivering. After cold-acclimation it responds by efficient and immediate NST, which must account for a substantial proportion of its total heat production, for the animal now maintains a high and constant body temperature (Figure 3.2). However, the dog is different; the proportion of its total heat production attributable to NST is much smaller than in the rat, and the relative contribution from NST remains approximately the same whether the animal has been cold-acclimated or not.

There are many species differences of this sort, so generalization is difficult. Moreover, there has not yet been a systematic survey in homeothermic animals of the occurrence of NST and the heat-generating brown adipose tissue (BAT), nor of the importance of NST throughout adult life. NST can be induced by injections of noradrenalin. Studies have been carried out to determine not only the extent and importance of NST in different species, but also how the contribution made to temperature regulation by NST might be related to body size.

■   What could you say about this relationship from the evidence presented in Figure 3.3 (which shows the relationship between the noradrenalin-induced increase in oxygen consumption and body mass in mammals)?

The regression line shown in Figure 3.3 suggests that the importance of NST is much reduced in larger animals, and is perhaps insignificant in mammals of more than about 10 kg. It seems that adults with a relatively large surface area:mass ratio have, in addition to shivering, a metabolic defence associated with BAT that allows them to maintain body temperature and activity at the cooler end of their thermal habitat. It is interesting, however, that many larger mammals capable of little or no NST as adults do use NST in infancy. Both in phylogenetic and ontogenetic terms (i.e. evolutionary and individual development, respectively), we might therefore conclude that the potential for NST has been lost as the need for it declines.

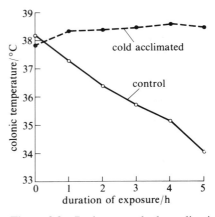

Figure 3.2   Resistance to body cooling in cold-acclimated rats exposed to −15 °C compared with control (warm-acclimated) animals. The cold-acclimated rats were previously exposed to −7 °C for 16 hours a day over a 7-week period.

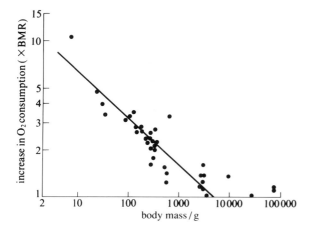

Figure 3.3   The inverse relationship between the noradrenalin-induced increase in oxygen consumption and body mass in mammals. Note that the increase in oxygen consumption is expressed as a multiple of the BMR.

3.2.2 Shivering

The term 'shivering' is used to describe the involuntary, periodic contraction of voluntary (skeletal) muscle, and includes all grades of contraction from the initial increase in pre-shivering muscle tone to vigorous overt oscillations.

The great majority of studies of shivering have been carried out on humans or laboratory animals that are not specially adapted for shivering, rather than on arctic species (birds in particular), which appear to rely on the intermittent use of this response throughout much of their lives. The willow ptarmigan (*Lagopus lagopus lagopus*), for example, shivers for about 16% of the time at an air temperature of $-10\,°C$, and it may be that shivering is important in all birds, even close to thermoneutrality. At any rate, it is clear that in these animals shivering cannot be dismissed merely as an emergency mechanism to be abandoned as soon as cold exposure has stimulated sufficient NST.

Shivering, in fact, is the most important initial mechanism to compensate for increased heat loss in cold conditions. It occurs in all warm-acclimated and cold-acclimated mammals and birds, although the threshold temperature at which it begins may change with adaptation. However, shivering is activated only when the rate of heat loss is so great that it nearly equals the maximum amount of heat that can be generated by NST. Indeed, the capacity for shivering often *increases* during prolonged cold exposure, a situation that we might predict for the pig, which lacks BAT, but one that is more surprising in rats.

It has often been said that shivering is an extravagant way to raise the body temperature. So it is, of course, in terms of an animal's energy reserves, especially as shivering often occurs at the time of the year when food is scarce. It may also be wasteful in that the tremor reduces external thermal insulation by disturbing the still air at the body surface and by raising the peripheral blood flow. In severe shivering there is also interference with voluntary muscular activity. We can estimate the efficiency of shivering as a method of thermogenesis by expressing the heat retained as a proportion of the extra heat produced, i.e.

$$\frac{(\text{heat production with shivering} - \text{heat loss with shivering})}{(\text{heat production with shivering} - \text{heat production without shivering})}$$

Measurements made on a naked man at 23 °C indicated that, without shivering, his heat production was 73 W and his heat loss 101 W. During shivering these values rose to 190 W and 135 W, respectively. Thus, the efficiency of his shivering was:

$$\frac{190 - 135}{190 - 73} = 0.47, \text{ or } 47\%.$$

Such estimates do vary sharply, however, some for naked men being as low as 11%, whereas the efficiency of shivering in goats and cattle with a thick hairy coat has been calculated at 100%. However, in all except the most unnatural conditions, shivering seems to be considerably *more efficient* than exercise in humans as a means of elevating metabolism. Energy is used to perform work during exercise and the extensive limb movements accelerate heat loss by convection. Indeed, many physiologists would now argue that shivering, with all its disadvantages, probably produces maximum energy and heat production for minimum muscle contraction.

Whatever may be the truth about the efficiency of shivering, no one doubts that it is highly effective in producing heat. Its full thermogenic potential is rather difficult to measure, but summit metabolism in adult animals lacking BAT, when virtually all skeletal muscles are participating, is eight to ten times the BMR. This value compares with a 20-fold increase over BMR in strenuous exercise, a form of heat production which (because it utilizes the same source of heat, namely the skeletal muscles) can only *replace,* rather than supplement, shivering. However, there is the advantage that heat production by exercise can be added to that produced by NST.

3.2.3   Thermal insulation

For thermoregulatory purposes, it is usual to consider a homeothermic animal as consisting of a **core** and a **shell**. Roughly speaking, the core of the body is represented by the organs in the head, trunk and abdomen, together with the deeper-seated muscles. The shell consists of the superficial tissues and the insulating coat of fur, feathers or clothing. The body core is where most thermogenesis (at least that responsible for BMR) takes place, and the shell represents a thermal buffer between the external environment and the core. Shell temperature may vary widely, core temperature usually very little. Since heat lost from the body is lost from its surface, this section is concerned with the shell's vital protective function in keeping this loss to a minimum.

In the cold, heat loss by non-evaporative means predominates, but evaporative cooling can be important during and after exercise. Essentially, the rate of loss of heat by non-evaporative means is a function of the thermal gradient from the animal's surface to the environment. A homeotherm cannot normally reduce this gradient by lowering its core temperature. Terrestrial endotherms have a reduced gradient because of the insulating properties of fur or feathers, which insulate by trapping a layer of still air over the skin surface and reducing heat loss. Evaporative loss may also be reduced, because the air trapped in the fur becomes saturated with water vapour, thus minimizing the vapour pressure gradient from the skin. The chief advantage of a fur or feather coat is its lightness, for the actual insulation is provided by the air it traps. Since it is the stillness of this air that is important, it is not surprising that dense coats, with more than 1 000 hairs cm^{-2}, are more effective insulators than sparse ones; the air within them is less susceptible to disturbance by wind or movement. However, even the densest animal coats, for example those of the red fox or husky dog, are no more than about 70% as effective as an equal thickness of still air.

The thickness of the coat is important too (see also Section 5.4.1). Not only can the effective thickness be altered rapidly by erection of hair or feathers, but growth and moulting also occur as natural processes which can relate the degree of insulation appropriately to seasonal change. The principal stimulus underlying seasonal changes in the coat is not the ambient temperature itself, but the more reliable indicator of changing daylength.

If you consider the insulating properties of the pelt (skin and fur) of different species of mammals, some interesting facts emerge (Figure 3.4 for arctic mammals and Figure 3.5, *overleaf*, for tropical mammals). Insulation was measured as the reciprocal of conductivity in $W m^{-2}$, with a heated plate (37 °C) on the inside of the pelt and cold air (0 °C) outside. The most important points to note about Figure 3.4 are the following:

(1)   The relationship between fur thickness and fur insulation is roughly linear.
(2)   In general, the larger the animal, the thicker its fur.
(3)   The points for the hair seal (*Phoca hispida*) are much lower in air than one might expect, because its insulation is provided mainly by blubber.
(4)   Small animals have relatively large surface areas, short fur, and poorer insulation. There is a limit to the amount of fur they can carry — if a mouse were encased in a really effective fur coat, its feet would not reach the ground!

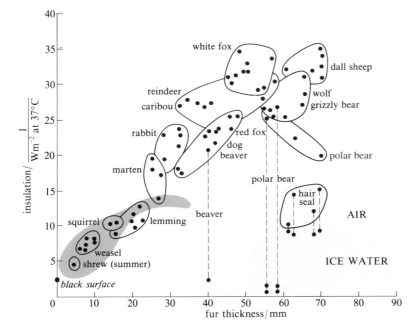

Figure 3.4   Insulation related to winter fur thickness in a series of arctic mammals. In the aquatic mammals, the measurements in °C in air are connected by vertical broken lines with the same measurements in ice water (blue shaded area). The distribution of points plotted from tropical mammals in Figure 3.5 is indicated by the grey shaded area.

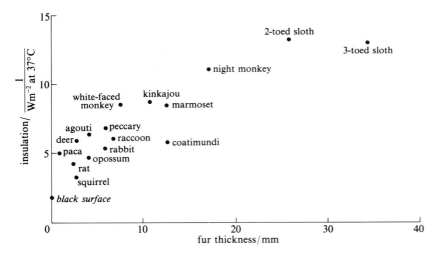

Figure 3.5   Insulation related to fur thickness in some tropical mammals. The insulation of the pelts may be over-estimates because the dead skin is a more effective insulator than live skin (in which blood circulates).

Figure 3.5 depicts the same types of measurements made on tropical mammals from Panama. In comparing these with the data in Figure 3.4 you should especially note the following:

(1)   Although many of these tropical mammals are quite large, the thickness of their fur corresponds to that of much smaller arctic mammals. For example, the paca (with a body mass of 2 kg), which is similar to the guinea-pig, and the peccary (20 kg), a type of hog, have a fur thickness comparable to that of the weasel and shrew.

(2)   Within the tropical mammals, there is no consistent relationship between body size and fur thickness, e.g. the marmoset is much smaller than the paca or opossum. Note the difference in fur thickness between the arctic and tropical squirrels.

(3)   The only tropical mammals with a fur thickness over 15 mm are those for which nocturnal cold is a slight problem. You may be familiar with the thick fur and low metabolism of the sloths, but the data on the night monkey (*Aotus trivirgatus*) are more surprising. This animal lives in the forest canopy at altitudes up to 2 800 m, and has a metabolic rate about 20% below that expected for a mammal of its size, which is probably unique for a primate. However, the combination of nocturnal habits, high body insulation, and low heat production when at rest is likely to confer significant energetic advantages. For example, because the animal is inactive during the day, when air temperature is highest, only the heat associated with resting metabolism has to be dissipated. At night, when air temperature is lowest, the extra heat produced by activity helps maintain the body temperature and minimizes the need for shivering, while the dense fur helps to conserve body heat.

3.2.4 Variability of surface insulation

The insulating properties of the body's shell are not inflexible. Obviously, an animal's pelt cannot be changed in response to the stress of sudden cold or heat in the way that humans can change clothing, but the rate of heat loss can alter to suit different circumstances, as Figures 3.6 and 3.7 illustrate.

■ What physiological changes are responsible for the effects illustrated in Figures 3.6 and 3.7?

The main physiological process underlying the uneven distribution of surface temperatures is a change in the peripheral circulation, which can cause enormous alterations in the temperature gradients from the sub-surface though the skin, fur or feathers to the air. In the cold, vasoconstriction reduces the flow of blood to the extremities, thus causing the 'withdrawal' of the core. In hot conditions, the peripheral vessels dilate, more blood flows through them, and the temperature of the nearby skin rises. The simple vasomotor changes available to all animals are supplemented in the limbs of many by a controlled **counter-current heat exchange system**. Body heat that might otherwise be carried from core to shell in the limb arteries is short-circuited by transfer to the adjacent veins. In such an arrangement, an adequate supply of oxygenated blood to the cold tissues can easily be maintained, especially as the oxygen demand of the metabolizing tissues falls at lower temperatures, while a considerable reduction in heat loss can be achieved. For example, at ambient temperatures down to $-10\,°C$, less than 10% of metabolic heat is lost from the legs of arctic gulls, whereas at $35\,°C$ most of the heat produced is dissipated through the legs. Often more than half the total is lost from the feet alone.

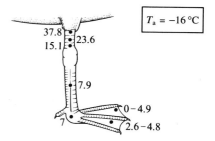

Figure 3.6 The distribution of superficial temperatures (°C) in the cold in the leg of an arctic gull.

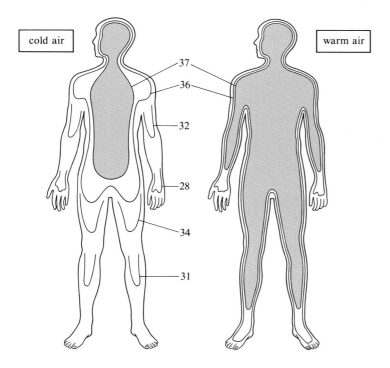

Figure 3.7 Isotherms (°C) in the human body on exposure to cold and warm air. An isotherm is a line joining points of equal temperature.

Counter-current heat exchange also occurs in the limbs of humans but the mechanism is evidently much less developed than in some animals. A rather crude method is used in the human hand, and in the ears of pigs and cattle, where blood flow is drastically reduced in the cold, and then periodically released by **cold-induced vasodilation,** which maintains gas and nutrient transport to the tissues. Skin temperature, and therefore the rate of heat loss, changes in a cyclical fashion as a result.

In creatures where adaptation to cold has taken the form of efficient insulation, the problem of heating up may be severe during vigorous exercise. Dogs and wolves can lose sufficient heat through the relatively short fur of their limbs (as long as counter-current exchange is not operating), and by panting (see Section 3.3). In the muskrat (*Ondatra zibethica*), the tail acts as an efficient and controllable heat exchanger; at rest the tail temperature can fall to as much as 35 °C below core temperature but, if the circulation to the tail is temporarily blocked and the animal made to swim, the body temperature begins to rise, indicating that the heat exchanger is normally bypassed during exercise and the tail used for cooling. Finally, it was discovered long ago by seal hunters that if they caused panic among their quarry on land, many deaths would result from exercise hyperthermia, which was believed to spoil the pelt. The excess heat produced by exercise cannot be dissipated to the air in a creature adapted so superbly to water.

Summary of Section 3.2

When a warm-acclimatized, adult homeotherm is exposed to cold, its first response is postural adjustment and acute vasoconstriction, both of which minimize the overall rate of heat loss. If the critical environmental temperature is reached and the core body temperature is threatened, the rate of heat production is increased by shivering. Many mammals also increase non-shivering thermogenesis (NST) from a variety of tissues. However, the importance of NST as a short-term response to cold stress is much reduced in larger animals.

During long-term cold acclimatization, there may be an increase in the basal metabolic rate (BMR). Heat loss is reduced even further by improved insulation using fur or feathers, and by vascular changes that allow the shell to cool. These factors combine to lower the critical temperature of the fully acclimatized animal.

3.3 Heat stress

The range of internal body temperatures over which the maintenance of self-regulating homeothermy can continue is seldom more than a few degrees. However, our consideration of homeotherms under cold stress has indicated that a number of birds and mammals tolerate external ambient temperatures substantially below this range for months. In rare cases, the ambient temperature may be as much as 70 °C lower. Their success is a measure of the efficiency of the insulation and the metabolic responses.

By contrast with this remarkable cold tolerance, few animals can survive in shade temperatures much above their deep body temperatures. The evolution of homeotherms has produced, as optimum, a range of core temperatures just 2 or 3 °C on either side of 40 °C. For the major part of every day, the core temperature is significantly above the level of shade temperatures, in most parts of the world, and the heat of metabolism can be lost readily enough. But at times of severe heat stress, as during very high air temperatures or exposure to the Sun, the animal cannot keep heat *out* for long by insulation, for it would soon be at risk from the heat of its increased metabolism. If these processes were accelerated by exercise, hyperthermia could soon become a serious threat. Rising tissue temperature accel-erates heat production and, if the body's cooling mechanisms are overwhelmed, denaturation of proteins (including enzymes) begins, and heat death results.

The most important mechanism for cooling the body under any form of terrestrial heat stress is the evaporation of water. The latent heat of vaporization of water at 37 °C is 2.4 kJ g^{-1}. This is the quantity of heat required to change the state of water from liquid to vapour and, under ideal physiological conditions, the latent heat is taken from the body itself. We know from common experience that the efficiency of evaporation from the skin is affected adversely by the 'dampness' of the air, so the degree of heat stress suffered is a function not only of ambient temperature and radiation but also of air humidity and air movement. Water evaporates from the respiratory surfaces as well, with an associated heat loss, so respiratory cooling may be an important means of thermoregulation.

If the ambient temperature remains below the animal's surface temperature, which in hot climates is close to that of the core, some heat loss can occur by radiation and convection. If the humidity of the air is not too high, much more heat can be lost by evaporation. However, extensive evaporation requires a high compensatory water intake, and of course hot, unshaded parts of the world also tend to be those areas where animals have most difficulty in obtaining water. On the other hand, regions where the heat is moderate but water plentiful are typically also areas of high humidity where evaporative cooling is less effective.

Another feature of hot, dry environments is the very large diurnal change in temperature arising from the lack of atmospheric moisture and cloud cover. Heat from the bare ground is lost very quickly by radiation to a clear sky and the nocturnal temperature may fall to near freezing. Thus, in southern Tripoli in Libya, extremes of 0.5 and 37.2 °C have been recorded within a single day. There may also be huge annual changes, for example at Wadi Haifa in the Sudan where the temperature ranges from −2.2 to 52.5 °C within 6 months. Many desert animals need adaptations, behavioural or otherwise, to cope with temperatures well below the thermoneutral zone, as well as highly developed methods of coping with heat stress.

3.3.1 Evaporative cooling

In studying 'dry heat' transfer, we are interested in the thermal gradients from an animal's surface to the ambient air; in the same way, with evaporative transfer we are concerned with the vapour pressure gradients. **Vapour pressure** is the partial pressure exerted by water vapour in the air, and it is the vapour pressure difference between the surface and the atmosphere that represents the driving force for vaporization. Atmospheric vapour pressure is commonly measured in millibars (mbar); to convert mbar to kPa, which are the SI units of pressure, multiply by 0.1.

It is important to realize that vapour pressure provides a measure of **absolute humidity**, whereas the familiar concept of **relative humidity** (r.h.) gives the prevailing vapour pressure as a percentage of the maximum amount of water vapour that air at that temperature can hold (i.e. the saturation vapour pressure). So, if the vapour pressure of air remains constant and air is warmed, then the r.h. falls, because at higher temperatures, the saturation vapour pressure increases. In Figure 3.8, the solid line shows the saturation vapour pressure at a variety of air temperatures. For instance at 20 °C, the saturation vapour pressure is 2.4 kPa, which is obviously equivalent to a relative humidity of 100%. When the r.h. falls to 50%, the vapour pressure is only 1.2 kPa. However, consider an air temperature of 30 °C, where the saturation vapour pressure is 4.3 kPa. If the vapour pressure is the same as before (2.4 kPa), the r.h. is now only about 55%. If the vapour pressure is 1.2 kPa (equivalent to 50% r.h. at 20 °C), then at 30 °C the r.h. is only 27%.

It is worth remembering that the most significant measurement for physiological purposes is not r.h. but the difference between the saturation vapour pressure and the vapour pressure actually prevailing, because this difference is a measure of the ability of the air to take up water by evaporation.

Under very dry conditions, evaporative cooling can, for limited periods, provide extraordinary heat tolerance. In 1774, Dr Charles Blagden, Secretary of the Royal Society, remained in a room at 126 °C for 45 minutes without undue distress. He took with him his dog (in a basket to prevent burning of its feet), a piece of raw steak, and a jar of water with a layer of oil over the surface. Soon the water was boiling beneath the layer of oil, and the steak was said to be cooked, but he and the dog, by prodigious sweating and panting, were all right until the humidity was raised by pouring water on the floor, at which point they had to be hastily removed.

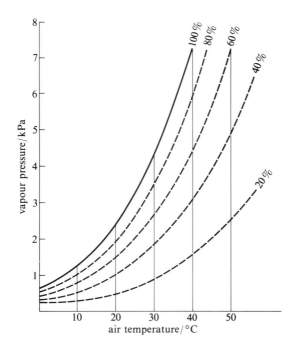

Figure 3.8 The relationship between vapour pressure (expressed in kPa) and air temperature, at different relative humidities.

3.3.2 Cutaneous water loss: sweating

Animal integument is permeable to water, so some loss occurs by passive diffusion and evaporation from the surface. In homeotherms generally, at thermoneutral or low temperatures, the rate of water loss by this means is of the order of $10\,g\,m^{-2}\,h^{-1}$, which in humans dissipates an amount of heat equivalent to some 25% of that produced by BMR. Under warm conditions, the rate of such loss may treble.

However, passive diffusion is a process that must be clearly distinguished from active thermoregulatory sweating. The first is the inescapable consequence of vapour pressure gradients, the second, in those mammals adapted for sweating, is a highly efficient heat-dissipating device utilizing a specific secretory process geared accurately to the individual's state of heat stress. Sweating is found more often in larger animals (over 10 kg), although there is no phylogenetic pattern that predicts whether or not a particular species uses cutaneous, as distinct from respiratory, evaporation (Section 3.3.3). Many animals use both. Cutaneous water loss in humans is often estimated by using sweat capsules, which cover a known area of skin. By ventilating each capsule at a fixed rate, and by measuring the change in r.h. as the air flows through, the amount of water added to the capsule from the skin is easily found. This figure is then used as a basis for calculating overall cutaneous water loss.

In young men, where the sweating mechanism is exceptionally efficient, maximum rates of water loss while working at high temperatures are in excess of $1\,000\,g\,m^{-2}\,h^{-1}$. Cattle can sweat at about one-tenth the rate, but pigs, despite a bare skin which might seem ideal for unimpeded evaporation, seem to be incapable of thermal sweating from the appropriate-looking glands that are present in the skin.

The glands that secrete sweat are structurally of two types (Figure 3.9, *overleaf*). Those found over a wide range of mammalian species are the **epitrichial** (= around hair) **glands**, which develop only in association with the hair follicles (Figure 3.9c). They vary considerably in morphology and in functional role, the glands of the pig and dog evidently playing no part in thermoregulation, whereas those in cattle (there are about $1\,800\,cm^{-2}$) and sheep (about $300\,cm^{-2}$) are of marked thermoregulatory significance, and those of the horse are of vital importance.

The second type of sweat gland, the **atrichial** (= without hair) **gland** is characteristic of primates, although the glands occur also on the pads of cats and dogs. The glands develop directly from the epidermis, independently of the hairs, and open on to the free surface of the skin. They are at their most dense (some $2\,000\,cm^{-2}$) on the human palms and soles, where sweating is induced by emotional not thermal, stimuli, and occur elsewhere over the body at a density of $100–300\,cm^{-2}$.

It is worth mentioning that the presence or absence of hairs on the skin surface can have an important influence on the efficiency of evaporative cooling. In this respect, the relatively bare human skin is ideal, for the heat of vaporization is taken very largely from the body itself. Hairy skin, on the other hand, gives rise to more complex conditions and to the likelihood that water evaporating from the coat will take a good proportion of its heat from the air, rather than from the skin itself, and thus be of less value in cooling the body.

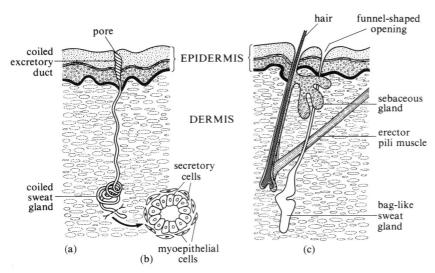

Figure 3.9   The chief structural features of sweat glands known to function in temperature regulation. (a) A human atrichial gland, with the secretory coil shown in cross-section (b). (c) An epitrichial gland of the ox with its accompanying structures.

Much more is known about sweating in humans than in any other animal. In fact, we know most about its occurrence in men where there are age differences, but sex differences are unlikely to be profound. An adult man performing moderate work in hot dry conditions may secrete 12 litres of sweat per day, and over shorter periods of high heat stress, as much as 3 litres per hour. The actual rate of secretion reflects the state of activity and exposure (Figure 3.10). Where humidity is not too high, a man can lose heat by evaporation at least ten times as fast as it is produced by the BMR. Thus he normally has a large reserve of cooling capacity and can cope with severe heat loads, either those of an external environment or from vigorous muscular work (which can be up to an order of magnitude greater than external heat loads), provided that *humidity remains low*.

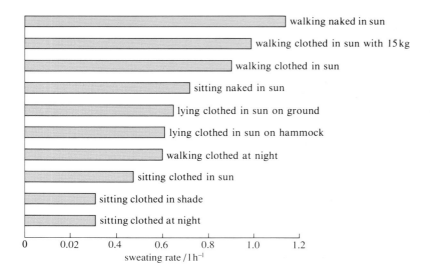

Figure 3.10   Average sweating rates in men, expressed as the rate of loss of water under various conditions of exposure in the desert, all at temperatures of 38 °C.

However, such an efficient mechanism depends critically on the availability of drinking water. A man marching in the desert may take on a solar and terrestrial radiation load of $2\,000\,kJ\,h^{-1}$, even allowing for the reflectance of his skin and clothing. On the basis of a latent heat of vaporization of $2.4\,kJ\,g^{-1}$, some $800\,cm^3$ of sweat would be needed every hour to dissipate such a load, even on the assumption that all the heat of vaporization is drawn from the body itself. This calculation does not, of course, take into account any direct heat loading from air hotter than the body, or the substantial metabolic generation of heat. In these circumstances, figures of 2 or 3 litres of sweat every hour soon become understandable. The entire plasma volume is unlikely to exceed 4 litres, so the physiological problems underlying this method of losing heat are also very obvious.

Sweat is an ultrafiltrate of the plasma, containing sodium chloride (in humans, between 0.2 and 0.4 g per $100\,cm^3$), as well as other ions, lactic acid and urea. However, because the tubules of the glands normally absorb much of the electrolytes, sweat is hypotonic to plasma, i.e. it has a lower osmotic pressure. The concentration of salts may rise at first during high rates of sweating, but generally falls again with acclimatization. In either case, it is clear that heat stress can soon deplete the body of salts as well as water. Initially, fluid lost from the plasma is replaced from various 'non-essential' reserves, for example, from the digestive glands and gut, and there is a concurrent increase in anti-diuretic hormone (ADH) secretion by the pituitary and a consequent fall in the flow of urine from the kidneys. Later on, some fluid is withdrawn from the intracellular compartments of the body and there is a reduction in plasma volume.

Unfortunately for humans, the plasma contributes a disproportionate share of the overall fluid lost. A level of dehydration equivalent to a 4% loss of body weight is accompanied by a reduction in plasma volume of about 10%. Since there is no corresponding fall in blood cells or plasma proteins, the viscosity of the blood rises at just the time when the circulatory system, which bears the main burden of maintaining the body's heat balance, is already under strain as a result of maximal cutaneous vasodilation for the transport of heat to the surface and water to the sweat glands. The demand on the heart is therefore great as it tries to maintain the blood pressure and peripheral circulation. Hypotension (falling blood pressure) and fainting may follow. If corrective action is not quickly taken, the result is an explosive rise in body temperature and death through hyperthermia.

The efficiency of the human sweating mechanism is thus acutely dependent on the ability to drink. Under prolonged heat stress, however, it seems that even when water is abundantly available, the limited human drinking capacity (about 1 litre an hour) leads to a 'voluntary' dehydration of 2–4% of the body weight; there is thus a chronic condition of decreased plasma volume and raised osmotic pressure, coupled with a fall in urine output by as much as 80%.

Other sweating animals, such as the donkey and camel, handle their water balance problems much more effectively. In the first place, they lose much of their water during progressive dehydration, not from the plasma, but from the intracellular water outside the vascular system. The camel, for instance, can lose 30% of its body weight (some 10% above the lethal limit for man) before serious changes can be detected experimentally, in either its circulation or in its mechanisms of heat loss. In the second place, both species can drink vast quantities of water rapidly when it does become available. They can regulate the quantity drunk so that it balances the fluid lost, because the amount they can drink at one time is greater than the amount needed to balance water loss.

In humans, the body water is often itself maintained during intense sweating by the intake of water, but electrolyte imbalance occurs from salt depletion. Muscle cramp is an early symptom. It may be relieved or prevented by taking salt directly, as sportsmen do, or by consuming copious quantities of rough cider rather than tea or water — a traditional method favoured by West Country haymakers which, if it failed to replace the salts lost (as might fondly be supposed), could always be relied upon to minimize any heat stress due to overwork.

If preventative steps are not taken, the physiological consequences of salt deficiency can initiate a vicious cycle.

■   From what you have learnt previously, could you describe the likely sequence of events?

Loss of salt first affects the plasma and other extracellular spaces, which then lose water by osmosis to the cells. The intracellular fluid therefore increases in volume. The reduced osmolarity then causes the kidney to re-absorb less water in the renal tubules, which is followed by a further drop in extracellular fluid volume. There is now a loss of appetite which reduces salt intake, and the continuing depletion leads to vomiting and diarrhoea, and thus still more salt is lost from the body.

A behavioural response to heat stress which suffers none of the disadvantages of sweating is the wetting of the skin by *wallowing,* a method that promotes heat loss by both conduction and evaporation. The source of water applied to the surface of the body for cooling purposes is of no consequence provided that, when it evaporates, the heat of the body rather than that of the air contributes to vaporization. In some tropical species, such as the water buffalo, which has few sweat glands, a wallow or some equivalent water appears to be essential for survival. The same may well be true of the massive hippopotamus which, with short legs and small ears, must have an especially low surface area:mass ratio (lower, for example, than the elephant) but which nevertheless enjoys wallowing in water whenever possible. It is notable that all species that make use of external water for cooling have relatively hairless skin and in one, the pig, it has been shown that evaporation of external water can proceed at a rate ($800\,g\,m^{-2}\,h^{-1}$) almost equivalent to that in a sweating man. Liquid mud is even more effective, because it prolongs the period of effective evaporation (Figure 3.11).

Finally, a word about another form of evaporative cooling, often used in emergency only. This method is saliva spreading, known to be important in heat-stressed rodents, cats and marsupials. In the red kangaroo, saliva spreading exploits elaborate vascular networks beneath the thinly furred arms and legs, and rats, by licking their fur, can maintain homeostasis at an air temperature $3\,°C$ above that of the body.

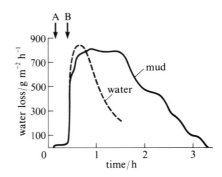

Figure 3.11   Evaporative water loss from the skin of a pig. At A, control measurements begin. At B, mud or water was smeared over the skin.

3.3.3 Respiratory water loss: panting

The lining of the respiratory tract is moist and heat is lost by evaporation during normal breathing. In hot weather, or after exercise, this passive and inevitable loss is enhanced in most birds (which don't sweat) and many mammals into an efficient method of heat dissipation under the control of the thermoregulatory system. Control over the rate of evaporation is achieved by changing the volume of air ventilating the surface of the upper respiratory tract. Typically, this increase takes the form of an abrupt change to rapid shallow breathing, as seen in the dog, rather than by slower deeper breathing which, so far as heat loss is concerned, might achieve the same end. The former pattern of breathing allows for maximal ventilation of the respiratory passages without unduly increasing the exchange of air in the lung itself. Panting is only a modification of breathing movements which first ventilates the lungs, bringing oxygen to the gas exchange surfaces and washing out carbon dioxide. This function has to continue unabated even when the secondary function of promoting heat loss is added to it.

It has been known for about 20 years that the temperature of the exhaled air is often significantly lower than that of the body core; in small mammals and birds it is commonly close to the ambient temperature. This discovery was at first surprising because air coming from the lung is certainly at the temperature of the body core and is fully saturated with water. The explanation for the difference is that a temporal counter-current heat exchanger is at work in the nose analogous to the spatial exchanger you are familiar with (from Section 3.2.4) in the appendages. Whereas the spatial mechanism (Figure 3.12a) operates in two parallel channels — the arteries and veins of the limbs — the temporal mechanism, reciprocating in one channel only, operates in the respiratory system (Figure 3.12b). In this case, both heat and water are trapped inside the animal and therefore losses are less than would otherwise be the case.

To understand the physiology of thermal panting, it is first essential to appreciate how this exchange system works. For the heat exchanger to function, both the inspired and expired respiratory air must pass over the same surfaces, those of the nasal mucosa. Let us consider the situation in a dog with a core temperature of 38 °C, breathing dry air at 22 °C (Figure 3.13, *overleaf*). Before inspiration, there is a thermal gradient from the tip of the dog's nose (say 23 °C) all the way along the mucosa to the trachea (38 °C). As the inspired air passes along the nasal passages, it takes up both heat and moisture from the mucosa and is thus fully loaded before entering the lungs. In the short interval between inhalation and exhalation, the thermal gradient from nose to trachea is maintained; little heat or moisture is added to the mucosa by the animal. When air is exhaled from the lungs, at 38 °C and saturated with moisture, it encounters mucosal temperatures that are progressively cooler. The temperature and vapour pressure gradients between the mucosa and the adjacent air are reversed and heat is now lost from the air to the mucosa until, at the tip of the nose, it is expired at close to the ambient temperature. As the air is cooled during this process, water recondenses on the mucosal surfaces. The air that is expired is still saturated (or very nearly so), but because its temperature is much reduced, it carries far less water (see Figure 3.8); in fact, under the conditions specified, about 60% of the water is conserved.

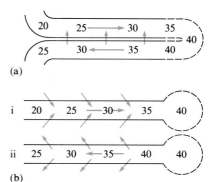

Figure 3.12   A diagram of spatial (a) and temporal (b) counter-current heat exchangers. The lower diagrams (b) represent the nasal heat exchanger, in which the inspired air draws heat and water from the walls of the respiratory tract (i) and gives both back again at exhalation (ii). The figures represent approximate temperatures varying from the deep body tissues (40 °C) to near the surface. The small arrows show the direction of heat transfer.

MOUTH CLOSED

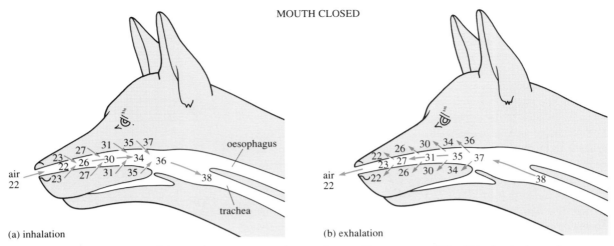

(a) inhalation

(b) exhalation

Figure 3.13 The operation of the nasal counter-current heat exchanger. Temperatures (°C) within the dog's nasal passages and at the mucosa during inhalation and exhalation indicate the conservation of heat and water when the mouth is closed. The small arrows show the direction of heat transfer from the mucosa to the air on inhalation (a) and in the reverse direction at exhalation (b).

By now you may have realized that this nasal counter-current heat exchanger conserves both heat *and* water and that it is therefore working *against* the animal's need to increase its heat loss by losing extra water from the respiratory tract during environmental heat loading or exercise. Can the exchange system be bypassed when evaporative heat loss is more important than heat or water conservation? The first point to make here is that the temperature and vapour pressure of the expired air automatically rises as the ambient temperature increases, and the heat exchanger is therefore abolished when the inspired air temperature reaches that of the body core. However, even under these relatively uncommon circumstances, the proportion of metabolic heat dissipated is small (about 12% for dry air at 38 °C), and decreases as the humidity increases.

The most obvious way to enhance evaporation from the nasal mucosa is by increasing the amount of air ventilating it. But this solution is only effective if it can be accomplished without, at the same time, over-ventilating the lungs and washing out too much carbon dioxide. The bicarbonate buffer system of the blood is in equilibrium with a level of 5% CO_2 in the alveoli; if this level is reduced, the partial pressure of carbon dioxide in the blood (P_{CO_2}) will fall while the pH rises, leading to the condition called respiratory alkalosis. In many panting animals this unlikely balance is achieved by exploiting the fact that a good portion of the inspired air never reaches the lungs anyway. The upper parts of the respiratory passages represent a 'dead space' so far as gas exchange is concerned, and yet their increased ventilation is achieved by just the sort of respiratory response that we see in panting, namely, rapid shallow breathing. In cattle, for example, the ventilation of the alveoli and dead space is roughly equal during resting conditions (see arrow in Figure 3.14). However, on exposure to heat, when the total respiratory ventilation is increased, dead space ventilation constitutes a larger and larger fraction of total ventilation, increasing by tenfold before alveolar ventilation is changed. Evaporation from the nasal mucosa of the ox thus also increases by this amount before respiratory alkalosis becomes a problem and the creature can dissipate all of its metabolic heat in dry air up to 40 °C.

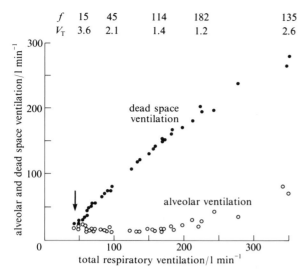

| f | 15 | 45 | 114 | 182 | 135 |
| V_T | 3.6 | 2.1 | 1.4 | 1.2 | 2.6 |

Figure 3.14   Changes in the alveolar and dead-space ventilation in the ox with increasing respiration when exposed to rising heat and humidity. Alveolar ventilation rises only when the volume of air breathed out per minute exceeds 200 litres. Tidal volume (V_T) measured in litres, and respiratory frequency (f) as breaths min^{-1}, are given at the top of the graph. The arrow indicates the values at rest.

In dogs, and probably in other species that pant efficiently, there is a simple mechanical device that further increases the effectiveness of respiratory cooling. A valve at the back of the throat oscillates in time with the breathing movements and directs a large proportion of the air that was inhaled through the nose out through the mouth, thereby largely bypassing the nasal heat exchanger (Figure 3.15). This mechanism can be used to modulate the rate of evaporative heat loss *without* affecting the respiratory frequency or volume, and is exploited to the full during thermal panting under most normal heat loads.

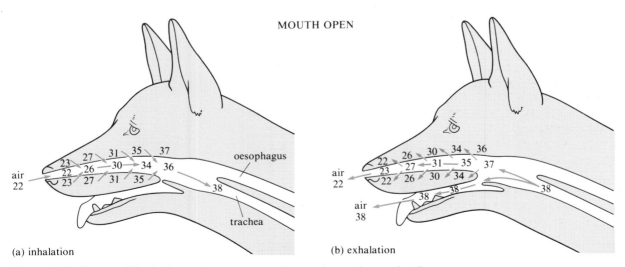

Figure 3.15   Bypass of the dog's nasal counter-current heat exchanger by opening the mouth, indicating how heat and water loss are enhanced.

During very severe heat stress another change is evident in the dog. The rapid shallow breathing of first-phase panting in which there is unidirectional air flow out of the mouth (Figure 3.15b), alters to a slower, deeper second-phase panting, in which air passes in and out through both nose *and* mouth. There is a very rich vasculature in the dog's tongue and the rate of blood flow increases greatly with a rise in body temperature. This factor, together with the quite different morphological characteristics of the buccal area as compared with the narrow nasal passages, ensures that, unlike the situation in the nasal passages, no significant heat-exchange mechanism operates in the mouth, so evaporation reaches its maximum during second-phase panting. It seems that this form of response normally occurs in the dog during exercise, when enhanced cooling is necessary as well as enhanced gaseous exchange. Recent experiments have lent weight to this interpretation by showing that most of the water that is evaporated from the nasal mucosa in the dog is derived from a gland situated in the nasal cavity; its copious secretions are probably essential to avoid desiccation of the mucosa during panting. During heat loading by exercise, on the other hand, most of the water seems to be supplied by the salivary glands, which maintain the dampness of the tongue and buccal surfaces.

The physiology of respiratory water loss is also complex in birds. Broadly speaking, there are two types of panting. In many birds, including the domestic fowl and house sparrow, breathing frequency rises roughly as a linear function of body temperature. However, in species with a particularly efficient panting response, such as the pigeon, the frequency changes abruptly as it does in the dog from the resting level to a panting level of about 500 times a minute. This resonant panting conserves energy because the frequency is close to that at which the entire thoracic cage of the species vibrates, if it is treated experimentally as a naturally oscillating physical system.

There has always been a certain controversy over the question of the site of respiratory evaporation in birds. It has been known for some time that the vibrations of the loose skin of the throat region, known as gular flutter, can be of considerable thermoregulatory significance. It accounts for some 20% of evaporative heat loss in the Japanese quail, and for all of the respiratory component in the poor-will (*Phaloenoptilus nuttalli*), one of the few birds that apparently do not pant. The tongue and the oesophagus have also been shown to play a part in some species.

But the main controversy concerns the role of the avian airsacs. Whereas in the panting mammal water loss can occur only from the surfaces of the upper respiratory tract, it has been postulated for well over a hundred years that the unique structure of the avian respiratory system might well be an adaptation for enhanced evaporative cooling, perhaps during the greatly increased heat loading imposed by the metabolism of flight. If so, then air would presumably have to enter the airsacs during the respiratory cycle either at a temperature below that of the body core, or at a vapour pressure below that of saturation. Recent experiments give no support to the hypothesis. Because the flow of gas through the avian lung is now known to be unidirectional, from caudal to rostral in both phases of the respiratory cycle, it follows that air entering both the anterior and posterior airsacs has already passed the gas-exchange surfaces of the lung and must be fully saturated at the deep-body temperature. Moreover, direct measurements of the surface temperatures inside the airsacs do not indicate that evaporation could be taking place, whereas temperatures on the surfaces of the upper respiratory tract are significantly lower than elsewhere (Figure 3.16). It seems therefore that, while the airsacs have an important 'bellows' function in avian respiration, they do not have a role in evaporative cooling.

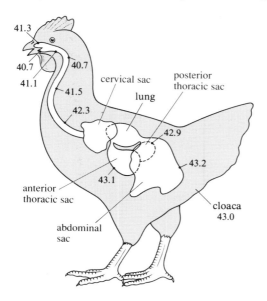

Figure 3.16   Surface temperatures (°C) from within the pharynx and respiratory tract (including airsacs) of the fowl, taken when ambient air temperature and body temperature (measured at the cloaca) were equal. The respiratory frequency is 41 ± 13 breaths min^{-1}. The lung and main airsacs are labelled.

Summary of Section 3.3

As ambient temperature rises towards the core body temperature, a homeotherm depends increasingly on the vaporization of water at the body surface to keep cool. When the air temperature equals the body surface temperature, evaporation is the sole channel for heat loss. Sweating can be a highly efficient means of combating heat stress, provided that drinking water is plentiful and ambient humidity not too high. In men, a loss if moisture of 1 litre per hour through sweating is not unusual during physical work in hot conditions, but if salt and water losses are not made good, there may be serious physiological consequences.

Many mammals and birds pant when exposed to heat. In this type of evaporative cooling, the respiratory and heat loss functions of ventilation can be in conflict. During quiet breathing, there is in many mammals a temperature gradient along the nasal passages, with a 'cold nose' at or below the ambient temperature. Exhaled air, saturated at body temperature, passes over the nasal surfaces that have been cooled by inspiratory evaporation, and here regains by condensation much of the heat that was previously lost. However, species that pant efficiently, such as the dog, can adjust the flow of air through the nose and mouth by a sensitive valving mechanism which, under most conditions, serves the body's thermoregulatory needs without over-ventilating the lungs. Thus, the panting dog normally inhales through the nose and exhales through the mouth, so bypassing the nasal heat exchanger. In severe heat stress, air passes very rapidly both in and out through the mouth (and nose) but the opportunity here for heat exchange is limited so the rate of heat loss is maximal, and such second-phase panting may cause alkalosis.

3.4 Heat storage

It is clear from what has been said already that evaporative cooling, when actively promoted by the physiological mechanisms of sweating and panting, can be very effective in maintaining body temperature in the face of heat loading from the environment or from exercise. However, the water lost in cooling the body must be replaced rapidly; when it is not available, panting and sweating can no longer function.

We have seen that dehydration leads to changes in the viscosity and osmolarity of the plasma that are physiologically undesirable. It also leads to a gradual rise in core body temperature which is also undesirable if prolonged or pronounced, yet the temporary storage of heat, as distinct from its immediate dissipation, can be the lesser of two evils when water is scarce.

You already know from Chapter 2 that the rate of gain and loss of heat by an animal is influenced by body size. Because of its higher surface area:mass ratio, a small animal gains heat from a very hot environment much faster than a large one, and consequently reaches the lethal limit of hyperthermia more quickly. If it is unable to escape the heat, then it must evaporate water at a very high rate to survive. For a very small animal (say 100 g) exposed to 40 °C, this rate would be at a rate equivalent to 10–15% of its body weight per hour — obviously an impossible situation. Even for a 2-kg animal, the figure would be 4–5% per hour — still unsustainable except for very short periods. The corresponding estimate for a 60–70 kg man is that he would lose about 1.5% of his body water per hour to remain in heat balance, and for a 500-kg camel, about 0.9%.

Although heat storage, like evaporative water loss, is not a realistic proposition for small animals, in those weighing over 10 kg it could reduce the need for evaporation. Simple calculations give us an idea of how much water might be conserved. A man weighing 67 kg would absorb some 450 kJ of heat if his body temperature were raised from 37 °C to 39 °C, and he would save nearly 190 cm^3 of sweat in so doing, which might be critical in desperate circumstances. The stored heat could be dissipated later, either by sweating when dehydration was ended, or by radiation and convection when the air had cooled down.

It seems that some animals, especially those accustomed to strenuous exercise, do indeed use this strategy as a matter of course. The African hunting dog, for instance, regulates its core temperature at a high level during the relentless running down of its prey. Sprinters, such as cheetahs, gazelles and the ostrich-like rhea, store the heat of their intermittent activity and cool themselves slowly afterwards by non-evaporative means. Of course, it is hardly possible to investigate such complex problems with these animals in the wild, but we are fortunate that in the last decade there has been a remarkable increase in understanding as a result of imaginative laboratory experiments, many of them on hand-reared animals, trained over long periods to accept physiological probes and to run on a treadmill. Once these conditions have been achieved, it is relatively straightforward to calculate a complete heat balance of the kind:

heat production = heat storage ± evaporative heat loss ± non-evaporative heat loss

The rate of heat production is usually determined from measurements of oxygen consumption, using a mask over the animal's face (as illustrated for an iguana in

Section 2.3). A fraction of the air is passed through an oxygen analyser which measures the difference in oxygen concentration between the air entering the mask and that flowing out. The product of this difference and the rate of air flow then gives a measure of the oxygen consumed by the animal. Heat storage is calculated from the change in the animal's core temperature. (For an animal with a body weight of 75 kg, the heat stored would amount to about 30 kJ for a rise of 1 °C.) Total evaporative heat loss is determined from the reduction in body weight during the experiment, with corrections for that due to defaecation, urination and the difference in weight between inspired oxygen and expired carbon dioxide. Non-evaporative heat loss is then calculated simply as the difference between the two sides of the equation.

By the use of these methods it is now known that when running at about 10 km h^{-1} for 15 minutes at 22 °C, the cheetah stores some 70% of the heat produced as a by-product of metabolism; at 18 km h^{-1} about 90% is stored. This species is known to be capable of speeds in excess of 100 km h^{-1}, but in the laboratory it has not proved possible to make measurements at running speeds greater than 22 km h^{-1}. In all experiments so far, heat production has risen linearly with running speed. If this relationship holds during full sprinting, the metabolism during these short bursts would increase by over 50-fold and the heat stored would push up core temperature by about 1.6 °C min^{-1}. This heat load may be the reason why, in the wild, cheetahs sprint for less than 1 km, because by the time this distance has been covered their core temperature would have reached about 40.5 °C, the level at which, in the laboratory, cheetahs refuse to run.

The fact that the cheetah can tolerate only moderate hyperthermia may be of considerable advantage to some of the species upon which it preys. Gazelles, for example, also store large amounts of heat when they run at high speed, but they tolerate a rise in core temperature of as much as 6 °C (compared to the cheetah's 2 °C), and can thus run fast for long periods. Consequently, if the gazelle can avoid capture during the cheetah's initial sprint, the predator overheats and abandons the pursuit, while the gazelle continues to store heat and escapes.

In gazelles, it appears that short bursts of exercise can occur without affecting water balance, because the raised metabolism increases the water formed by oxidation of food. Exercise also increases the amount of food eaten, and with it the free water taken in. Of course, any such benefit of exercise in terms of water balance would accrue only if most of the stored heat was lost afterwards non-evaporatively. Laboratory measurements with a treadmill suggest that most of the stored heat is lost in this way, *provided* the gazelle walks at less than 3 km h^{-1} or runs faster than 15 km h^{-1}; what extra water is lost by evaporation during and after exercise is then equalled by that gained from the raised metabolism. The important point is that the same *proportion* of the total heat production is lost by evaporation during both slow walking and fast running. Running, of course, generates a lot of extra heat but most is stored rather than being immediately lost through evaporation. However, at rates of exercise between these limits, the overall water balance is affected adversely because a higher proportion of heat generated is dissipated by evaporation. These results nicely match observations of wild gazelles, which spend much of the day grazing gently, interrupted only by short sprints to avoid predators.

3.5 Mammals in the desert: heat stress and water shortage

Arid and semi-arid regions occupy some 35% of the world's land surface, the desert environment representing one of the most stressful for animal life. In the hottest deserts, vegetation is very scattered or absent, and solar radiation levels can exceed $1\,000\,W\,m^{-2}$. Heat and drought are not the only characteristics, however, for animals on the surface must sometimes cope with near-freezing conditions at night. When nocturnal temperatures fall, condensation of water may occur, which can support the growth of plants in the absence of rainfall.

Despite the hazards of desert life, many different animals have adapted successfully, their mechanisms of survival depending to a considerable extent on whether they are large or small. Many small animals tolerate deserts essentially by avoiding the worst aspects of the climate: strictly speaking they are not adapted to heat stress.

3.5.1 Responses to heat in humans

In humans, the tolerance of hot dry conditions is excellent, on the one essential condition that losses of salt and water in sweating are made good. However, the most effective adaptations of people placed in hot environments are the obvious behavioural ones, rather than reliance on evaporative cooling. If work must be undertaken during the hottest part of the day then physiological improvement during acclimation is marked. From Figure 3.17 we can see that, after an initial period of considerable strain and discomfort, there is a progressive rise in sweating rate and a resultant decline in core temperature. The thermal threshold for the sweating response falls as acclimation proceeds, and so does the heart rate as blood volume rises. Overall, the responses provide an improved sense of comfort and of working efficiency, but at the cost of greater water loss.

Clothing can be important as a means of reducing the absorption of solar and reflected radiation, and also to prevent burning of the skin. It has been shown, for example, that men wearing only light khaki clothing absorb 55% less radiant heat than nude men under the same hot conditions. Looseness and porosity of clothing is more important for efficient cooling than colour (which affects radiation only within the visible spectrum), for it is important that air should circulate freely and moisture be able to evaporate. The heat gained by bedouins in the Sinai desert is the same whether they wear black or white robes, even though the former do absorb more solar radiation (with a surface temperature of 47 °C, compared with 41 °C for white robes). Evidently the ventilating action of the loose garments is more than enough to compensate for the difference in radiation absorption, for the skin temperatures of the individuals are identical (33 °C).

It is not possible for a human individual to accumulate a significant reserve of water before setting out on a hot journey. Few people can drink more than about a litre of fluid over a short period, and in any case the excess is soon eliminated by the kidney after it reaches the bloodstream. Renal conservation of body water commences only after loss has already occurred and then urine flow may be halved, and fall as low as $250\,cm^3$ per day (about one-sixth of the normal flow)

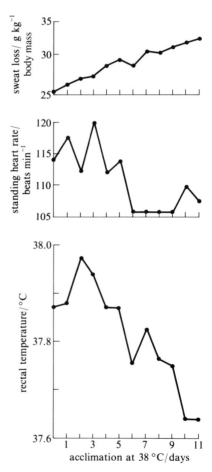

Figure 3.17 The development of heat acclimation in twelve young men trained into good physical condition, then alternating rest with work periods of 3 hours per day for 11 days in a chamber at 38 °C, with unsaturated air. Throughout the period of these measurements, drinking water was freely available.

during severe dehydration. The degree to which urine flow can be decreased depends on the ability of the kidney to concentrate salt and urea, which in humans is limited to solutions of about 2.2 and 6% of saturation, respectively. Thus, although drinking a slightly saline water is advantageous during heat stress, a solution as strong as seawater (2.8% solution of NaCl) is counter-productive.

3.5.2 The kangaroo rat

In marked contrast to humans, the kangaroo rat (*Dipodomys spectabilis*, Figure 3.18) survives under desert conditions with the aid of its powerful kidneys, which permit it to live entirely on metabolic (oxidation) water, and its behaviour by which it avoids the heat. This species represents an outstanding example of how behavioural and autonomic adaptation can combine to enable apparently ill-adapted animals (like other rodents, the kangaroo rat neither sweats nor pants, and some species weigh only 35–40 g) to flourish in harsh environments where air temperatures may rise to 45 °C, and ground temperatures to 70 °C. Kangaroo rats are typical of small desert animals in that they spend the day in deep burrows which are not only cool, but contain air which is humidified by the animals' own respiration. They emerge to feed at night and are subject to heat stress only if they become trapped in their shallow emergency burrows by the presence of a predator. However, these creatures are no more tolerant of hyperthermia and dehydration than are most other mammals, many dying with body temperatures of 40–41 °C if exposed for a few hours at an ambient temperature of 39 °C. At this temperature, the loss of body weight due to evaporation is about 1.82% per hour, which would be hopelessly inadequate to maintain heat balance even for an animal more than twice the size. It seems that kangaroo rats not only cannot afford to thermoregulate by evaporation, but lack the ability to do so. Their physiological fame rests rather on their ability to live without access to free water or damp food. They live chiefly on seeds and other dry plant material, selecting these even when green and succulent plants are available. They also produce faeces with only one-fifth of the water content of a laboratory white rat of the same size. The kidneys are exceptionally powerful, producing urine with concentrations of salt and urea of about 7% and 23%, respectively. When kangaroo rats are forced to drink by feeding them a diet of soya beans, which are very high in protein and hence yield large quantities of urea, they thrive even if provided only with seawater.

Some other desert rodents living in equally hot and arid regions are not adapted in this way, but instead depend upon a supply of food with a high water content, such as cactus. For instance, the American wood rat (*Neotoma floridana*) is also an avoider of heat and can survive without access to drinking water. Yet its kidney is less efficient in concentrating urine than that of the white rat. The wood rat's special adaptation is an ability to consume cacti rich in water and oxalic acid. Oxalic acid is highly toxic to most mammals, partly because it removes soluble Ca^{2+} from the blood, forming calcium oxalate crystals which damage the kidneys. The wood rat is known to have an unusual calcium metabolism and somehow manages to deal with the oxalic acid in its diet.

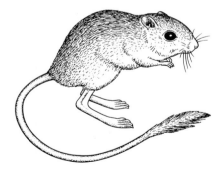

Figure 3.18 The kangaroo rat (*Dipodomys spectabilis*).

3.5.3 The jack-rabbit

A very interesting group of animals are the hares (or jack-rabbits, *Lepus californicus*) that occur in very hot deserts of North America. Although weighing only about 2 kg, they do not make burrows but live on the surface. For reasons that should now be familiar to you, they would need to lose at least 4% of body weight per hour to thermoregulate by evaporation, yet there is no free drinking water available over most of their range. The jack-rabbits live on a diet of green plant foods, and in the driest seasons eat some cacti. Work by Knut Schmidt-Nielsen has shown behaviour to play a large part in their survival. The animal selects a shaded depression in the ground, often in the lee of a bush, in which it crouches during the day (Figure 3.19). The bottom of such a depression has a much lower temperature than that of the rest of the surface, the hot desert winds and much of the radiation passing over the animal's head. From its sheltered position, the jack-rabbit's radiator-like ears can be exposed, not to the Sun, but to a clear blue sky. The radiation temperature of the north sky is only 13 °C, so if the ears, which have a rich circulation, are close to 40 °C and have a surface of 400 cm^2 that can be directed to the sky, they can radiate about 13 kJ h^{-1}, or about one-third of the resting animal's metabolic heat production. It seems likely that this mechanism does indeed provide the solution to what, on the face of it, looks like an unpromising situation.

Compared with the kangaroo rat, the jack-rabbit tolerates a considerable degree of heat stress, but neither species can afford to thermoregulate by evaporation. Large desert animals suffer the disadvantage that they can find little shelter from high temperatures or radiant heat, but this limitation is counteracted by the advantage of size. They can carry a good thickness of coat to insulate against solar radiation and have a proportionately greater water reserve for evaporative cooling. If water needs to be conserved, a large animal can also store a good deal of heat for non-evaporative loss during cool periods.

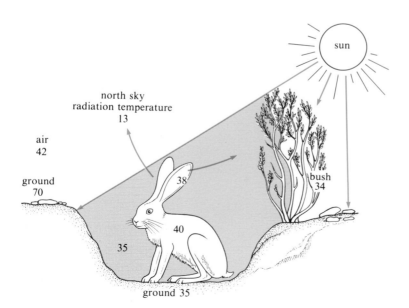

Figure 3.19 The desert jack-rabbit (*Lepus californicus*) in a shaded depression showing a behavioural adaptation to cope with the severe environment. Temperatures throughout are in °C.

3.5.4 Large desert mammals

Most of the large mammals that survive in arid regions are ungulate species, many of them exploited by humans. Morphological adaptation may play a part in their tolerance of heat, as in the long limbs, ears and tails of desert sheep, and the dewlaps (the loose skin beneath the throat) of some cattle. As a generaliz-ation, however, it is true that cattle are less well equipped than sheep and goats to cope with desert conditions, one reason being the structure and function of the kidney. The long loops of Henle in the renal medulla are associated with the reabsorption of water and production of concentrated urine; cattle mainly have short loops and sheep mainly have long loops. For cattle, a 1% salt solution for drinking is close to the physiological limit, whereas sheep can survive a solution of up to 1.5%.

When subjected to dehydration, ungulates show a decrease in both metabolism and evaporative water loss. There are complications when discussing dehy-dration, however, because the rumen of large animals can hold a considerable quantity of water. This water seems to protect the blood volume and viscosity by contrast with humans, although, again, cattle are less adapted to survive dehydration than sheep, and sheep less than camels. Thus, when deprived of water during exposure to 40 °C by day and 25 °C at night, cattle lose about 10% of body weight in the first day, sheep 8% and camels only 4%. The black Sinai goat may be one of the most tolerant species of all, retaining water in its rumen to be released into the blood gradually. It can survive dehydration of even 40% of its body weight, and continues to eat after a loss of 30%.

The hair of a desert animal can be important as an insulator, both against solar heat and nocturnal cold. There are three fairly distinct types — loose, tightly packed, or short and smooth — the value of each as insulation depending upon its ability to retain trapped air and to reflect radiation. Figure 3.20 compares the thermal properties of the coats of two breeds of heat-tolerant sheep with that of the short-haired camel. The raised core temperatures indicate that some heat is being stored. The sun penetrates the Awassi coat (a) and heats the middle layers so that the skin is relatively hot. In short-coated camels (b) (some varieties have much longer coats) solar energy is reflected, while sweating keeps much of the skin cool. Merino sheep (c) lose long-wave radiation from the hot tips of the wool and maintain a gradient of up to 43 °C across 4–5 cm of fleece, so the skin is protected from heating.

The camel, in fact, capitalizes to a remarkable degree on the capacity of its immense bulk (up to 500 kg) to store heat. If water is short in summer, it may maintain a normal core temperature throughout the cool night and then, at around 0600 h, allow its body temperature to fall to about 34 °C. Throughout the heat of the day, its temperature rises due to muscular work, solar radiation or both, but the animal makes no attempt to thermoregulate by sweating until the rectal temperature reaches 40 °C. Thus it absorbs heat over a range of 6 °C, compared with only 2 °C in humans. Given its large mass, the camel may save about 5 litres of sweat in a day, which is significant, considering that a 500-kg specimen resting in the full sun still loses a total of about 10 litres of water per day by sweating, breathing and excreting. There is no evidence that the camel's lethal body temperature is significantly different from that in humans, but it certainly is more tolerant of changes in body temperature.

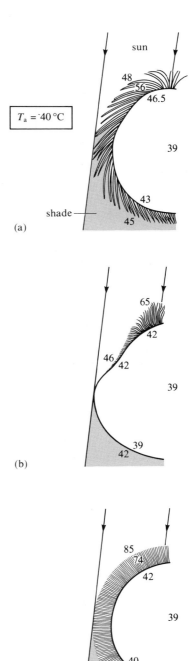

Figure 3.20   The gradients of temperature across the coat of (a) open-woolled Awassi sheep, (b) short-coated camels, and (c) Merino sheep with dense fleece. All the animals are exposed to sunlight and $T_a = 40$ °C.

Another difference between camels and people is in the distribution of fluid loss during dehydration, already mentioned in connection with sweating. You may recall that a 4% loss in human body weight is reflected in about a 10% reduction of plasma volume. Schmidt-Nielsen showed that, in a 290-kg camel, a 17% weight loss due to dehydration was accompanied by only an 8.8% reduction in plasma volume (amounting to 1.2 litres), and a 38% loss of fluid from the gut. Strain on the circulation is thus minimized, while camel tissues seem to be more resistant to high osmotic pressures than those of many animals.

The camel can also reduce urine flow to a greater extent than humans. Its kidney can produce a urine twice as concentrated as that of humans, and, under some circumstances, it can reduce the amount of urea that it excretes. According to Schmidt-Nielsen, much of the urea in the blood may be secreted into the rumen where bacteria resynthesize it into protein. This protein is later digested and some of it deaminated in the liver, the urea thus released returning to the blood. This cycle may help to retain nitrogen, and hence the water that would have been needed to secrete it, within the body during periods of water shortage.

The camel is also justifiably famous for its ability to make long, arduous journeys over waterless deserts. Its tolerance of such conditions has often been attributed to an alleged ability to store free water in its rumen and to utilize metabolic water derived from its fatty hump. The investigations of Schmidt-Nielsen have thrown a good deal of light on these claims.

Let us take the question of water storage first. It is certain that there are no special 'water sacs' in any part of the gut. Proportionately, there is no more intestinal water in a camel than in other ruminants, nor is there evidence of a generally higher tissue water content. However, a large camel does have up to 75 litres of fluid in the rumen (85% of it water) and another 8 litres in the intestine. We have seen that an unusually large percentage of the water lost during dehydration comes from the gut, 38% of 83 litres being nearly 30 litres. In a camel, daily loss may be in the region of 10 litres, so an 'available' reserve of this magnitude is not without significance.

As to the question of metabolic water, it has often been pointed out that since the oxidation of 1 g of fat yields 1.07 g of water, a 40-kg hump represents a reserve of 43 litres which can be drawn upon during a long journey. However, Schmidt-Nielsen makes the point that this mechanism involves the use of oxygen, which can be gained only by ventilating the lungs, leading to a loss of water from the respiratory tract when the camel breathes the dry desert air. Whether the fat reserves make a positive or a negative contribution to the animal's overall water balance therefore depends on the conditions prevailing in the respiratory tract.

More recent work by Schmidt-Nielsen and colleagues has addressed this question. Working under natural conditions in central Australia, on introduced camels (the camel is not native to that country), they measured body temperatures, oxygen consumption and respiratory frequency and volume, as well as the temperature and relative humidity of the inspired and expired air, by means of sensors inserted loosely into a nostril. The results showed that, during the daytime, severely dehydrated camels exhaled air that was at or near the core temperature and fully saturated with water vapour. At night, however, there was a marked difference, the exhaled air being at or near the ambient temperature with a relative humidity of about 75%.

We can best gain an impression of the camel's water balance by taking an example which uses hypothetical, but realistic, figures. Consider a camel resting at night in air at 28 °C and 40% r.h. Every 2 minutes it consumes 1 litre of oxygen, for which it inhales some 20 litres of air. This volume of air, under these conditions, contains 216 mg of water. This same volume, exhaled at core temperature (35 °C) and fully saturated, contains 784 mg of water, an overall loss to the camel of 568 mg. If 20 litres of saturated air were exhaled at ambient temperature (28 °C, water content, 538 mg), the loss would be reduced to 322 mg, while 20 litres of exhaled air at 28 °C and only 75% r.h. (the humidity measured by Schmidt-Nielsen) would have a water content of 403 mg, which would further reduce the water loss to 187 mg. The maximum saving of water could thus be calculated as follows:

$$\text{Saving} = \frac{\text{mass } H_2O \text{ in saturated air at 35 °C } - \text{ mass } H_2O \text{ in exhaled air}}{\text{mass } H_2O \text{ in saturated air at 35 °C } - \text{ mass } H_2O \text{ in inhaled air}}$$

$$= \frac{(784 - 403)}{(784 - 216)} = \frac{381}{568} = 67\%.$$

Although this mechanism seems to operate only at night, it obviously makes an important contribution to water conservation in the dehydrated animal, and probably ensures that there is a gain of water from the oxidation of fat.

3.5.5   Thermal gradients in the nasal passages

As you know already from Section 3.3, in many animals there are thermal gradients in the nasal passages and thus there is a remarkable similarity between the temperatures of the inhaled and exhaled air (Figure 3.21). The efficiency of the heat and water exchanger is of course a function of the structural characteristics of the passages over which air passes: those of small creatures with a large surface-to-bore ratio being generally more suited than the short,

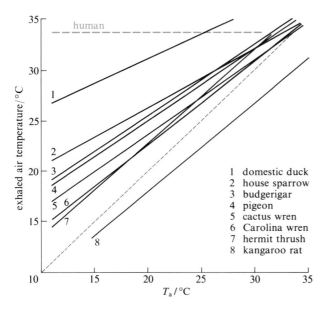

1 domestic duck
2 house sparrow
3 budgerigar
4 pigeon
5 cactus wren
6 Carolina wren
7 hermit thrush
8 kangaroo rat

Figure 3.21   Exhaled air temperatures of seven species of bird and the kangaroo rat at various ambient temperatures. (Much the same relationship applies in many small mammals.) The line labelled 'human' represents measurements on one individual only; those for other individuals did exhibit some slope. The light dashed isothermal line shows what the relationship would be if the temperatures of inhaled and exhaled air were equal.

wide passages of larger species. In this connection, it is significant that the camel's nose consists of many elaborately convoluted passages with a total interior surface area of more than 1 000 cm^2. For example, in the kangaroo rat breathing air at 25% r.h., the temperature of the expired air ranges from 31 °C at a T_a of 35 °C, to 13 °C at a T_a of 15 °C. The considerable water saving from this gradient is about 54% at 30 °C and 83% at 15 °C. By contrast, humans cannot recover more than about 16% at any air temperature in the range 12–35 °C.

The presence of temperature gradients in the nasal passages of small animals, or the exploitation of evaporative cooling from these areas in panting species, means that the venous blood returning to the head is cooler than the arterial blood supplying the 'nose'. It is now known that some animals make use of this temperature difference as a means of protecting the brain from overheating during periods of hyperthermia. The explanation for this protective mechanism is to be found in the anatomy of the blood vessels in the head. In both mammals and birds, the blood returning from the nasal regions (and much of the brain) drains into a capacious collecting vessel, the cavernous sinus (Figure 3.22), from which it then flows in the neck veins back to the heart. In many species, including the dog, sheep, pigeon and the gazelle, there passes through the cavernous sinus a network of small arterial vessels, the *rete mirabile*, formed from one of the two main arteries supplying the brain (the carotid). In species where nasal heat exchange is unimportant (such as monkeys, Figure 3.22a), there is no rete mirabile, the carotid artery simply passing intact through the cavernous sinus and giving little opportunity for the exchange of heat. However, where the rete is present (as in the oryx, Figure 3.22b), its large surface area permits an exchange of heat between the warm arterial blood and the cooler blood in the cavernous sinus. So, blood passing out of the arterial rete and entering the circle of Willis, from which the brain receives its blood supply, is at a lower temperature than it was in the neck arteries themselves. As a result, the brain can be maintained at a significantly lower temperature than the trunk and its essential function is maintained during hyperthermia in the rest of the body. Measurements of brain and core body temperatures confirm that the heat-exchange mechanism can keep the brain significantly cooler. In a range of species of bird from less than 50 g to over 30 kg in size, brain temperature during heat stress is maintained at about 1 °C below core temperature, whereas, among mammals investigated, Thompson's gazelle and the oryx can maintain a brain–body difference of up to 3 °C during sustained hyperthermia. It can hardly be doubted that this facility has survival value under desert conditions when heat storage is the normal means of combating water shortage.

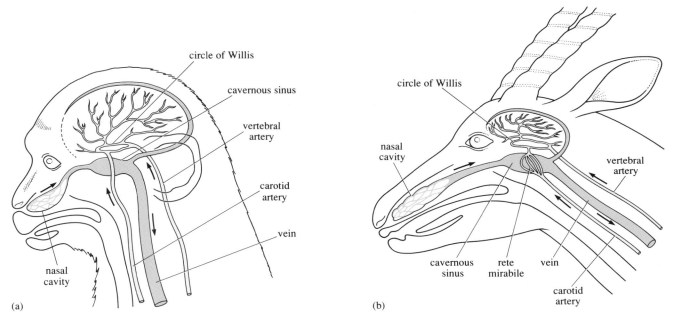

Figure 3.22   Simplified diagrams of the venous drainage from the nasal regions and the arterial supply to the brain in (a) a monkey, and (b) an oryx.

3.5.6 Birds

In contrast to mammals, where those that tolerate hyperthermia are chiefly large species, birds of all sizes seem to be tolerant of hot, arid conditions. Since the normal range of core body temperature among birds (41–42 °C) is 3 or 4 °C higher than that of mammals, hyperthermia can have considerable significance as a method of reducing the need for evaporative cooling. Temperatures of 32–44 °C can be tolerated for several hours by desert and non-desert species of bird, although it is not surprising that, as in the camel, a greater degree of hyperthermia is observed in birds deprived of water. The ostrich can maintain a normal core temperature for several hours in air temperatures as high as 51 °C by panting, but when unable to drink it reduces its rate of evaporation and allows the body temperature to rise. A similar response has been described in budgerigars, and it seems that an altered pattern of temperature regulation, with reduced evaporative cooling, may be a common avian response to intense heat and water shortage.

The avian kidney excretes uric acid instead of the urea of mammals. Uric acid is highly insoluble, and since water is reabsorbed, the waste material is lost as a semi-solid paste with very little water. The production of uric acid also means that birds gain about 20% more water from the oxidation of amino acids than do mammals producing urea. The excretion of uric acid is a feature that birds have in common with many reptiles. In most other respects, however, birds share with mammalian homeotherms a common set of responses to heat stress: in appropriate conditions they often adopt behavioural means of regulating temperature in preference to the more costly autonomic methods which are kept, as it were, in reserve.

Summary of Sections 3.4 and 3.5

Large species of animals have an advantage when heat stressed. Not only is sweating a more feasible strategy for losing heat, but appreciable quantities of heat can be stored during the day, for dissipation by non-evaporative channels at night. Thus the camel's body temperature may fall to 34 °C overnight and then rise to over 40 °C during the heat of the day, especially if the animal is dehydrated. Camels store heat by allowing their body temperature to rise in very hot conditions, reducing the thermal gradient between the environment and the body, and reducing the rate of heat flow from the environment into the body.

Many camels also have heavy insulation, which can retard the uptake of environmental heat. In addition, much of the water in the exhaled air that might be lost to the environment is saved by the nasal heat exchange mechanism, which significantly cools the exhaled air. The camel's nose allows the animal to reduce the relative humidity of the exhaled air, thus increasing water conservation even more. The lining of the nose is hygroscopic, readily taking up water vapour. By various mechanisms, the camel is able to endure the intense heat of the day without shelter from the Sun.

By contrast, small desert-dwelling animals avoid the heat as much as possible, often by burrowing underground. Behavioural strategies minimize exposure to heat, and many such animals, like the kangaroo rat, are nocturnal. Autonomic and behavioural adaptations go hand in hand; the urine of the kangaroo rat is highly concentrated and, as in the camel, a nasal heat exchanger can conserve water.

In many desert animals, including birds, the arterial supply to the brain passes close to cooled venous blood returning from the nasal respiratory surfaces, which provides the opportunity for heat exchange. In gazelles, for example, the brain temperature can be held about 3 °C cooler than core temperature. Thus a lot of heat can be stored during exercise without risk to the brain, which is the most heat-sensitive organ.

3.6 Conclusion

In this chapter, we have examined the interactions of homeothermic animals with one aspect of their external environment, namely temperature. The advantage for these animals of a relatively stable deep-body temperature, compared with one that conforms to changing external conditions, is that of an enhanced ability to exploit favourable opportunities and to survive environmental hazards. Since the rate of metabolic processes is temperature-dependent, it is not surprising that an optimum tissue temperature quite close to the upper lethal level has evolved. As a result, homeotherms are highly successful organisms, their range being limited only by insufficient food and/or water in habitats or seasons characterized by severe cold and heat. Within this range, they utilize both behavioural and autonomic responses which delicately match the overall rate of heat gain to the overall rate of heat loss.

We should stress that although this chapter has emphasized the thermal responses of mammals and birds, terrestrial ectotherms should not be regarded as 'primitive' or 'less successful' by comparison. As you know from Chapter 2, reptiles have behavioural and autonomic adaptations to both heat and cold which, in some ways, give them the edge over their homeothermic descendants. From a reptilian point of view, many mammalian adaptations (especially endothermy) would appear an expensive luxury!

Responses to the thermal environment may involve almost any organ or organ system of the body, as well, of course, as highly coordinated activities of the body as a whole. It is for this reason that a comprehensive study of such responses including the sensory and integrative actions of the nervous system represents a fruitful approach to an understanding of the general principles of biological control: the maintenance of a dynamic balance between the 'internal' and external environments.

Objectives for Chapter 3

When you have completed this chapter you should be able to:

3.1   Define and use, or recognize definitions and applications of, each of the **bold** terms.

3.2   Predict the short-term and long-term responses of a typical mammal acclimatized to a temperate climate, and then exposed to cold conditions.

3.3   Identify the characteristic features of shivering and non-shivering thermogenesis.

3.4   Describe the factors that may influence the position of the thermoneutral zone, the critical temperature and the magnitude of the metabolic response.

3.5   Identify the problems of animals in ambient temperatures above that of their thermoneutral zone.

3.6   Describe the characteristics of sweating and of panting, and identify the advantages and disadvantages of each mechanism.

3.7   Explain the advantage of storing heat, using at least two examples of animals that use this method, and explain how heat storage may limit animal performance.

3.8   Explain, using appropriate diagrams: (a) the operation of the nasal heat exchanger, and (b) the brain-cooling mechanisms involving heat exchange.

3.9   List the adaptations shown by the camel to existence in a hot desert, distinguishing between those which you would expect to be common to any large mammal, and those known only in the camel.

3.10   Predict the responses to heat loading of various species *not* described in the text, when provided with relevant observations or physiological data.

Questions for Chapter 3

(Answers to questions are at the end of the book.)

Question 3.1 (Objectives 3.3, 3.4 and 3.5)

Classify the following statements (a–e) as *true* or *false*.

(a) Below the critical temperature, metabolic rate increases above BMR.

(b) In homeotherms, the extra heat gained by increased metabolism below the critical temperature compensates for the extra loss of heat to the cold environment.

(c) The thermal conductivity of a homeotherm can be changed at temperatures within the thermoneutral zone.

(d) In the short term, acclimation to cold is likely to involve reductions in peripheral blood flow.

(e) Prolonged exposure to cold in rats (cold-acclimation) has no effect on their ability to generate heat by NST.

Question 3.2 (Objectives 3.2 and 3.3)

Rats acclimated to the warm (30 °C) were forced to exercise at a variety of low ambient temperatures. Such exercising, warm-acclimated rats would maintain a normal body temperature at ambient temperatures down to, but not below, 10 °C. By contrast, when cold-acclimated rats (6 °C) were exercised in cold environments, they could maintain their body temperature down to an ambient temperature of −20 °C. Interpret these observations. (Think of the ways in which exercise relates to heat production by shivering and non-shivering means.)

Question 3.3 (Objective 3.4)

Figure 3.23 shows the response to lowered ambient temperatures of two homeotherms, X and Y, of approximately equal BMR.

(a) Which animal has the greater thermoneutral zone?

(b) Which animal has the lower critical temperature?

(c) Other things being equal, which animal is likely to be better adapted to the cold?

(d) If the animals were of unequal size, which animal would be the smaller?

(e) If the animals were of equal size, which animal would have less insulation?

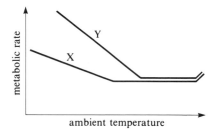

Figure 3.23   For use with Question 3.3.

Question 3.4 (Objective 3.6)

Classify the following statements (a–f) as *true or false*.

(a) Spreading saliva onto fur is likely to be an extremely effective method of heat dissipation under most circumstances.

(b) Gular flutter in birds, as opposed to sweating, may have the advantage of minimizing salt loss from the body.

(c) Increased ventilation during panting always causes increased loss of carbon dioxide from the pulmonary blood and an elevation of blood pH.

(d) The work of the respiratory muscles involved in panting (and therefore the extra metabolic heat production) is minimized because many animals pant at the resonant frequency of the thoracic cavity.

(e) During shallow panting in dogs, most of the air flow is unidirectional, with inhalation mainly through the nasal passages and exhalation through the mouth.

(f) It is likely that the panting dog varies the extent of heat loss mainly by changing the ventilation frequency and the depth of breathing.

Classify the following statements (a–f) as *true* or *false*.

(a) Many small desert animals are able to endure stressful hot conditions by storing heat.

(b) The coat of camels has an insulating effect in a hot environment and camels shorn of their coat are likely to have an increased evaporative water loss.

(c) Most desert-dwelling animals have a higher lethal temperature than temperate species.

(d) In general, cattle and horses are less well equipped to cope with heat stress than are sheep and goats.

(e) Panting is a thermoregulatory response shown exclusively by large mammals.

(f) When faced with severe heat stress, mammals resort to autonomic responses, whereas reptiles and birds respond behaviourally.

The following strategies (a–f) are adopted by various desert-dwelling species:

(a) avoidance of the heat (by burrowing or moving into shade);

(b) the production of concentrated urine;

(c) substantial insulation;

(d) a high-threshold body temperature for the onset of sweating;

(e) heat storage;

(f) radiative heat loss from extensive bare surfaces.

Which of these strategies does each of the following animals employ?

(i) the jack-rabbit

(ii) desert reptiles

(iii) the kangaroo rat

(iv) the camel

Question 3.7 (Objective 3.10)

Interpret the following behaviour in terms of how such actions might help avoid or limit heat stress.

(a) Reptiles often orientate themselves to face the Sun, rather than being 'side on'.

(b) The ostrich erects its plumage in very hot conditions.

(c) Some species of stork urinate on their legs when heat stress is severe to produce a white coating of residual salts.

(d) Some of the bird species that nest in exposed sites in warm climates tend to remain on the nest almost continuously, even after their eggs have hatched.

Question 3.8 (Objectives 3.8 and 3.10)

(a) Many birds exhale air at a temperature that is substantially lower than body temperature and often very close to the ambient temperature (see Figure 3.21). Note that the domestic duck has nasal passages that are much wider than those of other birds. In Figure 3.21, only the cactus wren and the budgerigar can be regarded as desert species.

(i) Is nasal heat exchange typical only of desert birds?

(ii) What factor probably accounts for the difference in width of nasal passages between the domestic duck and other species?

(b) In some desert-dwelling birds (and rodents) the BMR is significantly lower than one would predict on the basis of their body size. In what way might a lower BMR be an advantage to a desert-dwelling species?

Question 3.9 (Objective 3.8)

Explain the following observations:

(a) Experiments were conducted on anaesthetized sheep, which have a local brain-cooling mechanism, and rabbits, which do not. When air was pumped into the nose of a sheep, the temperature of the brain soon dropped, although the temperature of the arterial blood as it left the heart *en route* for the head was unchanged. When the experiment was repeated with a rabbit, there was no such immediate cooling of the brain, although after a brief delay there was a small drop in the temperature of blood in the carotid artery.

(b) When dogs are put into a hot room, they do not to react to the abnormal temperature, although both the brain and body temperatures rise rapidly to the point where the distressed dogs have to be removed. However, if dogs are exercised on a treadmill in a warm room, the body temperature rapidly increases, but the brain temperature rises much more slowly and remains more than a full degree below the body temperature throughout the run.

CHAPTER 4 THERMAL PHYSIOLOGY OF THE FETUS AND NEONATE

Prepared for the Course Team by Bob Cordell and Alison Tedstone

4.1 Introduction

In this chapter, we shall study the thermoregulatory problems faced by the mammalian fetus and neonate, and the physiological mechanisms that address them.

At the moment of birth, an animal faces the impact upon its body of an environment that, compared with conditions within the uterus, is harsh and physiologically stressful in a variety of ways. One major stress is exposure to an environmental temperature that is normally much lower than that within the uterus. As a consequence, there is a temperature gradient—from warm neonate to cooler air—that favours the loss of heat from the neonate's body. As we shall see later, the magnitude of these losses can be considerable because of the physical characteristics of many neonatal mammals.

For body temperature to be maintained, the rate of heat production by the neonate must match the rate of heat loss. In common with endothermic animals of all ages and types, there are two basic means by which the balance can be achieved. As explained in previous chapters, the possibilities are *to reduce the rate of heat loss* and/or *to increase the rate of heat production* by accelerating metabolic rate. The second strategy, called thermogenesis, may involve *shivering* and/or *non-shivering thermogenesis* (NST). You met these in Section 3.2 in connection with the response of adult organisms to cold.

The thermoregulatory methods that are involved before and after birth depend upon physical characteristics and the stage of development, and are considered in this chapter, beginning with the fetus. Throughout the following pages you should be aware that the *principles* of thermobiology (i.e. all the physical principles and much of the terminology that you have already met in connection with adult organisms) underly the thermobiology of both fetus and neonate.

4.2 Energy exchange between the fetus and mother

To begin our analysis with the fetus might, at first sight, appear to be unnecessary. The fetus is totally enclosed within the womb, and the womb is effectively a thermostable incubator. However, at the moment of birth, the incubator is abandoned and the fetus becomes largely responsible for its own temperature regulation. You already know that the neonate's systems do not all 'leap into full activity' at the moment of birth. Some have been active for much of fetal life, while others take time to come into operation. In so far as the thermoregulatory activities of the neonate are an extension and development of what went before birth, it is appropriate to start with *in utero* energy production and usage.

The fetus generates heat by many biochemical reactions including, for example, the catabolism of glucose in many different tissues. Even the fetal heart generates metabolic heat by beating. Some heat, albeit a relatively smaller amount, is also generated by frictional losses in the walls of the blood vessels. The fact that the fetus is totally enclosed means that any excess heat generated is exported to the mother via the placenta and by conduction through the amniotic fluid. As implied by this statement, in almost all natural circumstances the fetus is a net exporter of heat.

■   The conduction of heat depends upon the existence of a temperature gradient, with heat flowing from a higher to a lower temperature, i.e. down the temperature gradient. Given thermistors capable of measuring *in vivo* temperature, and an artificial substance that, when injected into an adult, significantly increases its body temperature, what experiments could you devise to show that heat flow is normally from fetus to mother?

It is possible to monitor the temperature of the blood leaving the fetus in the umbilical artery of a sheep, and to compare it with the temperature of the aortic blood of the ewe. Recall that the umbilical artery carries fetal blood from the fetal heart to the placenta. In normal circumstances, one would predict—if the fetus is a net heat exporter—that the temperature of blood in the umbilical artery would be higher than that of the maternal blood (as measured in the maternal aorta). If, however, the ewe were given a *pyrogen* (a temperature-raising drug) so that the temperature of maternal aortic blood (and hence maternal placental blood) rises, one would predict a reversal of the temperature gradient. The results of such an experiment are shown in Figure 4.1. Before administration of the pyrogen, umbilical arterial blood is indeed the warmer. After injection of the pyrogen, there are initial small rises in the temperature of maternal aortic blood associated with the stress of the injection, followed by a large rise as a consequence of the drug. The temperature of the fetal blood rises similarly, with only a short time-lag, demonstrating the efficiency of heat transfer between mother and fetus. The brief transposition of solid and dashed lines shows a temporary reversal of gradient; in this zone, heat flow would have been from mother to fetus.

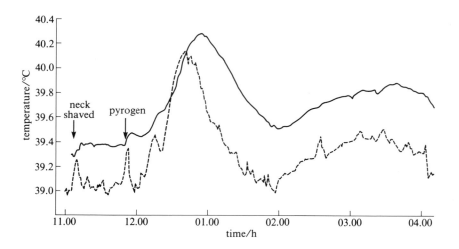

Figure 4.1   The temperatures of fetal blood in the umbilical artery (solid line) and maternal aortic blood (dashed line) in a term sheep. The shaving of the neck of the ewe causes a slight rise in temperature due to stress, and then the injection of the pyrogen in the neck causes another slight rise. The effect of the pyrogen itself is visible in the umbilical artery only 10 minutes after the injection.

The source of all heat exported from the fetus is, ultimately, the net energy made available by the sum of all metabolic reactions occurring within it. Measuring the rate of fetal heat production would be difficult by any direct method. However, a reasonable approximation to this rate (in $kJ\,kg^{-1}\,h^{-1}$) can be calculated from the rate at which the fetus consumes oxygen (in $cm^3\,O_2\,kg^{-1}\,h^{-1}$). To do this calculation, measurements and assumptions must be made as follows.

(1) The oxygen concentrations and rate of blood flow in both the umbilical artery and umbilical vein need to be measured, and from this the rate of oxygen consumption can be calculated.

(2) It is necessary to estimate — or to measure — the particular mixture of fuels being oxidized by the fetus (e.g. a particular molar mix of glucose and amino acids) in order to calculate the *energy liberated per cm^3 oxygen used*. This calculation depends on straightforward physico-chemical data of 'how many kJ are released per mole of oxygen used'. The calculated value is usually around $20\,J\,cm^{-3}$ (discussed in Section 2.4).

(3) It is necessary to assume that no *anaerobic* fetal catabolism occurs alongside the aerobic catabolism responsible for the oxygen uptake. In fact, this assumption is quite a reasonable one and any small amount of anaerobic catabolism that does in fact occur has relatively little quantitative effect on the final calculation of rate of heat production.

(4) From (1)–(3) it is possible to calculate a *metabolic rate* in $kJ\,h^{-1}$ and, with the mass of the fetus, in $kJ\,kg^{-1}\,h^{-1}$. To equate this value with *heat production*, it is necessary to assume that none of that energy is transformed into forms other than heat. If a fetus were able to do significant external work (using its muscles to impart kinetic or potential energy to the exterior), then that assumption would be a wrong one, but external work is in fact small enough to be ignored. Though rapid fetal growth (and hence biosynthesis) may make this assumption unsafe to some slight extent, the calculated value for 'fetal heat production' will still be broadly correct.

■ If fetal oxygen consumption were $x\,cm^3\,O_2\,kg^{-1}\,h^{-1}$ and the calculated conversion factor were $20\,J\,cm^{-3}\,O_2$, the quantity of heat apparently released per hour per kilogram of fetal tissue is $20x\,J$. If a significant amount of anaerobic respiration also occurred, would the value of $20x\,J$ be an overestimate or underestimate of the heat produced?

As heat is released in anaerobic as well as in aerobic respiration, and as this heat production is *not* reflected in oxygen uptake, calculation of heat production from oxygen consumption would, inevitably, be an underestimate. However, we noted earlier that anaerobic respiration is normally low; thus the 'error' is not normally a significant one.

The fetal metabolic rates calculated on the basis of these assumptions are generally higher than actually occur in free-living adult mammals of similar size. Typically an adult mammal of about 4 kg has a metabolic rate of around $9\,kJ\,kg^{-1}\,h^{-1}$, but in one study, the metabolic rate of a 4-kg fetal sheep was calculated to be as high as $12.2\,kJ\,kg^{-1}\,h^{-1}$. This result clearly indicates that fetal tissue has a higher energy turnover per unit mass than has adult tissue. The difference is very probably due to the high rate of tissue synthesis being undertaken by the fetus. A similar picture, shown in Figure 4.2, is obtained when the proportion of a ewe's metabolic rate attributable to the fetus is compared with the proportion of the ewe's total body mass attributable to the fetus.

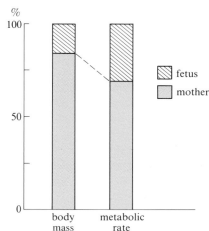

Figure 4.2 Although the fetal sheep represents about 16% of the body mass of the ewe, it contributes 30% of the total metabolic rate.

Two facts have now been established: (a) the fetus has a high metabolic rate, and (b) it is a net heat exporter. The percentage of the mother's total heat production that originates from the fetus is substantial, as shown in Figure 4.2. Effectively, the mother is accommodating a relatively large ancillary heat source within her, and this additional load must be managed by the maternal thermal control system. Yet, at the moment of birth, this ancillary source is ejected, and the mother's regulating system must readjust. Those of you who have given birth may have experienced a feeling of coldness afterwards, and this post-partum chill may very well be associated with the sudden loss of an internal heat source. However, as we shall now see, this effect is minor in comparison with the sudden chill experienced by the fetus as it leaves a well-insulated and controlled environment, and has to control its own temperature.

Summary for Section 4.2

As a consequence of (mainly aerobic) catabolic activities, a fetus generates a substantial amount of energy from nutrients supplied by the mother. Most of the liberated energy appears as heat, and this is transferred from fetus to mother mainly via the placenta. The heat exported by the fetus to the mother forms a significant proportion of the total heat lost from mother to environment. A mammalian fetus produces substantially more heat per kilogram of body mass than an adult.

4.3 Heat loss following birth

During labour and delivery, the human fetus has a mean core temperature of 0.5 °C above that of the mother (measured in the colon) and 0.2 °C above that of the amniotic fluid that surrounds it. Virtually no heat is dissipated over the body surface *in utero*, since the fetal circulation transfers heat to the mother so efficiently.

At the moment of birth, the core body temperature of the neonate begins to fall (illustrated in Figure 4.3), but as long as the neonate remains connected to the placenta its temperature does not fall very much. It appears that the role of the placenta is now reversed; instead of exporting heat from the fetus, the placenta conveys heat from the mother and heats the neonate. Once the cord is severed, however, the temperature of the neonate falls. The rapid cooling effect of the atmosphere has been demonstrated by measuring skin temperatures of the neonate during delivery: the temperature of the baby's scalp dropped from 36 °C to 34 °C within 10 seconds of delivery of the face. A thermistor attached to the chest showed that the first deep breath produced an instantaneous drop in temperature as air at 23 °C (T_a) filled the lungs.

In humans, the period following birth continues to be—without adult intervention—one of heat loss and declining temperature. Figure 4.4 shows how skin temperature and deep-body temperature fell in a group of newborn infants, each of whom had been dried. Here, of course, there has been intervention of sorts, as dryness is not the normal state at birth. The curves in Figure 4.4 would have been different had the babies been left wet.

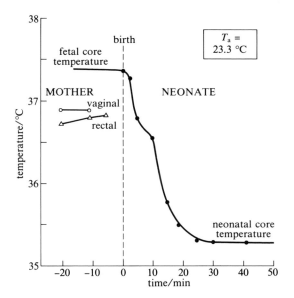

Figure 4.3 Serial fetal and neonatal core temperatures of a human infant, compared with the body temperature of the mother.

■ Why and in what way would they have been different?

Wetness would lead to much greater heat losses, and there would have been a larger decrease in core temperature over a 30-minute period (in fact, about 1 °C more). The reason for this is simply a question of physics. When water evaporates, a certain amount of heat energy is required to bring about the change from water to water vapour. This latent heat of vaporization is derived from the skin, and so a wet baby cools faster than a dry one.

It is not only the temperature gradient that affects heat loss from the newborn. In comparison with adults, the ratio of skin area to body mass is large in neonates. A typical value for the surface area:mass ratio in an adult man (of about 75 kg) is $0.025\,\mathrm{m^2\,kg^{-1}}$, whereas for a 2-kg infant it is $0.078\,\mathrm{m^2\,kg^{-1}}$. An average human newborn baby exposes 50–80% of its surface to the environment, depending upon posture. Thus it is not surprising that heat losses and temperature changes of the kind that you saw in Figures 4.3 and 4.4 occur.

Normal procedures for the care of newborn infants mean, as you would expect, that temperature stress is much diminished; warm air temperatures and clothing are, in varying arrangements, the norm. However, the newborn infant is itself capable of some response to the stimulus of initial cooling—a normal, healthy baby can triple its heat production in response to a cooling stress. An increase in the production of metabolic heat by the neonate requires increased oxygen and this is supplied as a consequence of another change that occurs at birth—namely a change over from maternal oxygen supplied via the placenta to atmospheric oxygen supplied via the lungs. The initial cooling that almost always occurs during and immediately after birth may have a positive role, as there is some evidence that the cooling itself acts as a stimulus to initiate breathing.

Even after breathing has started, however, there is no immediate surge of metabolic heat. It takes time for the lungs to take over from the mother as the source of oxygen. For neonatal arterial blood to become sufficiently oxygenated to sustain significant thermogenic catabolism, it has to become substantially

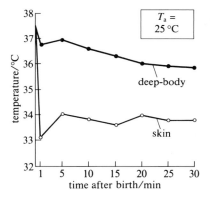

Figure 4.4 The mean abdominal skin temperature and the mean deep-body temperature of a group of newborn human infants kept dry and unwrapped for the first 30 minutes of life.

more oxygenated than fetal blood. Typically, the partial pressure of oxygen in the umbilical vein (blood flowing from placenta to fetus) is only 1.5 kPa, whereas it is around 8 kPa in the arteries of babies. It is only when newly established breathing has raised the oxygen partial pressure in neonatal arteries to 5.3 kPa or greater that heat production can be increased.

As Figure 4.5 shows, heat is lost from a 1.5-kg human infant (under these particular conditions) at a rate of nearly $90 \, kJ \, h^{-1}$, i.e. $60 \, kJ \, kg^{-1} \, h^{-1}$. This total loss occurs via the four different routes shown in Figure 4.5 in the proportions indicated. Clearly, the neonate would cool rapidly if it could neither generate heat internally, nor reduce the heat loss. If core temperature is to be maintained, by one means or another heat loss and heat production must, averaged over time, be equal. The response of neonates to cold stress — in other mammals as well as in humans — is considered in the next section.

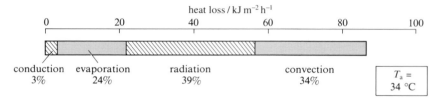

Figure 4.5 The heat loss from a 4-day-old naked baby weighing 1.5 kg, in a draught-free atmosphere of 50% relative humidity. The body temperature of the infant was 37 °C (rectal).

Summary for Section 4.3

From the moment of birth, a fetus is faced with much greater thermoregulatory problems than it had *in utero*. During birth (where T_a is much lower than in the uterus) the placenta transfers heat *to* the fetus, thus reversing its *in utero* role. When birth is complete, two main factors — the temperature gradient between fetus and environment, and the large surface area:mass ratio of the fetus — contribute to temperature stress. In humans, response to this stress leads *both* to the increased production of metabolic heat *and* to appropriate parental behaviour (provision of clothing etc.). To the extent that it is possible, heat production and heat loss are equal.

4.4 Behavioural thermoregulation in neonates

There are a number of stages in the progressive response of mammals to cold stress. An attempt to reduce the exposed surface area, i.e. behavioural thermoregulation, is normally made first. Next, there is a reduction in cutaneous blood flow and, finally, thermogenic tissue is activated. You already know something of the physiological control of heat loss from the skin (Chapter 3), and this section deals briefly with behavioural thermoregulation. A review of thermogenesis then occupies the rest of the chapter.

As noted earlier, metabolism generates heat, and below the critical temperature the regulated production of additional metabolic heat is crucial to the maintenance of body temperature. However, the load placed upon *thermogenesis* is lessened by any kinds of behaviour that result in the conservation of heat.

In the human neonate, there is little behavioural response to cold stress except to cry. Human infants are incapable of altering their posture to a significant degree. They tend to lie extended whatever the temperature, and are thus unable to reduce their effective surface area:volume ratio when cold-stressed. As noted earlier, it is adult behaviour, in providing clothes etc., that allows the infant to conserve sufficient heat. Such measures are essential in cold climates, as the thermogenic capacity of the neonate, even at triple the basal rate mentioned earlier, is simply not enough to achieve temperature constancy.

Different situations often apply in other species. Neonatal rabbits respond behaviourally when cold-stressed. In a cold environment, the almost hairless newborn rabbits hunch into a ball, wrinkle their skin, and rock from side to side. Wrinkling may help trap still air close to the skin (so increasing the degree of insulation), and hunching certainly decreases the surface area. There is also a pronounced thermogenic response to cooling immediately from birth with, as you would expect, oxygen consumption increasing as the ambient temperature falls. Despite these behavioural and thermogenic responses, the body temperature still falls when the neonate is exposed to cool air. The newborn rabbit, in common with many other small neonates, pays the price of temperature instability because of its small size and inadequate insulation. The goal of a stable core temperature, mentioned in Section 4.3, is simply not attainable.

The behaviour of newborn piglets illustrates another 'behavioural device' for heat conservation, namely *huddling*. Postural changes do occur in the individual piglet—at an air temperature of 30 °C, the average effective surface area of a newborn piglet was 0.114 m², whereas at 20 °C postural changes had reduced the exposed area to 0.095 m². But, in addition and more significantly, piglets huddle together in the cold so reducing still further the effective surface area. By comparing the metabolic rates of (a) single piglets between 3 and 6 days old isolated in a metabolism chamber with (b) a group of huddled piglets of the same age and (c) a 90-kg adult pig, it has been shown that huddling behaviour conserves heat very effectively. Results are shown in Figure 4.6.

■   From Figure 4.6, you can see that the metabolic rate (in kJ m⁻² h⁻¹) of the huddled piglets is closer to that of the adult pig than to that of the isolated single piglet. From data in Figure 4.6, at ambient temperatures of 30 °C and 10 °C, make approximate calculations of the metabolic rates of the huddled piglets and the adult as percentages of the single isolated piglet. What is the lower critical temperature of the adult pig?

At 30 °C, it can be seen that the huddled piglets and the adult pig both have exactly the same rates of heat production per square metre of surface area, namely about 70% of that of the isolated piglet. At 10 °C, the metabolic rates of huddled piglets and adults begin to differ, but both use substantially less energy than isolated piglets (60% and 50%, respectively). The plateau representing the thermoneutral zone for the adult pig ceases at the T_{lc} of 20 °C.

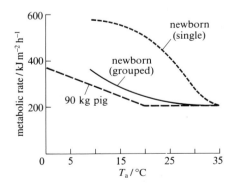

Figure 4.6   The metabolic rate of a single newborn piglet at different ambient temperatures, compared with those of an adult pig and with a group of newborn piglets.

Thus it is plain that, when the ambient temperature falls much below about 35 °C, piglets tend to huddle together and behave metabolically as if they were an adult pig. Below about 27 °C, the energy production of the huddled piglets and the adults begin to diverge, with the adult being slightly more efficient. However, energy continues to be saved by huddling down to the lowest temperature shown in Figure 4.6.

The phenomenon of huddling — which also occurs in newborn puppies, mice rats and chicks, and other species — emphasizes that heat conservation in the newborn often depends on complex behavioural responses. For instance, newborn rabbits, though born blind and relatively helpless, move towards each other, possibly because they are attracted by the warmth of each other's body. They move around all the time in a cold environment, but are inactive and sleep in a warm location. In a closed space, newborn rabbits wander and search until they come to the warmest spot, where they then remain. The adoption of a flexed posture also reduces surface area, but such adaptation to the cold is only possible for newborn mammals if the muscles are sufficiently well developed. As noted earlier, human neonates do not have this capacity.

Many mammals — particularly small ones such as rats and mice which have a high surface area:volume ratio, and especially those in cold climates — protect their young from extremes of temperature by building a nest. In many species, for example, the rat, the parents join their offspring in the nest, and the amount of time they spend there depends largely on environmental conditions. In mice, the warmth of the parent's body, the insulation of its coat, and the protection of the nest all keep the huddled offspring warm.

Young mice and rats are almost poikilothermic at birth and they rely on the presence of the mother to keep the nest warm. When the mother leaves the nest, the young mice or 'pups' cool and they start to produce calls. These calls are well beyond the range of human hearing (ultrasonic), but they can be heard by the mother, if she is nearby, and stimulate her to return to the nest. If a pup falls out of the nest, the calls it emits as it cools stimulate the mother to retrieve it and return it to the nest. The rate at which the pups call is inversely related to body temperature, although the relation is only approximate; at very low body temperatures the pups do not call very much, perhaps because they are too chilled. The call of the pup is an unspecific signal: a mother either cannot recognize her own pups from their call, or does not discriminate, for any pup that calls is retrieved.

Summary for Section 4.4

Although the neonates of some mammals are unable to maintain a constant T_b, homeothermic mechanisms are active in all mammalian species. These involve either heat conservation or heat generation (thermogenesis). Heat is conserved by reducing losses through the skin and by behavioural means. The latter may involve parental activities (clothing in humans, nest-building in rabbits and mice, etc.) or neonatal activities (posture changes in species such as rabbits, huddling in pigs, etc.). Young rats and mice (and others) emit calls as their temperature falls, to which the mother responds, indicating that behavioural thermoregulation may involve behavioural activities of *both* offspring *and* parents.

4.5 Shivering and non-shivering thermogenesis in neonates

Although we have focused principally on heat conservation by behavioural means so far in this chapter, there has been constant reference to thermogenesis, literally, the 'generation of heat'. As noted earlier, heat is produced in all metabolic activities. The term 'thermogenesis', however, is usually used by physiologists to mean the *involuntary* production of heat *as a consequence of cold stress*. By restricting the term to involuntary processes, heat produced by muscle contraction in exercise (voluntary behaviour) is not normally described as thermogenesis. Similarly, by restricting the term to heat production that is a consequence of cold stress, heat that is produced as a by-product of metabolic processes in general is also not usually described as thermogenesis.

Two points should be made about the strict definition of thermogenesis given above. First, heat produced by exercise is, or can be, physiologically important and, just because of a definition, should not be ignored when discussion of it is appropriate. Similarly, heat produced by metabolic processes *that are not sensitive to cold* is also important in the energy economy of an organism; it, too, should not be ignored when inclusion in a discussion is warranted. A second point about the definition of thermogenesis is that physiologists and physiology texts are not always scrupulous in their adherence to the strict definition! You need, therefore to be aware of possible confusing usage.

As noted in Section 4.1, one method of producing heat from metabolism depends on the *involuntary*, *cold-induced* muscular process known as *shivering*. Not surprisingly, this kind of heat production is described as **shivering thermogenesis**. Heat production by any other metabolic process that involuntarily occurs as a consequence of lowered temperature is termed **non-shivering thermogenesis (NST)**.

You know from Sections 3.2.1 and 3.2.2 that shivering is an important source of metabolic heat in many adult animals. In contrast, looking across the range of mammalian species, shivering is used less by neonates. It is, however, important in some animals whose newborn are comparatively large and also have relatively well-developed muscles at birth. Within minutes of delivery, the neonatal lamb can increase its rate of heat production to five times that of the BMR when cooled—and most of this increase is attributable to the onset of shivering. Similarly, shivering is important in newborn foals, piglets and other mammals whose size and development at birth make it a feasible mechanism.

As noted at the beginning of this section, NST properly includes all heat production that is not a consequence of shivering and is stimulated by cold stress. In fact, the *only* known process that conforms to this definition is the production of heat within **brown adipose tissue (BAT)**. Such heat production increases as ambient temperature decreases and involves the mediation of the **catecholamines**, especially **noradrenalin**.

■   From your knowledge of thermobiology, recall what kinds of metabolic process produce heat *other than shivering and heat production in BAT*?

The answer is, of course, all of them! All metabolic processes are inefficient to some extent, leading, therefore, to the conversion of chemical energy to heat. One important category is muscular activity other than in shivering, i.e. that involved in other movements. Other heat producing activities have nothing to do with movement: heat is produced in differing amounts in different tissues as a by-product of biosynthesis, active transport, etc.

Many neonatal mammals, however, depend on NST as either the sole or the major provider of extra metabolic heat for thermoregulation. Compared with a mammal such as a lamb, neonates of animals such as rats, rabbits, kittens or mice are physically small, and hence have a large surface area:volume ratio. Thus, proportionately, they have a consequently greater need for heat. These neonates also lack the muscle mass and muscle development necessary for shivering. They need, therefore, some other way to make their heat, and neonatal NST, i.e. BAT activity, is widespread among such species. Despite its large size, the newborn human infant, probably because of its relatively poor motor development, similarly uses NST and not shivering.

Such is the importance of BAT thermogenesis that much of the remainder of this chapter is devoted to the nature, biochemistry and regulation of this tissue. As a scene-setter, it is useful to distinguish shivering thermogenesis, BAT thermogenesis and non-BAT heat production in broad biochemical terms.

Figure 4.7a illustrates the well-established and apparently universal role of ATP as an energy transducer. *On the left*, catabolic processes degrade metabolic fuels such as glucose, glycerol, fatty acids and amino acids, and produce ATP within cells as a consequence. Heat is liberated during these processes as a result of the inefficiency of the coupling of ATP production to energy-liberating catabolism. For example, of the approximately 2 900 kJ of gross energy available when one mole of glucose is oxidized to carbon dioxide and water, in most cells only about 1 100 kJ is transferred to ATP as it is formed from ADP and inorganic phosphate. The remaining 1 800 kJ, about 60% of the free energy liberated in oxidative catabolism, is lost as heat. *On the right*, various energy-using processes, of which muscle contraction, active transport and biosynthesis are the most notable, lead to the reconversion of ATP to ADP, but again with very inefficient linkage, with the result that yet more heat is liberated. For an example of inefficiency in ATP usage, let us consider protein synthesis. When two amino acids are joined together, only about 13% of the potential energy in the ATP used is retained in the peptide bond; the rest is liberated as heat.

Despite this inefficiency, ATP production is *obligatorily coupled* to the oxidative catabolic processes. This means that a sequence of oxidation/reduction reactions within the electron transport chain of mitochondria is linked to the synthesis of ATP from ADP and inorganic phosphate in such a way that the *one cannot occur without the other*. Because metabolic heat depends on the *inefficiency* of ATP production and use, it follows that in **coupled mitochondria** heat cannot be liberated without ATP being made and ATP cannot be made unless it is also used. This means that heat production can only be increased by using more and more ATP, hence making more and more ATP. This process is the basis of heat production in shivering or in the deliberate muscle movements of various kinds of behaviour.

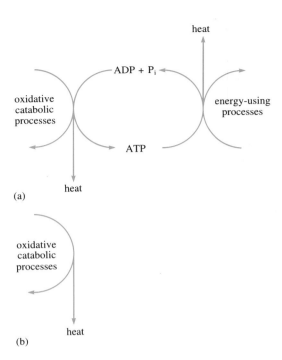

Figure 4.7   (a) Role of ATP as an energy transducer in cells of all tissues. (b) ATP production is abolished in fully uncoupled mitochondria in BAT.

Leaving aside BAT, Figure 4.7a also shows why tissues other than muscle cannot increase or decrease heat production in response to temperature and thermal need. As with muscle, heat 'leaks' during ATP formation or ATP usage and, as with muscle, ATP production is tightly coupled to catabolism. However, it is plain — in terms of economy and the organization of tissues — that these cells could not increase (say) their rate of biosynthesis or their rate of active transport simply to use more, and so make more ATP, purely for the sake of heat production. Interestingly, significantly increased heat production occurs in malignant tumours because of increased cell division, and hence increased biosynthesis. These can be seen as hot spots on infrared pictures of the body (see Figure 4.8, *overleaf*).

The final way in which a cell may increase heat production is to reduce the efficiency of ATP production so that more of the potential energy within the fuel is converted into heat instead of into ATP. This process has been shown to occur in BAT, which is specialized for heat production. In this tissue, the catabolic oxidation of intracellular fuel, mainly lipids, is progressively uncoupled from ATP production as the external temperature falls, and as a direct consequence, more heat is produced. Figure 4.7b illustrates the situation in fully **uncoupled mitochondria**: all chemical potential energy liberated by oxidation appears as heat, none being stored in newly synthesized ATP. The mechanism by which changes in external temperature are linked to the intracellular biochemical process of uncoupling is somewhat complex, as the following pages will show.

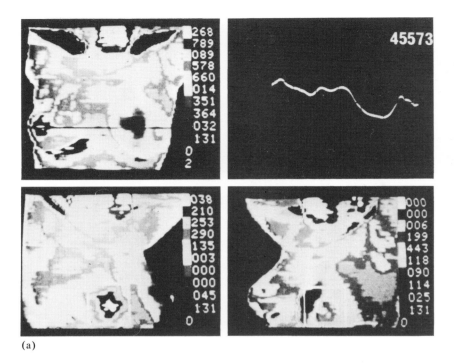

(a)

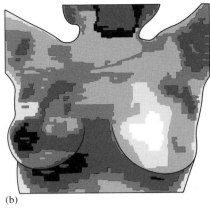

(b)

Figure 4.8 Infrared imaging is a very useful diagnostic tool for certain types of disease. This example of the practical use of diagnostic imaging shows how the presence of tumour cells can be revealed by their slightly higher temperature (and therefore infrared emission). The position of the tumour cells can be determined accurately by taking photographs from different angles (a). The temperature range is normally indicated by a scale of colours running from blue to red. As these photographs do not reproduce well in black and white, the top left one has been redrawn (b) with a grey scale running from white (coldest) to black (hottest).

Summary for Section 4.5

Thermogenesis is a term that encompasses processes in which heat is involuntarily generated as a consequence of cold stress. Defined in this way, there are just two categories of thermogenesis: *shivering thermogenesis* and *non-shivering thermogenesis* (NST). The only known example of the latter is thermogenesis in brown adipose tissue (BAT). Heat is also produced in other ways — namely by all other metabolic processes. This includes all other kinds of muscle contraction, whether cold-related (e.g. voluntary exercise) or totally unrelated to cold (e.g. heart beat), and also metabolism unrelated to muscle contraction (e.g. biosynthesis, active transport).

Some neonates depend very much on shivering thermogenesis, especially those that are relatively large and have comparatively well developed muscles at birth, e.g. lambs. Other neonates depend very substantially on NST, e.g. rabbits, humans. Some of these can also shiver whereas some, such as human neonates, cannot.

In NST (i.e. in BAT catabolism) heat production increases inversely with temperature by the mediation of the catecholamines, especially noradrenalin. In all tissues *other than BAT*, heat is produced as a consequence of the inefficient formation of ATP (in catabolism) and the inefficient utilization of ATP (in muscle contraction, biosynthesis and active transport). In the mitochondria of these non-BAT tissues, ATP production is *coupled to* the catabolism of cellular nutrients. In *BAT*, heat is directly produced as a consequence of catabolism without the formation and breakdown of ATP. The mitochondria of BAT are said to be fully or partially uncoupled.

4.6 Brown adipose tissue (BAT)

The thermogenic properties of BAT were first demonstrated using fine thermocouples implanted beneath the skin of neonatal rabbits. One was placed in the interscapular body, which contains a large deposit of BAT (known as IBAT, the 'I' denoting interscapular). A second thermocouple was placed over the sacrospinalis muscle in the lumbar region, which contains no BAT, and a third was used to monitor colonic temperature. Figure 4.9 shows the observations made during the experiment. After 14 minutes (t_1) at 35 °C the ambient temperature was dropped by 10 °C. The body temperature dropped rapidly at all sites, but after a further 20 minutes (t_2) the temperature over the IBAT had climbed back to 37 °C. Such data suggests that BAT increased its heat production in response to the drop in ambient temperature. The increase in BAT temperature occurred concurrently with an increase in oxygen consumption, indicating that metabolic rate was being increased by cold exposure. As shown in Figure 4.9, the effect is marked, oxygen consumption being three times greater at 25 °C as that at the higher temperature.

The final part of the experiment provides confirmatory evidence of the role of BAT in heat production. After 50 minutes, the oxygen content of inspired air was reduced from 21% to 5% (indicated by the grey band in Figure 4.9). Not only did oxygen consumption fall rapidly but all three body temperatures fell to about the same value. When the inspired oxygen level was returned to 21%, the temperature over the BAT rose rapidly.

■   What do you note from Figure 4.9 about the differences in the temperature in BAT, muscle and colon after 45 minutes? What explanation for these differences is likely?

Because of thermogenesis within it, the temperature of BAT is largely unchanged from the starting value of 37 °C. In contrast, muscle temperature has fallen by more than 2 °C. The temperature change in the colon—the core temperature of the neonatal rabbit—registers an intermediate decrease of just a little more than 1 °C. The likely reason for these differences is that the thermogenic power of BAT is partially able to buffer the colonic temperature (reflecting the temperature of the essential organs) against cooling caused by the lowered ambient temperature. Muscle temperature, itself lacking cold-induced thermogenicity, is less physiologically essential than the core, and so its temperature is less protected.

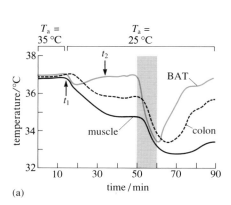

(a)

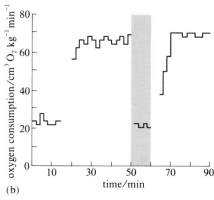

(b)

Figure 4.9   The total oxygen consumption and the temperature at three different body sites during cold and during hypoxia in the newborn rabbit. (a) Body temperatures measured near BAT (blue line), in muscle (solid black line), and in the colon (dashed black line). (b) Oxygen consumption. The grey band marks a period during which the oxygen content of the inspired air was cut from 21% to 5%.

4.6.1 Location of brown adipose tissue

At birth, about 20% of the body mass of a human is adipose tissue—that is, fatty tissue containing substantial amounts of triacylglycerol. Much of this adipose tissue—about 90% of it—is **white adipose tissue (WAT)**, whose comparative structure and function is briefly touched upon below. Of more interest in the context of non-shivering thermogenesis is the 2% or so (10% of the 20%) of BAT about which much has already been said. Other mammals contain both WAT and BAT, though only guinea-pigs rival humans in the preponderance of WAT. Most other mammals have much less WAT and in some, as we shall see, the proportion of BAT can be as high as 5% of the total body mass. In contrast, some may have no BAT whatsoever.

BAT has been found in many mammals, particularly small species, and is most readily identifiable in animals that are dependent upon NST to maintain their body temperature, such as neonatal mammals, small mammmals that are cold-acclimated, and mammals arising from hibernation (when body temperature is increased as part of the awaking process). In these animals, BAT is active and appears a dark brown/red colour. In animals where the tissue is relatively inactive, it is much paler in colour and less well defined.

Like WAT, BAT is found in a number of discrete deposits in locations throughout the body—mainly in the interscapular, cervical, axillary (armpit) and kidney regions, as well as round the aorta and the heart. The relative size and importance of each depot varies from species to species. Figure 4.10 shows the distribution of BAT in the human infant and Figure 4.11 in a fetal mouse. In rats and mice the largest site is found in the interscapular region (IBAT), just under the skin. Here the tissue is divided into two distinct lobes, each of which has its own nerve and blood supply. The accessibility of this site, with its clearly identifiable nerves and blood vessels, has made it the most studied BAT depot.

In most neonatal mammals the total amount of BAT existing in discrete depots (i.e. that which can be dissected from the dead animal) is 1–2% of the body mass. The exceptions are noteworthy. Piglets and many hoofed mammals appear to have no BAT; lambs, though born with some, lose it within a few days. In contrast, newborn rabbits, guinea-pigs and other very small neonates contain more BAT—about 5% of body mass.

Figure 4.10 The distribution of BAT (shaded grey) in the human infant. For clarity, the distribution of the thin sheets of tissue around the shoulder blades and neck is shown on a separate drawing.

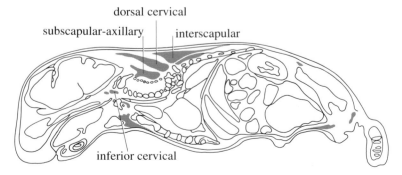

Figure 4.11 A longitudinal section of a fetal mouse, showing the areas of BAT as grey shading.

The proportion of BAT in different mammals correlates well with the apparent importance of NST in the 'armoury of thermoregulatory weapons' with which each species has been endowed by evolution. Piglets, as noted in an earlier section, are physically mature at birth and, as well as their huddling behaviour, can shiver violently from birth. Neonatal lambs, with their small surface area:volume ratio and well-developed muscles, have some BAT but rely more on shivering to produce the heat they need. In contrast, one finds a greater than normal proportion of BAT in neonatal mammals, such as the rabbit, that have a proportionately large surface area from which to lose heat, as well as feeble muscles that cannot support shivering. For animals such as these, thermogenesis via BAT is essential. Even then, without the shelter of their nests and without the care of the mother, poikilothermy rather than homeothermy becomes the norm.

A human baby usually has about 1–2% of body mass as BAT: thus, a baby of around 3.2 kg might contain around 32–64 g of BAT. As noted earlier, newborn babies lie fully extended and do not shiver: despite their comparatively large size their heat generating capacity depends solely on NST. In this respect, the newborn of humans more closely resemble those of rats or rabbits than of pigs or sheep.

It is important to note that the seemingly small quantities of BAT described above have a large and very significant impact upon BMR. The maximum aerobic capacity of BAT ($500\,\mathrm{W\,kg^{-1}}$) is about ten times that of skeletal muscle. Thus, in animals such as rats, 1 g of BAT could cause a doubling of metabolic rate and, in large animals such as man, 50 g could cause a 20% increase.

4.6.2   Histology of brown adipose tissue

In addition to the endothelial cells of the many blood capillaries that pervade brown adipose tissue, BAT is made up of brown fat cells (or **brown adipocytes**), interstitial cells and **preadipocytes** that can differentiate into mature brown adipocytes if an animal is subjected to a sustained thermogenic stimulus. The tissue is highly vascularized and is capable of a high rate of blood flow. This ensures that oxygen is delivered to the respiring cells, that the tissue's fuel reserves are replenished, that waste products of metabolism are removed from the tissue and, above all, that heat produced in the tissue is carried to other parts of the body. The latter is, of course, the evolutionary *raison d'être* of BAT.

Brown adipocytes and BAT blood vessels receive direct innervation by neurons of the sympathetic branch of the autonomic nervous system. The neurons that impinge on the brown adipocytes have been shown to contain only the neurotransmittor noradrenalin. Those that interact with the blood vessels contain at least one other neurotransmittor, which has been named *neuropeptide Y*.

There are many differences between the white adipocytes (of WAT) and the brown adipocytes (of BAT) which underlie differences in the function of the two kinds of tissue. The brown adipocyte is thermogenic and essentially a site of fuel oxidation, whereas the white adipocyte is essentially a site of fuel storage dedicated to the regulation of lipid fuel supplies to tissues remote from itself.

Brown and white adipocytes differ in a number of ways. These include the following:

(1) *Cell size*. White adipocytes are larger, on average, than brown adipocytes.

(2) *Number and shape of lipid storage vesicle*s. Brown adipocytes have numerous small vesicles (vacuoles) dispersed throughout the cytoplasm. In contrast, in a white adipocyte there tends to be a single large vesicle taking up most of the cytoplasmic space of the cell. These differences in lipid vacuoles have led to brown adipocytes being described as **multilocular** (literally, having many places) and white adipocytes as **unilocular** (having one place).

(3) *Mitochondria*. The mitochondria of brown adipocytes are larger, more numerous and have a more complex cristal structure than mitochondria in white adipocytes—or indeed of cells of other tissues. In BAT, the mitochondrial respiratory enzymes are present at higher concentrations than in WAT and in other tissues, e.g. the activity of cytochrome oxidase in BAT exceeds even that in heart muscle. This is a striking gauge of just how great is the oxidative power of brown adipocytes. The high degree of BAT vascularization together with the large amounts of cytochromes, gives active BAT its characteristic red/brown colour and hence its name. The major characterizing factor in brown adipocyte mitochondria is the presence of a unique protein, called **uncoupling protein (UCP)**, in the inner mitochondrial membrane, which will be discussed in detail in the following section.

(4) *Glycogen content*. Levels of glycogen are high in brown adipocytes, where it is stored as cytoplasmic granules. Much less glycogen is found in white adipocytes.

Figure 4.12 illustrates a number of these differences in diagrammatic form. Note that when the BAT cells contain a lot of fat, the individual lipid vesicles may coalesce to form one large vesicle and the mitochondria become masked. This is illustrated in drawing 4 of Figure 4.12b. These unilocular cells are largely indistinguishable from the non-thermogenic white adipocytes (drawing 2 of Figure 4.12a).

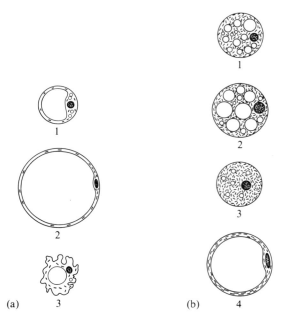

Figure 4.12 (a) White adipose tissue: (1) A developing cell. The nucleus is rounded and the cytoplasm contains a number of small fat vacuoles and one large one. (2) A mature cell. The nucleus is compressed against the cell wall, the mitochondria are few, small and rounded. (3) A fat-depleted cell. (b) Brown adipose tissue: (1) A developing cell. The cytoplasm contains a round nucleus, numerous large mitochondria and many fat vesicles. (2) A mature cell. The cell contains more cytoplasm and more fat than the developing cell. (3) A fat-depleted cell. The cytoplasm is filled with mitochondria and few small fat vesicles. (4) Note that the distinction between unilocular and multilocular adipocyte tissue is not always precise. Here the fat vacuoles in a BAT cell have fused to form a single vesicle.

BAT tissue that contains mostly unilocular cells appears yellowish rather than brown. The difference between multilocular and unilocular brown adipocytes suggests a difference in primary function. Although the distinction is somewhat imprecise, multilocular cells are associated with thermogenesis whereas unilocular ones (like the white adipocytes) store fat. Multilocular cells are thought to be engaged in rapid oxidation of fat substrate. The coalescing of the smaller lipid vacuoles would indicate a slowing down of fat oxidation. Observations of brown adipocytes in tissue culture, using time-lapse photography, have shown coalescence of fat droplets. In calves and lambs, the brown adipocytes are often unilocular at birth, and anatomical studies of still-born human neonates have, similarly, shown that the brown adipocytes are largely unilocular at birth. After birth, the brown adipocytes become multilocular.

In Section 4.7 we shall describe evidence showing that the catecholamines—especially noradrenalin—are involved in the triggering of lipolysis and thermogenesis. Tumours of the chromaffin cells of the adrenal glands (**phaeochromocytoma**) secrete catecholamines. In humans suffering from this condition, the level of catecholamines in the blood plasma is around twenty times the normal level, and patients with this disease show a marked proliferation of multilocular brown adipocytes.

The increase in thermogenic activity in phaeochromocytoma may be so great that infrared scans may fail to discriminate between the tumour and the very active BAT. Fortunately, because BAT is the only known site of uncoupling protein, it is possible to use a **radioimmunoassay** (with antibodies raised against UCP) to measure accurately the amount of UCP present in human BAT obtained either during surgery or at autopsy. Figure 4.13 presents some data that compare the amount of UCP found in adipose tissue in humans of different ages in two different sites. The presence of UCP is considered to be a conclusive indication of thermogenic potential.

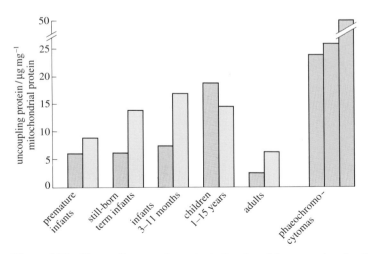

Figure 4.13   Uncoupling protein content of perirenal (grey tone) and axillary (blue tone) adipose tissue of humans of different age groups, and of perirenal adipose tissue from three cases of phaeochromocytoma. Mean values were significantly different from those of infants (3–11 months).

■ What conclusion can you draw from the comparative height of the three
bars on the far right?

The three right-hand bars all relate to adipose tissue in individuals suffering
from phaeochromocytoma; all show a substantially increased levels of UCP.
Given that these tumours actively secrete catecholamines into the circulation—
which therefore increases the exposure of the vascularized adipose tissue to noradrenalin—the hypothesis that increased levels of noradrenalin lead to
increased UCP in BAT is supported.

We now turn to the changes in BAT that occur under more normal (that is, non-
pathological) conditions. What histological changes, if any, have been observed
during cold stress? Warm-acclimated adult rats can be cold-stressed very
effectively by moving them from 25 °C to 4 °C for 48 hours. Figure 4.14
compares samples of IBAT from such cold-stressed rats with samples from
unstressed controls: (a) and (c) are controls at low and high powers, respectively, and (b) and (d) are equivalent preparations from the cold-stressed animal.

Figure 4.14 Sections of IBAT. (a) A
section from a warm-acclimated rat.
Arterioles (A) and blood capillaries (C)
are indicated. The unlabelled, white,
spherical structures are lipid vesicles
($\times$ 456). (b) A section from a cold-
stressed rat ($\times$ 456). (c) A higher
magnification ($\times$ 1 064) of the section
shown in (a). The four cell types
mentioned in the text are indicated: B,
brown adipocyte; E, endothelial cell; I,
interstitial cell; P, preadipocyte. (d) A
higher magnification ($\times$ 1 064) of the
section shown in (b). Three cell types
are shown.

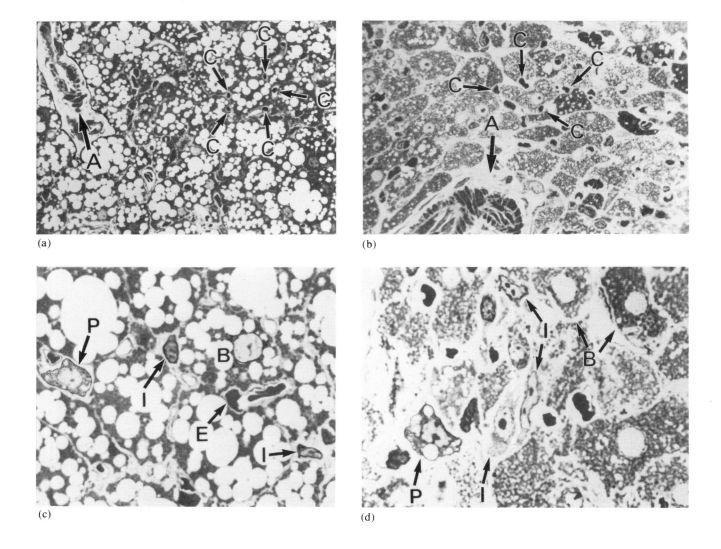

(a)

(b)

(c)

(d)

■   By comparing (a) and (b), what conclusions may be drawn about the effect of cold stressing on the IBAT arterioles, capillaries and the triacylglycerol vesicles?

The comparisons show that the size of both arterioles and capillaries is greater in the cold-stressed rat than in the control; the diameter of the fat vesicles has markedly decreased. Increased blood flow and decreased fat reserves are both consistent with increased thermogenesis, and this, in turn, is consistent with the increase in BAT activity that occurs as ambient temperatures fall.

Examination of the micrographs (b) and (d) shows the four cell types present in BAT tissue: brown adipocytes (B); preadipocytes (P), i.e. cells that are precursors of brown adipocytes; interstitial cells (I); capillary endothelial cells (E).

If the number of cells of each type is counted and frequency histograms are prepared, results of the type shown in Figure 4.15 are obtained. From this, we can see that the percentages of preadipocytes and interstitial cells have increased in the cold-stressed animals, whereas the percentages of mature adipocytes and endothelial cells have decreased slightly. Preadipocytes are rarely observed in the BAT of warm-acclimated animals, yet in rats that are cold-stressed for 8 days they form 5% of the cells.

It is plain from Figure 4.15 that some change in the proportion of different BAT cell types occurs during cold stress. Just how dramatic that change is, however, is only revealed by an investigation of cell division during the acclimation period. The rate of DNA synthesis taking place during mitosis can be measured by a technique called **autoradiography**. [³H]thymidine, injected intraperitoneally into the rat 4 hours prior to the tissue samples being taken, is incorporated into the nuclei of the dividing cells. Microscope slides are prepared in the usual way, except that a coating of photographic emulsion is put over the tissue. Since radioactivity causes deposition of silver grains, any nucleus containing [³H]thymidine (and which has therefore undergone DNA replication) has silver grains on it which show up as black spots when viewed under the microscope (Figure 4.16).

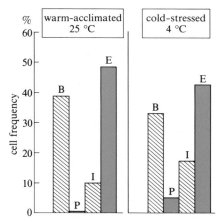

Figure 4.15   Cell frequencies in IBAT from warm-acclimated and cold-stressed rats. B, brown adipocyte; E, endothelial cell; I, interstitial cell; P, preadipocyte.

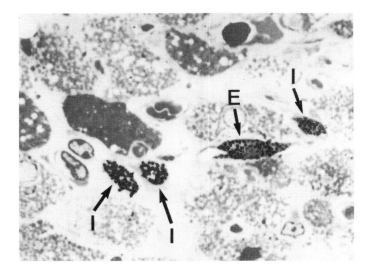

Figure 4.16   A section of IBAT from a cold-stressed rat. [³H]thymidine was injected 4 hours prior to the tissue sample being taken. The section has been coated with photographic emulsion. There are silver grains deposited over the nuclei of three interstitial cells (I) and one endothelial cell (E).

Examination of such preparations, with each different type of 'silver-speckled' cell being counted and tallied, permits the construction of histograms shown in Figure 4.17. This shows the percentage of cells with labelled nuclei in the four types we distinguished earlier. Apart from mature adipocytes, the other groups all show a remarkable increase in mitotic activity. Indeed, the increase in mitotic index of the cold-stressed rats over the controls is 70-fold. Mitotic index is the number of mitoses per thousand cells. Values in this experiment ranged from about 1 to about 90 per thousand.)

■   Taking Figures 4.14–4.17 altogether, how would you sum up the effect of cold stress on the cells of IBAT?

Figure 4.17 shows that there is a great increase, through mitosis, in the number of fat precursor cells (i.e. preadipocytes) and the associated interstitial cells. A parallel increase in capillary size occurs, as shown by the increased rate of division in the capillary endothelial cells. Such proliferation affects the directly observable proportions of cell types (Figure 4.15). Overall, there has been a marked *hyperplasia*, i.e. an increased number of cells, in the IBAT tissue.

It is not surprising, therefore, that the mass of IBAT was found to be greater in cold-stressed rats. This increase in mass can occur rapidly. The mass of IBAT in rats cold-stressed below 5 °C has been observed to double in 6 days. Further experiments have shown that the amount of BAT is also affected by diet, and appears to be linked with the fat content of the food (see Figure 4.18).

Various differences in the BAT of warm- and cold-acclimated rats have been reviewed in the preceding pages. These experimental observations, summarized in Table 4.1, must be accommodated within whatever biochemical mechanism is proposed for BAT function and regulation.

Table 4.1   A comparison of BAT in warm- and cold-acclimated rats, showing which factors increase (↑) or decrease (↓) on acclimation.

	Warm-acclimated	Cold-acclimated
Tissue mass	↓	↑
Protein content	↓	↑
UCP concentration	↓	↑
Sympathetic activity	↓	↑
Lipid content	↑	↓

4.6.3 Biochemical basis of thermogenesis in BAT

In the preceding section, we have seen that brown adipocytes are packed with large mitochondria that are, in turn, packed with respiratory enzymes. This indicates that mitochondrial pathways are involved in BAT thermogenesis. Indeed, it is now known that brown adipocytes contain mitochondria that are especially adapted for heat production. Before we look at the specialist BAT mitochondria, a review of the metabolic function of non-BAT mitochondria is now appropriate.

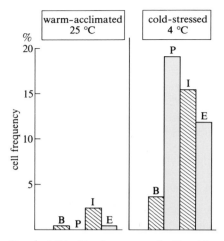

Figure 4.17   The frequency of cells with labelled nuclei in IBAT from warm-acclimated and cold-stressed rats.

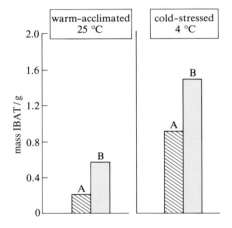

Figure 4.18   The mass of IBAT of rats fed on different diets before and after cold exposure. Group A received a low-fat, high-carbohydrate and high-protein diet. Group B received a high-fat, low-carbohydrate and low-protein diet.

As noted earlier (in Figure 4.7), metabolic energy is provided by the oxidative catabolism of substances provided to cells by the circulatory system. Within cells, the substances catabolized include glucose and glycogen, fatty acids and glycerol (derived from triacylglycerols), and a range of different amino acids. Each of these is catabolized by routes not discussed here — by glycolysis, by TCA cycle activity, by the β-oxidation of fatty acids, and so on — to yield continual supplies of *reduced coenzymes*, in particular NADH + H$^+$ and FADH$_2$. These coenzymes are delivered at the inner surface of the inner membrane of each of the many mitochondria that fill metabolically active cells (summarized in Figure 4.19).

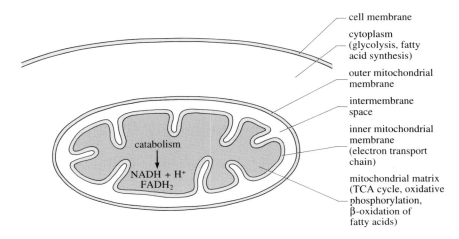

cell membrane

cytoplasm (glycolysis, fatty acid synthesis)

outer mitochondrial membrane

intermembrane space

inner mitochondrial membrane (electron transport chain)

mitochondrial matrix (TCA cycle, oxidative phosphorylation, β-oxidation of fatty acids)

catabolism

NADH + H$^+$
FADH$_2$

Figure 4.19 A mitochondrion. Most NADH + H$^+$ and FADH$_2$ is produced in the matrix (centre) of the mitochondrion. These reduced coenzymes reach the inner wall of the inner membrane when the next and final stage of oxidative catabolism occurs (electron transport chain).

The final stage of oxidative catabolism occurs at the inner mitochondrial membrane of each mitochondrion. Here, the molecules of NADH + H$^+$ and FADH$_2$ that have been produced by the other pathways are finally oxidized by molecular oxygen, and ATP is produced by the phosphorylation of ADP (**oxidative phosphorylation**). Some of the chemical energy made available by this oxidation is used in forming ATP and the balance is released as heat. The equations for the overall reactions accomplished at the inner membrane are:

$$NADH + H^+ + {}^\backprime O_2 \; (+ \; 3ADP + 3P_i) \rightarrow NAD^+ + H_2O \; (+ \; 3ATP + 3H_2O)$$

OR

$$FADH_2 + {}^\backprime O_2 \; (+ \; 2ADP + 2P_i) \rightarrow FAD + H_2O \; (+ \; 2ATP + 2H_2O)$$

These reactions take place via a series of linked oxidation/reduction reactions, termed the **electron transport chain** (**ETC**), within the mitochondrial membrane. Each component of this chain exists alternately in an oxidized or reduced state; the change in state is brought about by the addition of either a hydrogen atom or an electron (reduction) or by the loss of a hydrogen atom or an electron (oxidation). Successive components in the ETC have an increasing affinity for electrons (or hydrogen) and, in the reduced state, a decreasing chemical potential energy. The final acceptor of electrons (and hydrogen ions) is molecular oxygen — also delivered to the cell by the circulation — and the ultimate product is water. Some features of the ETC are illustrated in Figure 4.20 (*overleaf*).

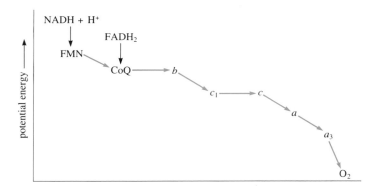

Figure 4.20 Illustrating the change in potential energy of reduced components of the electron transport chain. The flow of hydrogen atoms and of electrons is shown. CoQ is coenzyme Q; b, c_1, c, a and a_3 are cytochromes. FMN is a cofactor related to FAD. These components form part of the structure of the mitochondrial membrane.

The protons and electrons enter the chain at a relatively high energy level and leave the chain in the form of water at a relatively low energy level. As noted, passage down the chain has resulted in a stepwise reduction in the potential energy of the intermediate compounds as they are formed by successive reductions. The energy released by the oxidation/reduction reactions is then linked to the formation of ATP from ADP and inorganic phosphate (P_i) under the influence of the **ATP synthetase** enzyme (which is also part of the inner membrane). As noted earlier, the 60% or more of the energy is not captured in ATP and is lost as heat.

The exact process by which the energy released by the electron transport chain is used to make ATP from ADP and P_i is still not fully known. Most scientists, however, currently accept Peter Mitchell's **chemiosmotic hypothesis** as the most likely explanation. The hypothesis states that the constituents of the ETC are arranged in the inner membrane in a configuration which facilitates the sequence of reactions described above. As these reactions proceed, protons are transferred across the inner mitochondrial membrane from inside to outside. There is still uncertainty about precisely how many protons are moved to the outside per water molecule finally formed (i.e. per oxygen atom used or per pair of electrons transported). The representation in Figure 4.21a provides an acceptable summary of the relationship between electron transport and the movement of hydrogen ions.

Because the inner mitochondrial membrane is impermeable to protons, the movement shown in Figure 4.21a creates a **proton gradient**, i.e. a different concentration of protons (and hence a different pH and different electrical potential) on either side of the membrane. Any gradient of this kind possesses chemical potential energy, and it is this potential energy that seems to be put to work to form ATP. Protons can only pass though the inner mitochondrial membrane and so re-enter the matrix via a *proton permeable channel* that is structurally part of the ATP synthetase. The passage of protons through the ATP synthetase channel dissipates the energy of the gradient, which is then used to phosphorylate ADP and make ATP (Figure 4.21b).

The rate at which hydrogen atoms or electrons pass down the ETC from NADH + H^+ and $FADH_2$ to O_2 is determined by the rate at which H^+ ions on the outside of the inner membrane can re-enter the matrix. This, in its turn, is determined by the availability of ADP for phosphorylation to ATP.

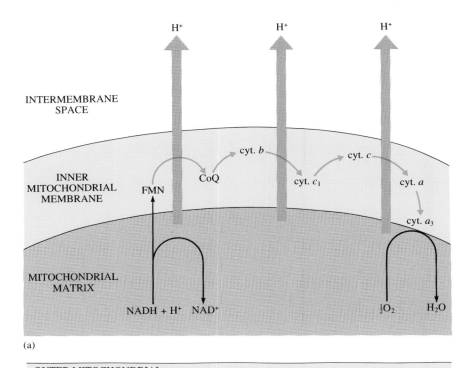

(a)

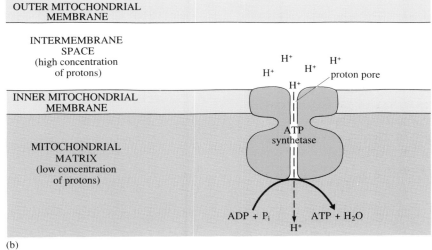

(b)

Figure 4.21   (a) A representation of the arrangement of components of the ETC within the inner membrane of the mitochondrion, and the associated movement of protons across the inner membrane. (b) A schematic representation of the proton channel through ATP synthetase, and the associated ATP synthesis.

■ (a) Assuming that the relationships described above are obligatory (i.e. that electron transport is tightly coupled to phosphorylation), what will happen to the rate of oxygen consumption if the intramitochondrial ADP concentration becomes very low?

(b) Assume that the mitochondrion is one of the many in muscle tissue. How could the ADP concentration be increased?

(c) What related comments might you make about cellular heat production?

When ADP concentration is low, the rate of respiration necessarily falls, as does the rate of ATP production. As the 'inefficiency' of the ATP-making process is the only source of heat, heat production falls. In muscle tissue, ATP is converted to ADP and, as a consequence, mechanical work is done. Thus, muscle contraction regenerates ADP, and permits electron transport and oxidative phosphorylation to recommence. As noted earlier, heat is liberated as a consequence of both ATP usage and ATP synthesis.

How do BAT mitochondria differ from non-BAT mitochondria? We have already seen in Section 4.6.2 that BAT mitochondria uniquely contain uncoupling protein, which is believed to confer upon BAT its thermogenic properties. The protein is relatively small: it is made up of 306 amino acids (M_r 32 000). A number of different techniques have been used to measure the levels of this protein in mitochondria: results from three of these techniques are shown in Table 4.2. Here we can see that mitochondria of cold-acclimated rats (exhibiting NST) have more UCP than warm-acclimated rats.

Table 4.2 The effect of acclimation temperature on the amount of uncoupling protein in rats, including a comparison of electrophoretic and immunological assays.

Method	Amount of uncoupling protein / µg per mg mitochondrial protein	
	warm-acclimated rats / 22 °C	cold-acclimated rats / 4–6 °C
RIA*	69	152
ELISA*	37	134
SDS–PAGE*	84	124

*RIA, solid-phase radio-immunoassay; ELISA, enzyme-linked immunosorbent assay; SDS–PAGE, mitochondrial proteins were separated using sodium dodecyl sulphate–polyacrylamide gel electrophoresis, and the area corresponding to the 32 000 M_r peak was measured.

Structurally, UCP in humans is very similar to that found in mice and rats. The gene that codes for UCP has been identified and transplanted into yeasts which then have the potential to be used as a source of UCP. UCP functions by uncoupling fuel oxidation from ATP production, so that, instead of the majority of the energy liberated from the fuel being used to produce ATP, it is dissipated as heat. The question is, 'How is uncoupling achieved?'.

It appears that the UCP is situated in the inner membrane of the mitochondrion, where it acts as a proton translocator. It provides a re-entry point for protons to the matrix via the inner mitochondrial membrane. When activated, the translocator prevents the establishment of a proton gradient by the actions of the electron transport chain and, therefore, prevents the generation of ATP by the passage of protons through the ATP synthetase-linked channel. All the energy (of the sequential oxidations) used to create the proton gradient is dissipated as heat. The activation of UCP, therefore, uncouples the mitochondria. This is summarized in Figure 4.22.

In this uncoupled state protons, deposited outside the membrane by electron transport, readily and rapidly re-enter the matrix. This process tends to speed up the flow along the electron transport chain as the mitochondrion continues its futile attempt to establish a proton gradient which is continually being dissipated because of the presence of the UCP. This process increases heat production, both by increasing substrate oxidation and by ensuring that little or none of the liberated energy is harvested as ATP.

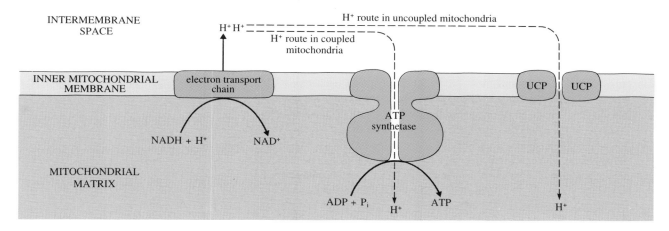

Figure 4.22   A schematic summary of the proton translocator actions of UCP.

Summary for Section 4.6

Experiments show that a marked lowering of T_a initially lowers the temperature in many parts of a rabbit's body, including the BAT-containing interscapular body (IBAT). However, the temperature of IBAT rapidly returns to normal (37 °C) because of thermogenesis within the tissue. In contrast, muscle temperature continues to fall because it has no temperature-related thermogenic power. The temperature of organs surrounded by or near to BAT show less of a temperature decrease. These results explain how core temperature, and hence the functioning of essential organs, is protected.

Mammals contain white adipose tissue (WAT) and, usually, BAT. The proportion of the total mass that is BAT varies from species to species, some having none but some having up to about 5% of body mass. The extent to which BAT produces heat in response to cold stress depends on the amount of BAT. Broadly speaking, mammals with small neonates, small mammals that are cold-acclimated, and mammals arousing from hibernation, all contain a significant amount of BAT and are substantially dependent on it for thermogenesis. BAT is *very* much more thermogenic than any other tissue, by about a factor of ten (per unit mass), and is located in discrete depots well supplied with blood. These contain brown adipocytes, which have a characteristic size and structure and are well endowed with numerous, large mitochondria with many cristae and a high concentration of cytochromes. The degree of vascularization and the concentration of cytochromes give BAT its brown colour. Brown adipocytes also contain more glycogen than white adipocytes. White adipocytes are mainly unilocular, whereas brown adipocytes that are thermogenically active are multilocular. Brown adipocytes uniquely contain uncoupling protein (UCP). BAT is well innervated by neurons of the sympathetic branch of the autonomic nervous system. Neurons innervating brown adipocytes contain the neuro-transmitter noradrenalin; those innervating blood vessels contain another neurotransmitter, neuropeptide Y.

WAT is primarily a store of fat that is mobilized to provide lipid fuel for tissues remote from itself. In contrast, the function of BAT during cold stress is that of thermogenesis. When a BAT depot is cold-stressed, the mass of BAT and the diameter of blood capillaries increases, and there are also changes in the histological make-up. Cold stress also leads to an increase in BAT sympathetic nervous activity and in the tissue concentration of UCP.

Non-BAT mitochondria (whether in WAT or any other tissue) are capable of transforming about 40% of the chemical energy of the respired substrates to the chemical energy of ATP; the other 60% appears as heat. However, because the rate of respiration is coupled to ATP production, the rate of respiration — and thus oxygen consumption and heat production — is comparatively low. ATP is produced by a mechanism that depends on the inner mitochondrial membrane being impermeable to hydrogen ions *except* via channels that are part of the ATP synthetase. In contrast, in BAT mitochondria fuel oxidation is uncoupled from ATP production, thus ensuring that all the energy released from oxidation is released as heat. As a consequence of uncoupling, which is brought about by the protein UCP, the rate of oxidation and heat production are greatly increased. UCP is situated in the inner mitochondrial membrane and acts as a proton translocator providing a route by which protons (built up on the outside of the inner membrane as a consequence of electron transport) are able to re-enter the matrix *without* passing through the ATP synthetase complex.

4.7 Control of the thermogenic response

What controls this uncoupling that leads to such physiologically important thermogenesis? Most information about the control of BAT has been gained from studying the interscapular deposits in small rodents. We have already noted that the IBAT deposit has a rich sympathetic nerve supply, indicating that this branch of the autonomic nervous system is important as a regulator of the tissue. This theory is supported by experiments with noradrenalin, such as that presented in Figure 4.23. Animals had their oxygen consumption measured and IBAT (solid line) and lumbar muscle temperatures (dashed line) were monitored. All three parameters were seen to increase in response to injections of noradrenalin. The increase in IBAT temperature paralleled changes in metabolic rate, but preceded and exceeded any changes in lumbar temperature. The effect of noradrenalin was seen to be abolished if the animal was pretreated with pronethalol (a noradrenalin antagonist).

Noradrenalin treatment also rapidly increases blood flow through BAT, which is an important part of the thermogenic response, as we have already seen. The mechanism underlying this is poorly understood. However, location of the sympathetic neurons on the blood vessels supplying the tissue suggests that neural stimulation brings about vasodilation and increases blood flow. It is difficult to separate experimentally actions here on blood vessels from those on brown adipocytes when noradrenalin is injected into an animal. Noradrenalin stimulates thermogenesis which may, in itself, cause an increase in blood flow through BAT by autoregulation of blood vessels, i.e. by vasodilation of blood vessels in response to the buildup of metabolites, such as carbon dioxide, produced by BAT when its metabolic rate is high.

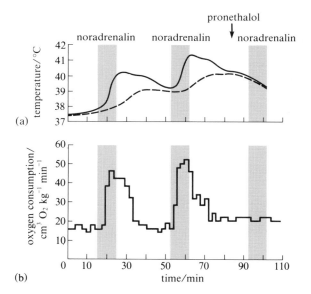

Figure 4.23 The effect of 10-minute intravenous infusions of 2 μg noradrenalin kg^{-1} min^{-1} (indicated by the grey bands) in a newborn rabbit on the oxygen consumption and body temperature, before and after the infusion of pronethalol. The upper curves show subcutaneous temperature over BAT (solid line) and over lumbar muscle (dashed line). The lower curve shows oxygen consumption.

The major central site of activation of the sympathetic nervous system is the hypothalamus. Detailed studies in anaesthetised rats have revealed that the **ventral medial area of the hypothalamus (VMH)** is of importance, though it is not the only area of the brain involved in BAT control. Figure 4.24 shows the results of experiments in which a small electrode was inserted in the VMH of an anaesthetised rat. The electrode was used to electrically stimulate the VMH, while IBAT, muscle and rectal temperatures were monitored using thermocouples. Electrical stimulation (indicated by the arrow) caused an increase in IBAT temperature that preceded and exceeded an increase in core temperature. Other experiments on the VMH have shown that BAT blood flow, lipolysis and lipogenesis are all increased. All of these effects are abolished if the IBAT pad is denervated—cutting all inputs from the sympathetic nerves—before the VMH is stimulated. It should be noted that other areas of the brain also are likely to be involved in the regulation of the tissue.

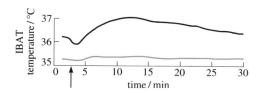

Figure 4.24 Changes in the IBAT temperature following unilateral stimulation of the ventral medial hypothalamus. The black line shows a normal response to an electrical stimulus (indicated with an arrow), with BAT temperature rising to a peak value of 37.0 °C 10 minutes later. During this period, rectal and muscle temperatures remained at 36.2 and 35.5 °C, respectively. Administration of 0.3 mg kg^{-1} of the β-adrenergic antagonist propranolol was found to reduce the rise in the IBAT temperature to less than 0.2 °C (blue line).

In tissues other than BAT, receptors for noradrenalin exist in two forms (alpha (α) and beta (β)). Both types of receptor interact with noradrenalin equally, but interact differently with other pharmacological agonists, meaning that one drug may selectively stimulate responses mediated by the α-receptors and another drug stimulate responses mediated by the β-receptors. What is the situation in BAT?

Receptors for noradrenalin are located on the brown adipocyte cell membrane. Although both α- and β-receptors have been identified in BAT, it appears that 80% of the BAT thermogenic response to noradrenalin is mediated by its binding to β-receptors. There has been much debate about the exact pharmacological nature of β-receptors on the brown adipocyte cell membrane. In other tissues (including WAT), two types of β-receptor are found: β1 and β2. It seems that the β-receptor in BAT is somewhat different from both β1 and β2—and in the literature it has been called the **β3 receptor**. The existence of a novel receptor such as this in BAT is of great interest to the pharmaceutical industry.

Though it is clear that activation occurs when the β3 receptors on the brown adipocyte membrane are occupied by noradrenalin molecules released from sympathetic nerve endings, the precise mechanism of action has been a subject of much debate. The binding of noradrenalin seems first to increase the cellular (cytoplasmic) levels of cyclic AMP (cAMP); this increase then activates a specific lipase enzyme thus increasing the rate of lipolysis (the breakdown of triacylglycerols stored in the vesicles to fatty acids and glycerol). The fatty acids thus liberated have two functions: they increase the supply of oxidizable fuel for thermogenesis and, in addition, they lead to uncoupling of the mitochondria.

The exact mechanism by which this uncoupling is brought about has also been investigated for many years. BAT mitochondria, in the absence of a thermogenic stimulus, are normally coupled, i.e. fuel oxidation is directed towards ATP production. A thermogenic stimulus brings about rapid uncoupling. It now seems likely that fatty acids are the major intracellular regulator of the UCP: fatty acids are the natural uncouplers of BAT mitochondria and have their effect by binding to UCP. Evidence for this conclusion is provided by experiments whose results are summarized in Figures 4.25 and 4.26.

In these experiments, brown adipocytes were incubated at 37 °C in the presence or absence of various substances; respiration rate (as oxygen consumption), and glycerol and fatty acid production were measured throughout. The addition of noradrenalin to the incubation medium caused a large increase in the respiratory rate of the cells and, at the same time, increased lipolysis which released fatty acids and glycerol into the incubation medium. The addition of propranolol inhibits the stimulatory effect of noradrenalin.

■ Look at Figure 4.26 and interpret the results. What parts of the proposed mechanism is supported by the results?

Fatty acids are said to act as an *intracellular messenger* (also termed **second messenger**), i.e. they are compounds that act as intermediate signals within the cell for a first messenger (in this case, noradrenalin). This is born out by Figure 4.26, which shows that propranolol inhibition is overcome by the addition of a free fatty acid (palmitic acid) which stimulates respiration. This, in turn, suggests that fatty acids can bypass the β-receptor and are thermogenic stimuli themselves. The results of other experiments have shown that fatty acids act as both a fuel for thermogenesis and as an uncoupling agent, i.e. they facilitate the action of the UCP, but the exact mechanism is unknown.

The account given in the preceding paragraphs is incomplete. The area is one of active research, and a number of experiments that provide evidence for further complexities are omitted here. One example, at the physiological level, is the effect of adrenalin; adrenalin from the adrenal glands, reaching BAT via the blood, can have the same effect as noradrenalin released from the terminals of the sympathetic nerves. This is in accord with the use of the term

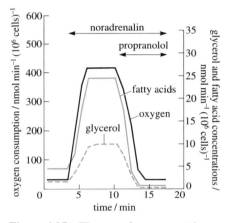

Figure 4.25 The rate of oxygen uptake (black line) and concentrations of glycerol (dashed blue line) and fatty acids (solid blue line) in brown adipocytes, during administration of 100 nM noradrenalin and subsequently 1 μM propranolol.

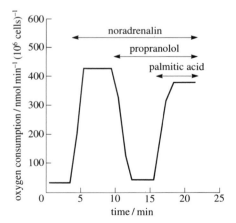

Figure 4.26 The rate of oxygen uptake in brown adipocytes, during administration of 100 nM noradrenalin, 1 μM propranolol, and subsequently 1 mM palmitic acid.

'catecholamines' earlier in describing BAT sensitivity: both adrenalin and noradrenalin are, chemically, amine derivatives of the aromatic diol known as catechol. Another example of further complexity is provided by events at the molecular level. It appears that various nucleotides (ATP, GTP and GDP) have an effect that is opposite, in a sense, to that of fatty acids such as palmitic acids—thus these nucleotides lead to the recoupling of BAT mitochondria that have been previously uncoupled by fatty acids. Figure 4.27 summarizes the information presented in this section about the mechanism of thermogenesis in BAT.

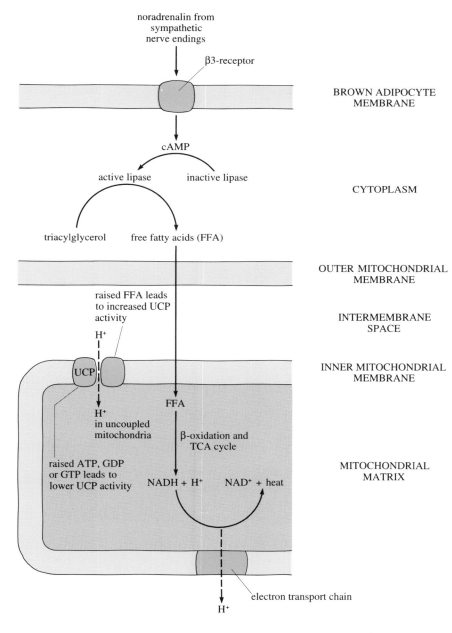

Figure 4.27 A summary of the information presented in this section, representing the thermogenic mechanism in BAT. Noradrenalin reaching β3-receptors leads to the release of cAMP in the cytoplasm. This stimulates the conversion of inactive lipase to active lipase, and the active enzyme catalyses the conversion of triacylglycerol to free fatty acids (FFA). FFA then have two effects: (1) they directly provide the substrate for β-oxidation, and (2) they stimulate UCP activity in the inner mitochondrial membrane. The former releases catabolic energy and the latter ensures that this appears as heat.

Other points, ancillary to the mechanism in Figure 4.27, are useful to note. These are:

(1) As noted in Section 4.6.2, chronic exposure to cold causes hypertrophy of BAT, including both an increase in mitochondria mass and the mass of UCP. The latter seems to occur because of an increase in the expression of the UCP gene; this results in an increase in the synthesis of the mRNA for the UCP and hence an increase in the synthesis of UCP. This process is facilitated by the binding of noradrenalin to receptors on the BAT cell membrane.

(2) A number of hormones (other than adrenalin) that are delivered to BAT via the blood have been implicated in the control of BAT either in the long term (i.e. controlling BAT growth) or in the short term.

(3) Though fatty acids are the major thermogenic fuel, brown adipocytes do take up glucose. Although they can and do under certain circumstances oxidize glucose directly, it appears that glucose is usually used for *de novo* synthesis of lipid.

Up to this point in Section 4.7, only the *efferent* parts of the control system, i.e those components involved in the route *from* the brain to the interior of BAT mitochondria, have been discussed. The physiological role of non-shivering thermogenesis lies, of course, in the capacity of an animal to generate heat in response to cold stress. Thus, there remains to be considered the *afferent* parts of the overall system, i.e. the route *to* the brain of information obtained from the external environment. In short, how do changes in the internal or external environment activate the brain to stimulate BAT?

While the experimental results presented in Figure 4.28 do not answer the question 'how' in any detail, they do provide direct evidence of the link between thermogenesis and exterior temperature and between efferent sympathetic activity and exterior temperature. A small part of the ear of an anaesthetized rat was cooled to and held at 4 °C for 20 seconds (see the shaded bars in Figure 4.28). In the following period, the 'percentage of normal' efferent sympathetic activity was recorded, as was the increase in IBAT temperature (using thermocouples inserted into IBAT).

■   Referring to Figure 4.28, describe the response to this cold stimulus (a) in terms of sympathetic nerve activity, and (b) in terms of the measured IBAT temperature. What relationship is there between the two graphs, and how would you account for your observations?

As can be seen from the figure, sympathetic nerve activity reaches 135% of its pre-stimulus activity during the duration of the stimulus. Thereafter (i.e. after the cessation of the stimulus), activity gradually falls to its normal level. After a very short delay (and an initial temperature decrease), IBAT temperature rapidly increases and thereafter declines slowly. The temperature curve can be seen to lag slightly behind the sympathetic activity curve, and also has a longer duration.

No changes in any of the parameters measured were seen if the ear was warmed, showing that information arising from cutaneous cold receptors increases thermogenesis in IBAT by increasing the activity in the sympathetic nerves supplying it.

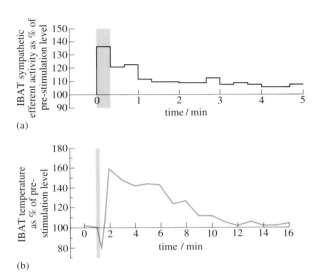

(a)

(b)

Figure 4.28   The effect of cooling a small part of a rat's ear to 4 °C for 20 seconds (indicated by the shaded area) on (a) subsequent sympathetic nerve activity, and (b) IBAT temperature.

There are a number of other afferent control systems that are involved in the activation of BAT in this and other situations, some of which will be discussed in Section 4.8.

Summary for Section 4.7

It appears that cold, sensed by cutaneous cold receptors, stimulates the ventral medial area of the hypothalamus (VMH) by the appropriate afferent pathways. Nerve impulses pass from the VMH, via efferent pathways of the sympathetic nervous system, to the nerve endings within BAT depots. Within BAT, sympathetic neurons stimulate both adipocytes and blood vessels (via the neurotransmitters noradrenalin and neuropeptide Y, respectively). Noradrenalin stimulates thermogenesis and, it would seem, neuropeptide Y stimulates blood vessel dilation, though some of the products of the thermogenic reactions in adipocytes (e.g. CO_2) may also lead to dilation of the nearby blood vessels. Noradrenalin receptors are located on the brown adipocyte cell membrane and are a special kind termed β3 receptors. Binding of the neurotransmitter noradrenalin to these β3 receptors triggers an intracellular cascade by which, ultimately, uncoupling and hence thermogenesis, occurs. The first consequence of binding noradrenalin is that the cytoplasmic concentration of cAMP increases. This then activates a lipase enzyme. Lipolysis increases and fatty acids are released which serve both as a fuel for subsequent oxidation and as *second messengers*. These facilitate the action of UCP (which opens up a route by which protons can re-enter the mitochondrial matrix without passing through the ATP synthetase channel).

4.8 BAT in the adult

The capacity of an animal for NST depends not only upon the thermal environment, but also upon its developmental stage. There are also considerable differences between species in the time course of BAT development (Table 4.3).

Table 4.3 Time at which BAT differentiation occurs in various animals.

Animal	time at which BAT differentiation occurs
guinea-pig	pre-natal
hamster	7–14 days post-natal
rat	perinatal (at birth)
rabbit	perinatal
human	pre-natal

Under thermoneutral conditions, BAT gradually loses its thermogenic capacity in the adult, though hibernators are an exception. Hibernators retain BAT in a thermoneutral environment, and uncoupling protein remains present in their BAT. The ability to increase and decrease body temperature is an essential part of the hibernation/awakening cycle. When hibernating, an animal's body temperature is lower than when it is awake, so the rates of all biochemical reactions are slowed. Rewarming is a stage for which BAT may be essential. The addition of heat to the body arising from BAT speeds up the biochemical reactions and aids awakening. In hibernators, BAT undergoes seasonal changes in appearance and thermogenic capacity. This topic will be discussed further in Chapter 6.

4.8.1 The non-hibernating adult

In non-hibernating adult animals, the thermogenic capacity of BAT declines with age. This change in BAT may be partially reversed by cold adaptation. Taking the guinea-pig as an example, the thermogenic capacity of its BAT can be assessed at different developmental stages by measuring the stimulus to respiration caused by a series of noradrenalin injections. From a peak value just after birth, there is a rapid decline in response, to a low level at 30 days (Figure 4.29). If IBAT is taken from fetal guinea-pigs, fully developed brown adipocytes can be found up to 18 days before birth. By contrast, the same observations made on fetal rats show no mature brown adipocytes until 1–2 days prior to birth, and the increased respiration on injection of noradrenalin is not apparent until 7 days after birth. At birth, the hamster is somewhat less mature than the rat, and mature brown adipocytes are not seen until 15 days after birth.

As you know, cold-acclimation acts as a stimulus to the retention of thermo-genic ability by BAT, and can also lead to hyperplasia. If cold-acclimated (4–8 °C) adult rats are brought to room temperature and injected with noradrenalin, the respiration rate increases much more than in rats acclimated to room temperature, as is illustrated in Figure 4.30. A rapid fourfold increase in the respiration rate is seen in cold-acclimated rats, compared with a slower doubling of the rate in warm-acclimated rats.

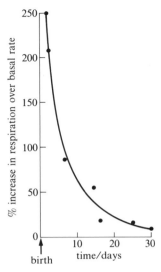

Figure 4.29 The effect of a series of noradrenalin injections on the respiration rate in a guinea-pig up to 30 days after birth. The effect of each injection, represented by a point, would have decayed long before the next injection was given.

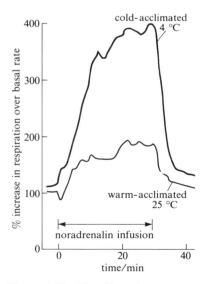

Figure 4.30 The effect of noradrenalin infusion on the respiration rates of a cold- and a warm-acclimated rat.

An alternative measure of BAT activity is the rate of blood flow through the tissue, since increased thermogenesis requires an increase in blood flow. It is technically difficult to measure the blood flow through BAT directly, so it is normally assessed indirectly using radioactively-labelled microspheres. Tiny balls (microspheres) that are slightly larger than the diameter of a capillary are injected into the left atrium of an anaesthetized animal (the side of the heart that feeds the systemic circulation). They then pass into the arteries and to the tissues where they jam in the capillaries. The tissues are then removed and the amount of radioactivity in each is assessed. The greater the blood flow through the tissue, the larger the number of microspheres trapped.

Using the microsphere method, it has been shown that sudden, acute cold stress increases blood flow in the BAT in all adult rats. However, the size of the response differs in cold-acclimated rats compared with warm-acclimated rats. In cold-acclimated rats, acute cold gives a 24-fold increase of blood flow in BAT (25% of total cardiac output) compared with a 12-fold increase (12% of cardiac output) in warm-acclimated rats.

Though the microsphere method shows clearly that blood flow has increased in BAT in response to a cold stimulus, we have no information about the respiration rate of the tissue. Recently, a technique has been developed to measure directly the respiration rate of IBAT *in vivo*. The method involves collecting the venous blood directly as it drains from the IBAT lobe, measuring its oxygen content, and then comparing it with that of arterial blood. Thus, the amount of oxygen extracted from the blood as it passes through the IBAT lobe can be calculated. Table 4.4 shows that the amount of oxygen extracted increases as the exposure temperature decreases—thus paralleling increases in IBAT temperature and the respiratory rate of the animal.

Table 4.4 The arterio-venous oxygen differences in the IBAT of warm-acclimated rats exposed to various temperatures.

Temperature / °C	Difference in oxygen content of arterial and venous blood in IBAT / cm^3 O_2 per 100 cm^3 IBAT
28	3.7 ± 0.6
20	14.5 ± 1.2
6	17.2 ± 0.7

It has been established that the thermogenic response seen in adult rats correlates with the amount of UCP. When the amount of uncoupling protein is estimated from SDS–PAGE, it is found to be present at a higher level in cold-adapted rats—in fact, as high as in the perinatal stage. When the rat is returned to a thermoneutral environment the amount falls rapidly.

One might wonder why the level of UCP fluctuates in this way. Consider a rat in a thermoneutral environment. As there is no cold stress, there is no massive release of noradrenalin to trigger a thermogenic response. Presumably, therefore, the presence of the UCP would be of no consequence (though very low levels would mean that the response to subsequent cold stress would be slower in developing). Why then is the level of synthesis of this protein inversely linked to external temperature?

At first sight, there is no evolutionary advantage in repressing synthesis of UCP during warm periods since there would be no triggering of thermogenesis by noradrenalin. However, if you remember the discussion of messengers (Section 4.7), you will realize that circulating free fatty acids can, on their own, produce a low level of thermogenesis independent of the sympathetic nervous system. It appears that the reduction in UCP is to ensure that thermogenesis is not triggered at the warm-adapted level by an increase in free fatty acids that is unrelated to temperature.

4.9 Conclusion

Neonatal mammals face problems of heat conservation after birth, when the temperature of most drops rapidly and remains relatively low and unstable for some time. Not surprisingly, many neonatal mammals, especially small ones, can tolerate a degree of hypothermia that would be unacceptable to the adult. At birth, some neonates are unable to generate much extra metabolic heat, but many, e.g. the rabbit, are immediately able to compensate partly for excessive loss of heat by increasing the rate at which they produce metabolic heat. So, from the moment of birth, the neurological and biochemical mechanisms responsible for increased heat production come into play. It is important to note, however, that the actual amount of extra heat produced may not fully compensate for heat loss across extensive and poorly insulated surfaces. The thermal protection offered by nests and the behavioural responses of the young (e.g. huddling) also help to avoid excessive heat loss. During the first few weeks of post-natal life, the increase in size and the development of good thermal insulation means that the newborn mammal becomes more able to regulate its body temperature independently over a wide range of ambient temperatures.

The newborn of most species, in contrast to many adults, increase their metabolic heat production primarily by non-shivering thermogenesis (NST). Brown adipose tissue (BAT) appears to be the only tissue able to produce heat in this way. During cold stress, BAT produces extra metabolic heat via stimulation of the sympathetic nervous system; its strategic location in the thorax means that the vital thoracic organs are protected against excessively low temperatures. The amount of BAT in neonates, and its relative importance in thermogenesis, varies considerably. BAT may be particularly significant in small mammals that are born relatively immature; larger species that are more mature at birth and have more advanced motor development appear to rely more on shivering thermogenesis. Even in those species that rely heavily on BAT thermogenesis in the neonate, the importance of BAT declines with post-natal development, although the tissue maintains its importance in cold-acclimated adults.

Lipolysis in BAT produces free fatty acids, which can be oxidized to provide $NADH + H^+$ (and $FADH_2$) and are then oxidized in the electron transport chain (ETC). In BAT, mitochondrial ATP synthesis is short-circuited because the mitochondrial membrane is rendered leaky to protons. This is due to the presence of uncoupling protein (UCP), which is unique to BAT. Thus, protons bypass ATP synthetase, and the energy accompanying proton translocation is dissipated as heat. The rate of electron transport, being no longer constrained by the rate of ATP synthesis, increases. It is now known that proton conductance of the inner mitochondrial membrane can be decreased by the binding of various nucleotides (including ATP, GTP and GDP) to the uncoupling protein. Free fatty acids, released by lipolysis, reverse the effect of this nucleotide binding, and increase proton conductance across the mitochondrial membranes. The amount of UCP can vary depending on the degree of cold exposure and the developmental stage of the tissue.

Objectives for Chapter 4

When you have completed this chapter, you should be able to:

4.1   Define, use or recognize definitions or applications of each of the **bold** terms.

4.2   Describe or interpret experiments concerning the energy budget of the fetus.

4.3   Describe or interpret experiments concerning the change in body temperature that occur immediately after birth in humans.

4.4   Describe behavioural heat conservation in neonates (including reference to species differences).

4.5   Describe the role of shivering in neonates (including reference to species differences).

4.6   Describe the structure and function of white and brown adipose tissue (including histological detail).

4.7   Describe shivering and non-shivering thermogenesis, and the biochemical principles that underlie these processes.

4.8   Describe or interpret results from experiments that suggest BAT is under the control of the sympathetic nervous system.

4.9   Describe, or interpret results from experiments about, the effect of cold-acclimation on IBAT.

4.10 Describe or interpret experiments concerning the biochemical mechanism for the control of thermogenesis in BAT.

4.11 Outline the role of BAT in neonates of different species.

4.12 Describe or recognize true or false statements about BAT in adults.

Questions for Chapter 4

(Note that these are not computer-marked questions and are open to discussion! Answers to questions are at the end of the book.)

Question 4.1 (Objective 4.2)

In the discussion of fetal heat production in item (4) of Section 4.2, it is suggested that rate of heat production cannot be equated with metabolic rate calculated from oxygen consumption *in rapidly growing tissue*. Which do you think would be larger? Explain your answer. (*Note*: you may find the detail about ATP consumption in peptide bond formation in Section 4.5 a useful pointer.)

Which of the statements (a)–(e) *about humans* are true? Qualify or explain your choice, where appropriate. You may need to refer to the text or Figures 4.3–4.8 in Sections 4.3–4.5.

(a) Fetal core temperature drops throughout the perinatal period, starting from the beginning of birth.

(b) Shivering thermogenesis plays only a modest part in neonatal homeothermy.

(c) Non-shivering thermogenesis is apparent soon after birth.

(d) Behavioural (voluntary) movements play no part in the neonatal response to cold.

(e) The thermobiology of human neonates is more closely allied (e.g. in the effect of surface area:volume ratio) to those of pigs, sheep or horses than to those of rats or rabbits.

Each of the following statements (a)–(h) applies to WAT or BAT, or both, or neither. Categorize these statements by writing the letters W, B, W + B, or N (= neither) against each. Explain your answers as necessary.

(a) … contain(s) unilocular adipocytes.

(b) … contain(s) triacylglycerol.

(c) … produce(s) ATP.

(d) … is/are characterized by the presence of UCP.

(e) … produce(s) fatty acids by lipolysis, most of which are oxidatively catabolized within the tissue.

(f) … is/are innervated by sympathetic nerve endings and is/are highly vascularized.

(g) … often contain(s) mitochondria that are at least partially uncoupled.

(h) … is/are stimulated to increase thermogenic output by propranolol.

Section 4.6.1 notes that 'the maximum aerobic capacity of BAT ($500 \, \text{W} \, \text{kg}^{-1}$) is about ten times that of skeletal muscle'. Summarize in 80–100 words the biochemical basis for this difference. Which diagram in the text would you choose to support your statement?

Imagine that you are comparing IBAT in warm-acclimated rats with IBAT in cold-acclimated rats. What differences between them, if any, would you expect in each of the following respects (listed in (a)–(e))?

(a) proportion of UCP

(b) diameter of fat vesicles

(c) mass of BAT (per unit mass of whole rat)

(d) proportion of preadipocytes

(e) sympathetic activity

CHAPTER 5 POLAR BIOLOGY

Prepared for the Course Team by Caroline Pond

5.1 Introduction

This chapter is about animals' structural and physiological adaptations to living permanently in cold climates; hibernation, a special response to transient or seasonal cold, is dealt with in Chapter 6. Living in a polar climate involves adaptations of many physiological systems: appetite, diet, energy storage and reproductive habits as well as thermoregulation. In many cases, such changes involve 'ordinary' physiological mechanisms being pushed to extremes. The study of such physiological adaptations can help us to understand how humans and domestic animals could cope with similar conditions that arise under artificial or pathological conditions. For example, obesity is rare among wild animals, even when food is very plentiful, but in humans the condition is common and often leads to numerous physiological complications, ranging from susceptibility to diabetes to mechanical damage to legs and feet. Nearly all naturally obese animals occur in cold climates, and there is no evidence that they suffer from the complications of the condition that are observed in people and their domestic livestock. Perhaps we have something to learn about the natural regulation of appetite and the organization and metabolic control of fat from these cold-adapted species that have evolved ways of combining fatness with fitness.

On the evolutionary time-scale, polar environments, and hence polar organisms, evolved relatively recently. The study of polar organisms provides the opportunity to study physiological adaptations of quite recent origin that evolved in organisms which were already complex and well-integrated. Such changes are comparable to artificial evolution in domestic animals, whether by manipulation of the genome (i.e. intensive artificial selection, gene transfer, etc.), or by drastically altering the diet and husbandry conditions. Polar organisms may help us to understand the physiological and psychological implications of the rapid, often drastic changes that we impose upon our own lives and those of our domestic animals.

Antarctica has been isolated from other continents since the Mesozoic supercontinent Gondwanaland broke up and the fragments that became India, Australia and New Zealand drifted away. The rich fossil record in Antarctica shows that a diverse tropical fauna, including early eutherian and metatherian mammals, once lived there. As the continent became colder, many species disappeared and adaptations to the climate evolved *in situ* in surviving lineages over many millions of years. Consequently, much of the fauna and flora of Antarctica and the surrounding oceans are endemic.

In contrast, much of the Arctic* is a large ocean, connected to the Pacific Ocean by the Bering Strait (that became a land bridge several times during the last million years) and through wider channels to the north Atlantic Ocean.

* When used as an adjective, 'arctic' refers to the regions around both poles and does not have have a capital letter. 'Arctic' and 'Antarctic' are the northern and southern arctic regions, and do have capital letters.

Prevailing winds and deep currents bring plenty of mineral nutrients to the Southern Ocean but the Arctic Ocean, particularly the areas north of Siberia, Alaska and Canada, is nutrient poor. Consequently, the Southern Ocean supports a much greater abundance of marine life than is found in most of the Arctic, except in a few areas such as the Barents Sea around northern Norway and Finland.

Biological evolution in the Arctic has been much affected by the Pleistocene Ice Age, which produced several periods of glaciation over much of the Northern Hemisphere that began about a million years ago and continued until as recently as 10 000 years ago. There were Ice Ages in the Palaeozoic and early Mesozoic, but until the Quaternary Ice Age began about 1 Ma ago, the climate had been mild, often warm, over the whole globe for the previous 250 Ma. The climate became colder and drier, promoting rapid evolution in many different lineages of animals and plants. Many species became extinct, but others, particularly descendants of cold-adapted organisms that lived on high mountains, adapted to the new conditions: numerous modifications of the skin and fur, endocrine mechanisms and behaviour and circulatory, respiratory, digestive and excretory systems evolved in many different species over a comparatively short period. Among them was an almost hairless primate, *Homo*, which adapted successfully to the cold climate in Europe and northern Asia after several million years of evolution in tropical Africa. Many such cold-adapted species ranged over much of the Northern Hemisphere until the climate became warmer during the interglacial period of the last 10 000 years, and are now confined to the Arctic.

The polar environment

At high latitudes, the Sun's rays always strike the Earth at wide angle from the vertical so they travel through a thicker layer of atmosphere and are attenuated by the time they reach the ground. Because the Earth's axis of rotation is inclined to its path around the Sun, there are large seasonal changes in daylength and the Sun is continuously below the horizon for a period in winter and continuously above the horizon for an equivalent period in summer. The annual changes in daylength and average temperature recorded just inside (Tromsø, Norway) and far into the Arctic Circle* (Longyearbyen on the island of Spitsbergen, Svalbard Archipelago) are summarized on Figure 5.1. The range of annual temperature change is much greater at the higher latitude, and in mid-winter (January and February) the range about the mean is more than 12 °C. In arctic climates, the temperature can change abruptly and often unpredictably. In fact, both the localities featured on Figure 5.1 are on coasts, where the sea keeps the climate much more equable. Further inland, fluctuations in temperature are even greater. Arctic organisms are thus adapted both to the extreme cold and to abrupt fluctuations in temperature.

Warm, moist air from the temperate zone rarely reaches high latitudes, so in most arctic areas precipitation is low. Much of the water is locked away as ice, which has a low vapour pressure, and the air is very dry (often as dry as a tropical desert) and ground water is inaccessible to plants as well as to animals.

---

* The Arctic Circle (66° 30′ N), and the equivalent latitude in the Southern Hemisphere, are defined as the latitude above which the sun is continuously below the horizon for at least 1 day each year.

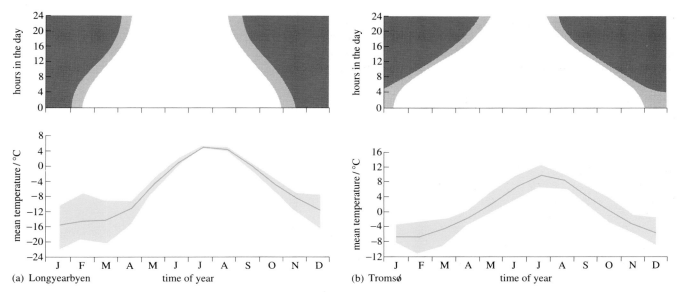

Figure 5.1 The number of hours of daylight (white), twilight (grey) and darkness (black), and the mean temperature (blue line) from January to December at (a) Longyearbyen, Svalbard (78° N), and (b) Tromsø, Norway (70° N). The pale blue shading shows the range about the mean temperature.

As explained in the previous section, arctic environments are, by geological standards, relatively new, most of the land having been completely covered with a thick layer of ice as recently as 10 000 years ago. Consequently, the soil is thin and fragile, and poor in organic nutrients. The optimum temperatures for plant growth do not coincide exactly with peak sunshine. At Longyearbyen, continuous daylight begins in late April, but the mean temperature does not rise above 0 °C (and so the snow and ice do not melt) for another 2 months (Figure 5.1).

These circumstances, combined with the severe climate, mean that the growing season for plants is short but intensive and total productivity on land is low, producing little food and still less shelter for animals. Consequently, relatively few species of terrestrial organisms live permanently at high latitudes. On Svalbard, for example, there are only a few hundred species of insects and other invertebrates, two resident terrestrial mammals (reindeer, Plate 5.1, and arctic fox, Plate 5.2), one bird (ptarmigan) and no reptiles, amphibians or completely freshwater fish, although more than 30 species of migratory birds, including geese, auks, puffins, skuas, terns, gulls, eider ducks and snow buntings, and mammals such as polar bears, walruses and several species of seal spend part of the year on or near land there. The vast continent of Antarctica has no indigenous terrestrial vertebrates, although many birds, including penguins, skuas, terns and gulls, and six species of seal spend time on or near land. The simple ecosystem on land and the severe, erratic climate tend to produce 'cycles' of population abundance followed by mass mortality or migration (e.g. lemmings in Scandinavia and Russia). Some interesting physiological and behavioural adaptations to these fluctuations in food supply have evolved in some of the larger animals.

The situation in the sea is very different. Seawater freezes at −1.9 °C, but because of the anomalous relationship between density and temperature of water, ice floats, insulating the water underneath from the cold air above.

Except in very shallow areas, the ice does not extend to the sea-bed, even at the North Pole. Storms and currents sometimes break up the ice, creating many temporary, and some permanent, areas of open water even at high latitudes in mid-winter. Such turbulence also oxygenates the water and admits more light, making the environment much more hospitable to living organisms. The movements of ocean currents are complex (and may change erratically from year to year), often resulting in an upwelling of deep water rich in nutrients and promoting high primary productivity in the sea. In most arctic regions, the sea is both warmer and more productive than the land, so at high latitudes there are many more organisms in the sea than on land, at least during the brief summer and, as in the case of the baleen and sperm whales, some are very large. Some groups of animals, such as bears, that are terrestrial in the temperate zone have evolved adaptations that enable them to feed from the sea in the Arctic.

5.2 Environmental regulation of physiological processes

All plants and animals respond to environmental changes such as the light–dark cycle and temperature, but the impact of the environment on essential physiological processes such as eating, fattening and breeding is more evident and often more finely controlled in arctic species than in those that are native to warmer and more equable habitats. Large effects are nearly always easier to quantify and to investigate experimentally, so arctic species offer an excellent opportunity to study the subtle but often important action of environmental changes on physiological processes.

5.2.1 Nutrient budgeting

Energy is expended in the search for food, and in ingesting and digesting it. If food is so scarce that searching is inefficient, or its nutrient content so low that little nourishment is obtained from it, animals may be able to save energy by suppressing appetite and fasting. In arctic environments, food is widely scattered both in space and in time. Consequently, the physiological mechanisms that regulate appetite and energy storage are sophisticated and effective in arctic species. Herbivorous animals such as reindeer are directly dependent upon plant productivity and synchronize their foraging and other energetically expensive activities, such as mating and breeding, with it. Daylength (photoperiod) is a more reliable indicator of season than temperature (see Figure 5.1) and is often an important regulator of physiological mechanisms.

To investigate seasonal changes in the behaviour and metabolism of species native to the high Arctic, a few specimens of the subspecies of reindeer that is endemic to Svalbard (*Rangifer tarandus platyrhynchus*, Plate 5.1) were transported to northern Norway and kept in small outdoor pens there, alongside specimens of the native subspecies, *Rangifer tarandus tarandus*. All the animals had continuous, unrestricted access to forage but, as shown on Figure 5.2, the Svalbard reindeer ate three times as much food in August as in March.

■ Are these seasonal changes in the appetite of Svalbard reindeer simply a direct response to the environment?

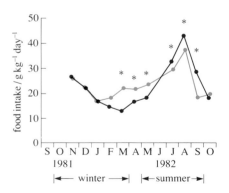

Figure 5.2 Seasonal changes in the voluntary food intake (in grams per kg body mass per day) of Norwegian reindeer (blue) and Svalbard reindeer (black) with unrestricted access to food. Asterisks mark significant differences between subspecies.

No. There were seasonal changes in the food eaten by local Norwegian reindeer as well, but they were less pronounced than those of the animals native to high latitudes. In addition, the largest differences between the two subspecies were observed in mid-March and mid-September, around the equinoxes when day and night are equal in length over the whole globe.

■ Do seasonal differences in energy expenditure explain these data?

No. Being confined in small pens, the reindeer took little exercise all the time. Energy expended on thermoregulation should be greater in cold weather, so if thermogenesis (Section 3.2) was important, one would expect them to eat more, not less, in the winter.

Reindeer (Plate 5.1) grow thick coats of long, hollow hair that insulates the warm skin so effectively that snow accumulates on their backs without melting. Energy expenditure on shivering or other forms of thermogenesis seems to be minimal even in the coldest weather. Foraging is slower and less efficient in winter, and the lower total daily intake is supplemented by utilization of the fat reserves built up during the brief summer, when they eat almost continuously. However, as these experiments show, the seasonal changes in food intake arise primarily from the endogenous control of appetite, and are not imposed upon the animals by food availability. The fine control of appetite is slightly different in subspecies adapted to different climates. The investigators also found small but significant differences at certain times of year between Norwegian and Svalbard reindeer in the rates of lipogenesis measured in adipocytes *in vitro*, and in the responses of adipose tissue to hormones such as adrenalin.

Metabolic rate, food intake and other aspects of energy balance also change seasonally in birds and mammals that are native to high latitudes. The red, or common, fox (*Vulpes vulpes*) occurs throughout Europe and northern Asia except in high mountains and arctic regions, where is it replaced by the smaller arctic fox (*Alopex lagopus*). As shown on Figure 5.3a, at above 10 °C, the fox's BMR is about the same in summer and winter, but as the temperature falls, the rise in BMR is delayed and is slower in winter-adapted animals than in those caught in summer.

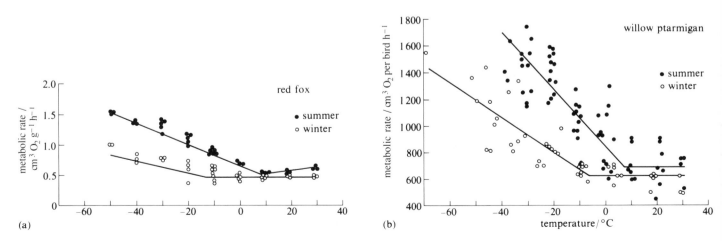

Figure 5.3 The resting metabolic rates at different temperatures of (a) red fox and (b) willow ptarmigan acclimatized in captivity to summer and winter conditions.

Such phenomena have been intensively investigated in ptarmigan (Plate 5.3) which are non-migratory, mainly ground-dwelling grouse-like birds that eat twigs, shoots and other plant material. There are two species in Scandinavia and Russia: the willow ptarmigan (*Lagopus lagopus lagopus*) and the rock ptarmigan (*L. mutus mutus*). ('*Lagopus*' means 'foot of a hare' and refers to the feather-covered or fur-covered feet of the ptarmigan and arctic fox, see Plates 5.2 and 5.3 and Figure 5.12.) A subspecies of rock ptarmigan, *L. mutus hyperboreus*, occurs only on Svalbard; it is larger than the mainland forms, and has almost pure white plumage during the 8 months of winter. As shown on Figure 5.3b, the metabolic rate of willow ptarmigan measured at a wide range of temperatures is lower in winter than in summer. The seasonal differences are even greater in Svalbard ptarmigan. Svalbard ptarmigan also eat much more in the late summer than in winter and accumulate fat in the autumn. The experiments summarized in Figure 5.4 reveal some of the physiological mechanisms that control these changes in appetite and energy storage.

When exposure to continuous light was started in July (Figure 5.4a), the birds' usual autumnal fattening proceeded as normal, but their body mass remained high and food intake fairly low, right through to the following September. Throughout this period, their plumage remained white and they failed to breed. It was as though the continuous light held them indefinitely in their autumnal condition. However, when exposure to continuous light was started in November (Figure 5.4b), the birds underwent a complete cycle of changes in body mass and food intake (and began to develop speckled summer plumage) before settling into continuous high body mass and low appetite.

■ What do these experiments show about how seasonal changes in appetite and body mass are controlled?

They are not simply a response to environmental conditions but are at least partly controlled endogenously.

Exactly how such control mechanisms evolve and what happens when animals (or people) are abruptly transported into environments in which their endogenous controls of appetite and energy expenditure are inappropriate are not known.

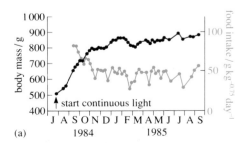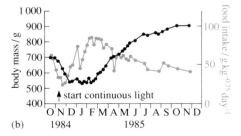

Figure 5.4   Changes in food intake (grams per kg body mass per day, blue) and body mass (black) in Svalbard ptarmigan (*Lagopus mutus hyperboreus*) during 14 consecutive months kept in captivity with unlimited access to food at Tromsø. (a) Birds kept outside and then indoors in continuous light from July onwards. (b) Birds kept outside and then indoors in continuous light from November onwards.

Although many species live in mountains and arctic regions, no ruminant mammal, even the few very small species, is known to hibernate in the strict sense of the term (see Chapter 6). One reason might be that substantial changes in body temperature would kill the micro-organisms in the rumen that are essential to digestion. Another possibility is that in ruminants, both storage and membrane lipids contain mostly saturated lipids, which have a higher melting point than unsaturated lipids. Laboratory experiments in which animals were fed diets rich in saturated or unsaturated lipids just before hibernation showed that, at least in small rodents, a larger proportion of unsaturated lipids in cell membranes and adipose tissue is essential to successful hibernation. Finally, pregnancy, which lasts a relatively long time in ruminants and usually takes place during the winter, could not be sustained at lower temperatures.

Birds also do not hibernate, but like reindeer, many species undergo daily or seasonal changes in energy expenditure and appetite and many of the endocrine changes that are an integral part of true hibernation in other groups. The fact that the preliminary stages of hibernation are widespread among vertebrates may help to explain why true hibernation has evolved several times in distantly related taxa (see Sections 6.2.2 and 6.6).

5.2.2   Environmental regulation of breeding

As pointed out in Section 5.1, primary plant productivity occurs for only a few months in the summer, so the reproductive physiology of most arctic animals, particularly herbivorous species, is tightly synchronized with the seasons. On Svalbard, more than 90% of the reindeer calves are born in the first week of June, and the mothers of those born too soon or too late are often unable to find enough food to support lactation. As shown on Figure 5.1, the onset of continuous daylight and that of the conditions that support plant growth are several months out of phase. This situation poses little problem for reindeer, because the duration of pregnancy is almost constant and they mate only during a brief rutting period in September, when the daylength is changing rapidly. But this environmental cue alone would not be an accurate control on the timing of breeding of resident herbivorous birds such as ptarmigan that breed in mid-summer.

The physiological mechanisms that control the timing of several aspects of mating and breeding in the Svalbard ptarmigan (*Lagopus mutus hyperboreus*) have been investigated in detail. Their plumage is almost pure white in winter but speckled brown feathers appear in summer and the adult males have a red fleshy 'comb' over each eye. Figure 5.5 shows the seasonal changes in these secondary sexual characters, the maturation of the gonads, and the concentration of luteinizing hormone (LH) in blood plasma in ptarmigan shot on Svalbard. In males (Figure 5.5), LH levels are low from August until February, when the sun reappears (see Figure 5.1). The LH levels in blood plasma and body weight (see Figures 5.4 and 5.5) start to increase slowly, and in March the combs begin to grow, and first primary, then secondary, spermatocytes appear in the testes (Figure 5.5b). However, there are no mature spermatozoa until the end of May, so the gonads mature much more slowly that in most other seasonally breeding birds. Pigmented feathers also do not appear until June, just before the snow melts (Figure 5.5a).

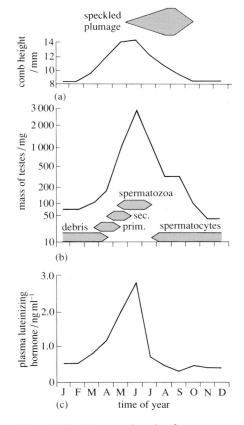

Figure 5.5   The annual cycle of maturation of the gonads and formation of external secondary sexual characters in male Svalbard ptarmigan. (a) Height of combs and appearance of pigmented feathers. (b) Mass of testes and appearance of cells in various stages of spermatogenesis. (c) Concentration of luteinizing hormone in blood plasma. The vertical axis of (b) is on a logarithmic scale.

■ Are there any advantages in delaying the development of pigmented feathers?

Speckled plumage is probably much more conspicuous to potential predators (i.e. arctic foxes) against a background of snow than pure white feathers, so it would be advantageous not to produce the breeding plumage until it is essential for courtship and mating.

Throughout the year, LH levels are lower in female (Figure 5.6) than in male ptarmigan, but, as in males, there is a sharp peak in June that coincides with maximum weight of the ovary and egg laying (Figure 5.6a). However, LH is also fairly high in March (Figure 5.6b), several months before the gonads become active. Some other factor, perhaps non-photoperiodic inhibitory input from the environment (e.g. cold weather), must be delaying the maturation of the ovary.

5.2.3 Variable fecundity

The food supply for most arctic species depends on several unpredictable factors so successful breeding is far from certain, even if births are tightly synchronized with the seasons. Maintaining pregnancy and feeding the offspring after birth (or hatching in birds) are energetically expensive. The death of the offspring before its maturity represents an irredeemable loss of 'reproductive investment' for the parents, particularly the mother, although the earlier in parental nurturing that the death occurs, the smaller the loss to the parents. Various mechanisms of environmental determination of fecundity have evolved among large birds and mammals and are particularly evident in arctic species.

Like most large ungulates, reindeer produce only one calf a year and suckle it for more than 6 months, by which time the next pregnancy may be well underway. Observations on Svalbard reindeer show that in December, nearly all adult females are pregnant, having conceived during the mating season in the previous September. But as winter progresses, the proportion that are pregnant falls, and by June the following year any fraction from over 90% to less than 10% of the adult females give birth to a calf. The other pregnancies must have ended in abortion or reabsorption of the fetus. In each year, the proportion giving birth is approximately the same in all areas of Svalbard that can be studied, suggesting that it is related to the climate. Exactly how the animal 'knows' when to terminate a pregnancy which she is unlikely to be able to complete successfully is currently under investigation, but the quality or quantity of the food available during the winter is the most likely factor.

The fecundity of arctic foxes is also very variable: in years when prey and carrion are abundant, some litters consist of as many as 20 pups (with an average of 10–12 in Canada and 6.4 on Svalbard), a very large number for a canid (dog-like) mammal, but very few breed at all in years when food is scarce. A similar pattern is found in predatory birds such as the snowy owl, which also feeds on rodents and hares that undergo population cycles. When prey are abundant, the fox or owl parents can raise a large number of pups or chicks but if food availability suddenly falls (due to mass mortality or migration of prey or a change in the weather), most or all of the offspring may starve in the nest. Food intake and/or energy stores somehow regulate the number of oöcytes

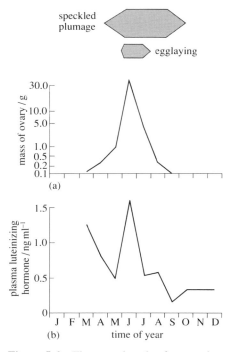

Figure 5.6 The annual cycle of maturation of the gonads and the formation of external secondary sexual characters in female Svalbard ptarmigan.
(a) Appearance of pigmented feathers, mass of ovary, and period of egg-laying.
(b) Concentration of luteinizing hormone in blood plasma. The vertical axis of (a) is on logarithmic scale.

ovulated and/or the number that implant successfully and develop, so that as far as possible, fecundity is adjusted to food supply in a fluctuating environment. However, very little is known about the mechanisms involved: the formation and maintenance of the placenta depend upon several different hormones, some of them secreted from the pituitary and brain. The body may respond to stress or insufficient nutrition and it may terminate the pregnancy promptly, thereby preparing the mother for another try when the prospects of a more successful outcome appear brighter.

Summary of Sections 5.1 and 5.2

Large seasonal changes in temperature and sunlight dominate primary plant production and hence the food supply. Food intake is regulated by the endogenous seasonal control of appetite, fattening and activity, as well as by food availability. Energetically demanding activities like breeding and migration are only feasible during a brief period and must be tightly synchronized to season. Arctic ecosystems involve relatively few species, some of which are prone to abrupt, cyclic changes in population abundance, so food supplies change erratically from year to year and from place to place. Most physiological adaptations to these features of the arctic environment probably arise from modification and refinement of mechanisms that occur in temperate-zone species.

5.3   Natural feasting and fasting

It is clear from Sections 5.1 and 5.2 that seasonal or irregular periods of fasting are an integral part of living at high latitudes, especially for large animals. When people (and many tropical and temperate-zone mammals) lose weight, either because they are eating less or because they are suffering from a metabolic disorder such as diabetes or cancer, protein is broken down in substantial quantities long before the lipid stores are exhausted. Even very vigorous exercise cannot prevent the breakdown of lean tissue, although it can often reduce or delay the process, particularly in young people. The loss of protein causes muscles to become weak and wasted, and the skin and hair to appear shabby. Immune function is also impaired, weakening resistance to parasites and infectious diseases. These undesirable side-effects of fasting do not normally afflict mammals and birds that naturally go without food for long periods.

5.3.1   Penguins

Penguins (order Sphenisciformes) are an ancient and distinctive group of flightless, short-legged birds that evolved in the Southern Hemisphere, probably around New Zealand, about 65 Ma ago in the late Cretaceous, although the oldest known fossils date from about 45 Ma ago.

At a maximum body mass of more than 40 kg, the emperor penguin (*Aptenodytes forsteri*, Figure 5.7, *overleaf*) is the largest living penguin (some fossil species were much bigger) and is found further south than any other vertebrate. Like other penguins, emperors feed on fish, squid and large crustaceans that they catch by diving and chasing the prey underwater. They breed on the iceshelf, away from predators such as skuas and seals, on breeding

Figure 5.7 Emperor penguins with chicks (*Aptenodytes forsteri*).

grounds that may be as far as several hundred kilometres from the open water. The males leave the feeding areas in early April (autumn in Antarctica) and fast during 6 weeks of courtship and for a further 2 months while brooding. Only one egg is laid, and the male carries it on his feet and broods it in a special flap of feathered skin that extends from his abdomen. Brooding penguins are inactive, keeping close together in large groups and walking an average of only 30 metres per day, thereby minimizing energy expenditure to near BMR. If his mate has not returned by the time the chick hatches, the male feeds his offspring on 'curds' formed from deciduous tissue in the oesophagus and broods it as he did the egg (Figure 5.7). As soon as he is relieved by his mate, he walks back to the open water in what is by then mid-winter, continuously dark and very cold.

The female also fasts during courtship, but she returns to the sea after presenting her mate with a single egg that is large relative to her own size. The female fattens quickly while at sea, eating 6–8 kg per day and increasing her body mass by about one-third, before returning inland to take her turn to feed the chick on curds and partially digested food regurgitated from her stomach.

René Groscolas and other French biologists from Strasbourg spent many months in Antarctica studying the physiological mechanisms behind these habits. Figure 5.8 shows the measurements that they made on wild penguins during the breeding season and in the following 3 weeks, while the birds were artificially prevented from returning to the sea to feed at the end of the natural fasting period. Every few days, marked penguins were caught, weighed, their rectal temperature measured, and a sample of venous blood taken.

While fasting at the breeding colony, the mean body mass of the males fell by 40.5%, from 38.2 kg to 22.75 kg, at an average rate of 135 grams per day. After falling slightly during the first few days, the body temperature, and plasma glucose and fatty acids levels were constant (Figure 5.8a), and well within the ranges of values measured in penguins that were feeding regularly. The ketone β-hydroxybutyrate is produced by partial oxidation of fatty acids and can substitute for glucose in some energy producing pathways in some tissues. Its concentration increased steadily, reaching a peak when the fathers began to feed their chicks. The smaller females lost only about 22% of their initial body mass during their shorter fast. Except during the period of egg-laying, the pattern of changes is similar to that of the males.

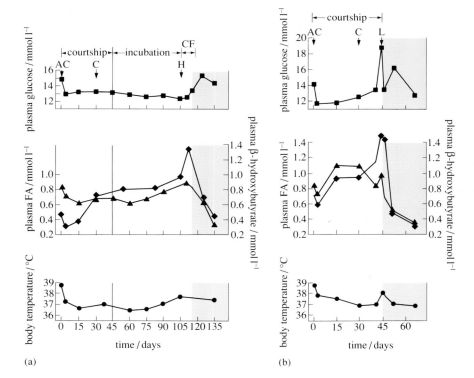

Figure 5.8   *Changes in the concentrations in the blood plasma of glucose (■), non-esterified fatty acids (FA, ▲) and β-hydroxybutyrate (◆), and body temperature (●) in (a) male and (b) female breeding emperor penguins. The white areas show natural habits, the start of the blue shading marks the end of the fast in the colony, and the blue shaded areas show measurements during the period in which the penguins were penned, preventing them from returning to the sea and feeding (after day 115 in the males, and day 45 in females). The observation period began at the end of March and continued until the end of August (early in the Antarctic winter) for the males (a) and until the end of June for the females (b). Abbreviations: AC, arrival at the colony; C, copulation; H, hatching; CF, chick feeding with oesophageal secretion; L, laying.*

■   Why should egg-laying affect body temperature and metabolism?

Egg production involves the synthesis of large quantities of protein and lipid (for yolk), and withdrawal of calcium stores (for shell formation), which require higher levels of circulating glucose and generate heat.

The tenfold increase in the concentrations of β-hydroxybutyrate is small compared to changes of up to 40-fold observed in the blood of pigeons, poultry and humans after just a few days of starvation. When artificially prevented from returning to the sea at the end of their normal fast, plasma fatty acid and β-hydroxybutyrate concentrations decreased sharply in penguins of both sexes. Their rate of weight loss also increased abruptly, reaching a mean of 542 grams per day for the lightest penguins that weighed only 17.5 kg.

■   What can you deduce from these observations about the penguins' fat stores and energy metabolism?

Production and utilization of free fatty acids decrease, probably because stores of triacylglycerols are almost exhausted. So the penguins start utilizing protein at a much higher rate. Because much less energy is produced from the breakdown of each gram of protein, a much higher rate of weight loss is necessary to meet the energy requirements of maintaining an almost constant body temperature.

This conclusion is confirmed by increased excretion of uric acid during enforced starvation. Other measurements indicate that during natural fasting, 93% of the penguins' energy comes from oxidation of fatty acids released from adipose tissue (Figure 5.9). The small quantity of glucose needed to support glucose-dependent tissues (e.g. the brain) is formed mainly from the glycerol in triacylglycerols, and only small quantities of protein are utilized.

■ Are the reserves replenished in the same way as they are depleted?

No. As shown on Figure 5.9, protein is withdrawn last during fasting but replenished more rapidly than lipid when the penguins start feeding again.

These observations suggest that, as in other animals, loss of protein has serious disadvantages and is only a 'last resort' when other energy reserves are exhausted.

The mean body mass of male penguins leaving the colony is around 23 kg, which, from calculations based upon the data in Figures 5.8 and 5.9, indicates triacylglycerol reserves of about 2 kg. This amount is just sufficient to sustain the penguin as it walks, using energy at 2.8-4.5 times BMR, as far as 100 km back to the open sea. Under normal circumstances, the birds begin feeding just before exhausting completely the lipid in their adipose tissue (Figure 5.9). Utilization of protein reserves involves drastic alterations in metabolism and they do not last long, so if the weather is unusually severe, or the sea-ice is exceptionally extensive, or stocks of fish at the feeding grounds are low, penguins that were even slightly underweight at the start of the breeding season may not survive. Indeed, Dr Groscolas suggested that the decrease in the plasma concentration of fatty acids and/or of β-hydroxybutyrate may be the metabolic signal (the arrow on Figure 5.9) that prompts the parent to abandon its chick and return to the sea, even if its mate has not yet come back. Each year around 30% of eggs and chicks are abandoned for various reasons, and without parental care they always die. However, mortality among adult penguins is quite low, and each bird may breed many times during a long lifetime.

Comparison between different species of penguin shows that, in general, larger species can fast for longer, suggesting that the very large extinct penguins may have undergone fasts lasting many months.

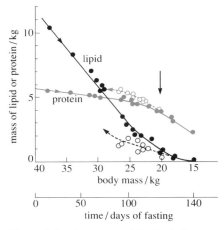

Figure 5.9 Summary of the depletion and replenishment of lipid (black circles) and protein reserves (blue circles) in breeding emperor penguins. The arrow indicates the body mass at which most penguins abandon the egg or chick and return to the sea to feed, even if its mate has not yet come back. Closed symbols show measurements from fasting penguins; open symbols, refeeding.

5.3.2 Bears

Brown or grizzly bears (*Ursus arctos*), and black bears (*U. americanus*) feed throughout the summer on grass, fruit, nuts, fish, small mammalian prey and carrion. In autumn, all brown and black bears fatten rapidly before entering caves or hollows where they become dormant for weeks or months. The terms 'hibernation' and 'torpor' are sometimes used to describe this state in bears. To avoid confusion with true hibernation (Chapter 6), this phenomenon is here called '**dormancy**'. Much of the research on the metabolic basis of this physiological state has been carried out in USA on the black bear, which occurs over most of USA and southern Canada and is smaller and easier to maintain in captivity than brown bears or polar bears.

Polar bears (*U. maritimus*) are almost entirely carnivorous and are the only species of bear to obtain almost all their food from the sea. They catch their main prey, ringed seals (*Phoca hispida*), as pups or when the adults come up to breathe through holes in the ice, so food is most accessible during the winter and during the seal breeding season in early spring. Males and non-breeding females remain active throughout the year, but in early winter the pregnant females migrate to areas where there are deep snow drifts suitable for making dens, where they give birth and suckle their cubs. Around Alaska, polar bears find suitable denning places on the sea-ice but those around Svalbard and Hudson Bay in Canada travel inland, sometimes substantial distances. The mothers are inactive and do not feed at all, but they remain alert when settled in the den. The limited physiological data indicate that metabolism during this period, which can last for up to 5 months, resembles that of dormancy in the more herbivorous brown and black bears.

Dormancy in black and brown bears

The dormant state of bears differs from true hibernation in that the body temperature does not fall below 31–35 °C and a major disturbance (such as an intruding biologist) can arouse them to full activity in a few minutes. Dormant bears do not eat, drink, urinate or defaecate, the heart rate drops from 50–60 beats min^{-1} to 8–12 beats min^{-1}, and oxygen consumption is only 32% of that of actively foraging bears. Nonetheless, the rate of protein turnover, as measured by the rate of dilution of ^{14}C-labelled amino acids injected into the blood, is three to five times higher during dormancy than in normal activity. Protein synthesis, particularly of enzymes involved in lipid and protein metabolism, also continues unabated during dormancy. The degradation of proteins to urea, however, is greatly slowed in dormancy. In these respects, the reciprocal changes in protein metabolism of the hibernating bear resemble those of humans and other mammals of tropical origin living on protein-deficient diets: essential amino acids are incorporated into proteins in the liver, but oxidation of amino acids and excretion of nitrogen are greatly reduced.

A small, but significant quantity of urea is produced throughout dormancy but it is not excreted. Instead, it passes across the gut epithelium and into the lumen, where it is further degraded to ammonia and carbon dioxide by the gut bacteria. The carbon dioxide is excreted with the respiratory gases, but the fate of the highly soluble, and in high concentrations toxic, ammonium ions is more interesting. In dormant bears, the blood concentrations of amino acids, total protein, urea and uric acid during dormancy are similar to those of active bears that are feeding regularly. Since there is almost no net elimination of the nitrogen, it must be re-incorporated into amino acids. The most important source of carbon for this process is glycerol. If ^{14}C-labelled glycerol is injected into a dormant bear, the label quickly appears in alanine, then in other amino acids, and finally in plasma proteins.

■   Where could the glycerol come from normally in a dormant bear?

Glycerol is produced from lipolysis of triacylglycerols.

The fatty acids released by lipolysis are used in energy metabolism, but much of the glycerol (that in other mammals is mainly oxidized) is combined with ammonia to form amino acids, which are incorporated into proteins in the normal way. This mechanism recycles the nitrogen so efficiently that the concentration of urea in the blood actually decreases slightly after several weeks of dormancy.

The rate of excretion of nitrogen can be estimated as the ratio of the concentrations of urea (U) to creatinine (C) in the blood (U:C ratio). Creatinine is formed from the breakdown in muscle of phosphocreatine, a high energy phosphate compound, and is a minor but constant source of excreted nitrogen. In bears, the concentration of creatinine in blood plasma increases about threefold during the first 1–2 days in dormancy and then remains constant. The U:C ratio is around 50 in most mammals, especially carnivores that are eating regularly, and does not normally fall lower than 25, even during prolonged fasting. But U:C ratios of less than 10 are frequently measured in dormant black bears, indicating that during dormancy a high proportion of the urea is re-incorporated into proteins instead of being excreted. Consequently, the bears' lean body mass is hardly diminished even after months of dormancy and their muscle strength is unimpaired.

In starving humans and most other fasting animals, β-hydroxybutyrate and acetoacetate (ketone bodies) are formed by partial oxidation of fatty acids (see Figure 5.8). They are normally eliminated by further oxidation, but sometimes the presence of high concentration of ketones disturbs the acid–base buffering of the blood and a comatose state called ketosis develops. In many hibernators, very high concentrations of ketone bodies trigger arousal (see Section 6.3.6). Ketone bodies increase in dormant bears as well but only to a maximum of ninefold between normal activity and dormancy and the toxic effects of ketosis have never been observed. Experiments in which labelled glycerol is injected into the blood of dormant bears show that, as well as being incorporated into amino acids, substantial amounts of labelled glycerol also appear in triacylglycerols.

■   What does this observation show?

It shows that, as well as lipolysis of lipids stored in adipose tissue, resynthesis of triacylglycerols from fatty acids and glycerol is also occurring at a significant rate. The rate of triacylglycerol turnover may be higher during dormancy than during normal activity, and may limit the rate at which free fatty acids can enter the pathways that produce β-hydroxybutyrate and acetoacetate, thereby preventing ketosis and enabling the bears to sleep undisturbed for long periods.

■   Are there any other metabolic advantages of utilizing fat during dormancy?

Oxidation of fat produces water. Since the bears do not drink during dormancy, and the surrounding air is very dry, such metabolic water probably makes a significant contribution to water balance. Total body water, blood volume and the water content of red cells and plasma remain normal during dormancy, indicating that the water generated by such metabolism is indeed sufficient to offset the small losses due to respiration of the dry, cold air. Thus the large quantities of adipose tissue triacylglycerols in bears are much more than just an energy store: they are central to the bears' metabolic adaptations to dormancy.

Measurements of composition of the respiratory gases reveal that the respiratory exchange ratio (RER) falls from 0.78 when the bears are fully active to 0.62–0.69 during dormancy. Such values are exceptionally low: the normal minimum RER for mammals, representing oxidation of lipid only, is 0.71. The low RER shows that some of the carbon dioxide that would normally be excreted through the lungs fails to appear. Carbon dioxide cannot be stored in significant quantities (because as bicarbonate it alters the acid–base balance of body fluids), so it must be converted into non-volatile compounds, possibly by the micro-organisms in the gut or by enzymes in the bears' liver.

Like other metabolic processes, the urea cycle and protein synthesis generate quite a lot of heat and the high rate of these processes during dormancy, together with the bears' large size and thick, insulating fur, combine to maintain a much higher body temperature than that of small mammals in deep hibernation. Fully functional brown adipose tissue has not been demonstrated in bears, even in neonates, although small areas of white adipose tissue have some structural features that resemble those of BAT. Nonetheless, at a body mass of less than 1 kg, bears are smaller at birth, relative to the size of their parents, than any other eutherian mammal, and they are born in mid-winter.

Fasting in polar bears

How often are polar bears successful in finding food? Do they fast when out on the ice, as well as when in dens? Polar bears range over such a wide area of inhospitable terrain that such questions, though vital to the management of the species in the wild, are not easily answered by direct observation. The study of nitrogen metabolism in black bears suggests an indirect way of investigating such topics.

Figure 5.10 shows some measurement of the U:C ratio in blood samples collected from polar bears in northern Canada that were temporarily sedated with drugs injected from a dart gun.

■   What do these data suggest about food sources and hunting success in bears?

More than 75% of bears in dens (Figure 5.10a) had U:C ratios of 10 or less so they were obviously not eating, but the U:C ratios were 19.9 or lower in 70% of those caught on land in summer and autumn, showing that they were also fasting (Figures 5.10b and c). Out on the sea-ice in spring (Figure 5.10d), more than half the bears sampled had U:C ratios of 30 or more, indicating that they were feeding regularly. At least 10% of the bears in this sample were fasting: either they were inexperienced, inefficient or unlucky hunters of seals or (as quite frequently happens) they were forced to give up their kills to larger bears that threatened them. Alternatively, they may be 'voluntarily' anorexic while mating: during the spring, large males attend oestrous females closely and may fight with rivals, leaving little time for hunting.

Ice conditions that favour catching adult seals are strongly dependent upon weather and water currents, and so are widely scattered in space and time. Food supply is probably erratic even for the most proficient bears. Seal hunting is almost impossible for several months in the summer and autumn when the sea is unfrozen, and the only food available to polar bears is the odd bit of carrion and a very small quantity of plant food. The data in Figure 5.10 show that nearly all polar bears fast for long periods in the summer and that, for many, the food supply is unreliable even in winter and spring. Thus polar bears seem to adopt many of the metabolic features of winter dormancy in the omnivorous brown and black bears, while remaining active enough to be able to travel long distances between seal-hunting grounds. They become lethargic and remain inactive for long periods when weather conditions or terrain make hunting impossible, suggesting that they have become 'dormant' without actually being asleep in a den.

This theory is confirmed by observations on polar bears held temporarily in captivity. Bears caught in autumn were starved for 5–7 weeks, fed for 3 days,

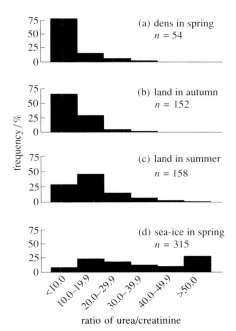

Figure 5.10   The frequency (as a percentage of the total) of U:C ratios measured in free-ranging polar bears caught in different areas of northern Canada at different seasons.

and then fasted again. Blood samples were taken just before and for several days after feeding, and the concentration of urea and creatinine measured. During the imposed fast, the U:C ratios averaged only 11.0, but rose abruptly to 32.0 after feeding and then declined to 22.8.

Polar bears are a relatively new species, evolving from brown bears during the last 100 000 years. They must have inherited the capacity for dormancy from their omnivorous ancestors that fed mainly in the summer and autumn. In polar bears, dormancy takes the form of inactivity during the summer months and in winter, irregular, intermittent fasting between widely scattered feeding opportunities.

5.3.3 The structure of adipose tissue

Since food is only available seasonally or intermittently at high latitudes, many arctic birds and mammals, including polar bears, Svalbard reindeer, arctic foxes, seals and walruses, naturally accumulate large stores of fat. In Sections 5.2 and 5.3, we saw that the quantity of energy stored and the metabolic control of its use are finely adjusted to the habits and habitat of the species. This section is concerned with the cellular structure and anatomical organization of adipose tissue in such naturally obese species. Most laboratory mammals do not naturally become obese, and must be induced to do so by drastic measures such as changes in diet, drugs or surgery. Although it is impossible to carry out as detailed measurements or carefully controlled experiments on wild animals as it is in the laboratory, arctic species provide a rare opportunity to study fattening and obesity as natural, rather than as pathological or artificial phenomena. Observations on these naturally obese animals can help resolve discrepancies between mechanisms that can be demonstrated experimentally in rats and those that seem to happen in people.

One important aspect of obesity is the contribution of adipocyte enlargement and the formation of additional adipocytes to the expansion of the animal's capacity for storing lipid. In adult rats and mice, fattening is achieved almost entirely by enlargement of adipocytes: the number of cells does not change. The matter is not easy to investigate in humans because there is no really accurate, non-destructive way of measuring total adipocyte complement, but indirect estimates suggest that the accumulation of more adipocytes makes a significant, in some people the dominant, contribution to obesity. In order to establish whether adipocyte proliferation is also essential to expansion of the lipid storage capacity in naturally obese arctic animals, we have to find a way of calculating how many adipocytes would be expected in an animal of any particular body mass. Figure 5.11 shows some measurements of the numbers of adipocytes in some temperate-zone and tropical mammals. The equations for the regression lines drawn on Figure 5.11 can be used to calculate the number of adipocytes expected in an animal from its body mass. The predicted adipocyte complement can then be compared with the measured adipocyte complement.

Such comparison shows that naturally obese arctic mammals such as polar bears, arctic foxes, wolverines* and reindeer have more adipocytes than expected, usually between twice and four times as many, although a few

---

* Wolverines (*Gulo gulo*) are large mustelid carnivores, related to otters, stoats and badgers.

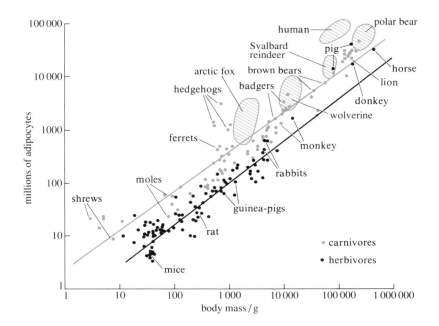

Figure 5.11   The numbers of adipocytes in some temperate-zone and tropical carnivorous and herbivorous mammals, compared with similar measurements on some naturally obese arctic species: polar bears, arctic foxes, wolverines and Svalbard reindeer. The large shaded circles enclose numerous measurements from wild specimens of the same species.

specimens have almost exactly the predicted number of adipocytes. Such proliferation of adipocytes is modest compared to that of humans: some obese people have more than ten times as many adipocytes as expected from comparison with the data in Figure 5.11.

However, the adipocyte complement of the wild mammals was found to be quite variable in otherwise similar specimens collected from the same area at the same time. Many factors such as hunting ability and appetite determine individual differences in fatness, but among the carnivores there was no evidence that individuals with more adipocytes were normally any fatter than those with fewer adipocytes: the adipose tissue of the former simply consisted of numerous, relatively smaller adipocytes. Individual variation in adipocyte complement is also observed in humans, with some people having relatively few, large adipocytes and others more numerous smaller ones, but it is not conspicuous in laboratory rats, all of which seem to have about the same adipocyte complement in relation to their body mass unless artificially manipulated to make them unnaturally obese.

■   Do these observations suggest that people who have large adipocyte complements are, or will inevitably become, obese?

No. In the wild carnivores, fatness does not correlate with adipocyte complement.

We know very little about the origin of such individual differences in adipocyte complement: adipocyte proliferation takes place mainly during the suckling period, and the exact course of growth at this age may differ from one individual bear, arctic fox, wolverine and reindeer to another, depending upon the number of littermates and the amount of food available to its mother.

■   Would it be possible to determine the fatness of a particular bear or reindeer by measuring the volume of a sample of its adipocytes?

No. Adipocyte volume would not be an accurate measure of fatness because the relationship between the total mass of adipose tissue and the volume of its adipocytes would be different in specimens that have large or small adipocyte complements.

Unfortunately, assessment of fatness from biopsy samples of adipose tissue is much more satisfactory in rats (because their adipocyte complement is more constant) than it is in either naturally obese arctic mammals or in humans.

Summary of Section 5.3

Penguins and many other large arctic animals fast for long periods while remaining active and at near-normal body temperature. Emperor penguins fatten before the breeding season and fast for weeks during courtship and reproduction. Very little protein is broken down until lipid stores are nearly exhausted. Energy reserves determine an individual's behaviour such as feeding or abandoning the chick. Omnivorous brown and black bears feed in summer and become dormant in winter: they stop feeding and enter dens, where their metabolism slows and is supported almost entirely by lipids released from adipose tissue. Urea is recycled and very little nitrogenous waste is excreted, so the protein in muscle, liver and other lean tissues is not depleted, as normally happens in prolonged fasting. Similar physiological processes occur in carnivorous polar bears when food is scarce but, except for breeding females, there is no regular, prolonged period of dormancy.

5.4   Thermal insulation

The principles of thermal insulation in birds and mammals are described in Section 3.2.3. For organisms of similar size and shape in a similar thermal gradient, the rate of heat loss from convection is up to 90 times as fast in water as in air, so in temperate climates, aquatic endotherms need much more efficient insulation than terrestrial species. Since seawater freezes at $-1.9\,°C$, but the temperature of the air around the poles can fall below $-50\,°C$, the insulation requirements of aquatic and terrestrial arctic animals are not very different. Nonetheless, there are important differences in the tissues involved and in their responses to different environments.

5.4.1   Insulation in terrestrial endotherms

Relatively minor changes in body shape can contribute much to reducing heat loss. Thus Svalbard reindeer (Plate 5.1) are smaller and stockier, and have shorter ears, legs and snout than subspecies that live further south. Polar bears also have relatively small, round ears, huge, shaggy feet and the tail is greatly reduced.

The insulating properties of furs and feathers can be easily compared by wrapping pelts around heated objects such as bars and measuring their rate of cooling under various conditions. Such observations indicate that in still air, the insulation of all coats of fur or feathers is proportional to their length and thickness, but the texture and secretions from cutaneous glands produce very different properties when exposed to wind and water (see Figure 3.4).

Some small arctic mammals such as lemmings and hamsters spend the winter in burrows and tunnels under the snow, where the air is effectively still all the time. Arctic foxes, and sometimes bears, shelter in snow drifts, and their young are born in dens, but in polar regions there is little shelter from plants, because trees and large shrubs are absent, and there are not many caves or other geological structures formed by flowing water. The effects of wind are important for large mammals, particularly if, like reindeer, they spend a large proportion of the time foraging in exposed places. In such animals, the outer guard hairs are long and relatively stiff, providing mechanical protection and support for the fine, dense underfur that traps layers of warm air near the skin. Stiff outer feathers and fluffy down combine to insulate birds in much the same way.

In arctic homeotherms, fur or feathers often extends over parts of the body that are usually naked in temperate-zone species: the feathers extend along the legs and over the feet of ptarmigan (Plate 5.3) and snowy owls, and the pawpads of arctic foxes and arctic hares are covered in short, tough fur (Figure 5.12). The fur of Svalbard reindeer is longer and denser than that of Norwegian reindeer and it covers the ears, eyelids, snout, lips and feet much more extensively.

■   Could there be any disadvantages in fur covering all parts of the body?

The animal's ability to dissipate heat during strenuous exercise or in warm weather is reduced and it risks overheating. When overheated, seals hold their flippers up in the wind or try to get back into water. Reindeer, bears and other terrestrial mammals pant vigorously, but hyperthermia is a real risk, especially for very large or pregnant specimens. The need to dissipate heat during prolonged, strenuous exercise may be one reason why the large hunters, such as wolves, that occur throughout the Russian and Canadian Arctic, are not completely covered in thick fur. In husky dogs (and their wolf ancestors), counter-current blood flow in the legs and nose results in much lower temperatures of the peripheral parts of these organs (Figure 5.13), greatly reducing heat loss from them. When the animals are asleep, of course, they tuck their feet and nose into their coat or cover them with their thickly furred tail, but they avoid overheating during long chases by retaining some exposed surfaces through which heat can be lost rapidly. All animals with wettable fur lose heat faster when wet, and most species, including polar bears, shake themselves vigorously (as dogs do) immediately after swimming.

The surface temperatures of red foxes, kit foxes (another temperate-zone species native to USA) and arctic foxes at air temperatures from −25 to +30 °C have been compared using infrared thermography (see Section 1.3.1). There were surprisingly few differences: all foxes lost heat through their legs, paws, ears and snout, but while the two temperate-zone species also lost heat through their thinly furred forehead, this area of the arctic fox is efficiently insulated. In the winter, the forehead of arctic foxes is covered in long, dense fur (Plate 5.2), making the animal look like a pet dog, but far from being a trivial character, this tuft of fur is an integral part of the species' adaptation to extreme cold. It is greatly reduced in the greyish-brown summer pelt.

People's breath freezes on beards and eyelashes but ice does not accumulate on the fur of many arctic mammals, notably that of arctic foxes, wolves and wolverines, probably because the microscopic structure of the hair surface

Figure 5.12   Photograph of the underside of the hind paws of an arctic fox in winter coat, showing the paw pads covered with fur.

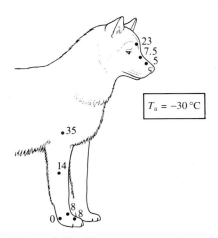

Figure 5.13   The temperatures at various areas of the skin of a husky dog.

and/or oily secretions from the skin prevent the formation of ice-crystals. Although less soft and silky than mink, arctic people value such fur, particularly for trimming hoods and mufflers.

For reasons associated with the erratic food supply (Section 5.2), many arctic mammals are obese, particularly in the winter, a situation that has led to the notion that thick subcutaneous adipose tissue makes an important contribution to insulation. Although as long ago as the 1950s, measurements on people swimming the English Channel and on men on polar expeditions failed to reveal any firm association between thickness of superficial adipose tissue and the capacity to withstand exposure to cold, the statement that subcutaneous adipose tissue is subcutaneous because it is essential to insulation appears in many recent textbooks.

■   How could you test this hypothesis?

The hypothesis predicts that there is normally a thermal gradient across the adipose tissue. In practice, it is quite difficult to measure such a thermal gradient over a long period, and demonstrating it would not prove that adipose tissue (rather than any other superficial tissue such as muscle) is essential to insulation.

Another approach is to compare the partitioning of adipose tissue between internal and superficial depots in arctic and tropical species and look for evidence of selective expansion of the superficial fat in the cold-adapted forms. Polar bears eat seals, and occasionally swim long distances in ice-cold water between hunting grounds. Ice conditions often make their prey inaccessible, forcing them to fast for long periods (Section 5.3.2), so bears fatten when prey are readily available and are usually obese for large parts of the year. These facts have given rise to the idea that, as in fully marine mammals such as walruses and arctic cetaceans (that often occur in the same habitats), adipose tissue makes an important contribution to insulation in polar bears. The data in Figure 5.14 enable us to test this hypothesis directly. The order Carnivora includes species that share a common ancestry and many habits and range in size from weasels (with a body mass of about 0.1 kg) to bears (with a body mass of up to 700 kg) and are adapted to live in very hot (e.g. fennec fox) and very cold (e.g. arctic fox, polar bear) climates.

■   Is the partitioning of adipose tissue between internal and superficial depots in semi-aquatic arctic polar bears different from that in fully terrestrial temperate-zone carnivores?

No. The mass of the intra-abdominal depots becomes proportionately smaller and that of the superficial adipose tissue larger with increasing body mass in all species studied. The data for polar bears fit closely to the regression line fitted to the data from the temperate-zone species. There is no evidence for adaptive redistribution of adipose tissue in polar bears. Their skin is warm to the touch and the coarse guard hairs and woolly underfur are probably the principal insulating tissues. The distribution of adipose tissue in mammals native to cold freshwater, such as otters, beavers and muskrats, is also not different from that of related terrestrial species (e.g. badgers, squirrels and lemmings respectively), providing no evidence that their adipose tissue is adapted to function as an insulator.

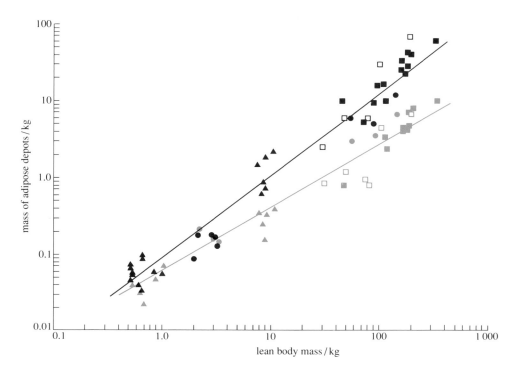

Figure 5.14 The mass of superficial (black symbols) and intra-abdominal (blue symbols) adipose tissue in some relatively obese carnivores. There was no significant correlation between fatness and body mass in this sample of 44 moderately obese carnivores. To compare arctic species with temperate-zone and tropical Carnivora, the regression lines are calculated from all the data except those from polar bears. (▲) Mustelidae (weasels, ferrets and badgers); (●) Felidae (cats); (■) polar bears; (□) brown bears.

As much as 50% of the body mass of large adult bears can be lipid, and selective expansion of the superficial adipose depots relative to the internal depots seems to arise mainly because 'there is nowhere else for so much fat to go'. The surface area also declines with size in animals of similar shape (see Section 2.7.1), so the superficial layer of adipose tissue becomes thicker with increasing body mass, even if it does not become proportionately more massive. There is also proportionately more superficial adipose tissue in large, naturally obese birds: the subcutaneous depots amount to more than 80% of the total adipose tissue in emperor penguins.

5.4.2 Insulation in aquatic endotherms

Most seals and sealions (order Pinnipedia) are furred. The young, which are always born on beaches or icefloes, have long guard hairs and dense underfur similar to the coats of terrestrial mammals. Before they start swimming regularly, they moult and grow their adult fur, which usually consists of short, dense stiff guard hairs that are oily from profuse secretions of the sebaceous glands. The hair probably acts like a wet suit of a human diver: a layer of water is trapped around the hair, where it is warmed by body heat and prevents much colder water from coming into direct contact with the skin. Short, oily fur dries quickly when the seals come onto land. Two genera, the northern fur seal, *Callorhinus ursinus*, in the north Pacific, and eight species of southern fur seals, *Arctocephalus* sp., in the Pacific and Southern Oceans, also have a dense layer of underfur that traps small bubbles of air and keeps the skin dry.

■   Are there any disadvantages of such insulation for aquatic mammals?

During deep dives, the pressure of the water would compress the air bubbles, greatly reducing the insulating efficiency of the fur and increasing the possibility that the skin is wetted. The air also makes the mammal or bird more buoyant, thus hindering diving and swimming underwater.

This kind of insulation is most common in semi-aquatic mammals such as beavers, muskrats and otters, and in the feathers of ducks and penguins, which live mainly in shallow water and spend long periods exposed to very cold air. Newborn seals have a fluffy neonatal coat, quite different in both colour and texture from that of the adults, that provides good insulation in air but is ineffective in water. Because the fur is an efficient insulator in air, adult fur seals and the juveniles of many other seal species have long been hunted for their pelts.

In view of the effectiveness of insulating fur among seals, it may seem surprising that one of the most northerly pinnipeds, the walrus (*Odobenus rosmarus*), and all the whales and dolphins (order Cetacea) are almost hairless, even as neonates. In these marine mammals, the skin and a specialized form of fibrous adipose tissue called blubber are the major insulators. Walrus skin is up to 5 cm thick and the blubber, although minimal or absent over the tail, flippers and parts of the head, is up to 15 cm thick over some areas of the trunk. Measurements on dead tissues indicate that conductance of heat is about half as efficient through adipose tissue as through aqueous tissues such as muscle. However, such passive properties are probably much less important to thermal insulation than counter-current systems of blood vessels (see Section 3.3.3), and control of the rate of flow of blood through the tissue, that brings heat from the warm core to the surface. Blood flow through the superficial adipose tissue can be reduced almost to zero for hours without damaging the adipocytes.

■   Why cannot the blood flow to muscle be similarly reduced?

Muscle is much more metabolically active than adipose tissue and cannot remain functional unless supplied with sufficient blood-borne nutrients and oxygen. Deprivation of blood for longer than a few minutes causes permanent damage to most muscles.

When basking out of the water, the skin of walruses is so flushed with blood that it appears pink, particularly in warm weather, which is when they are most often seen by hunters and biologists. As soon as walruses enter the water, blood vessels in the skin and outer layers of the blubber constrict, shutting off the circulation almost completely, so the animals become dull grey and much less heat is lost at the surface. During strenuous exercise, or when in warmer water, perfusion can be increased, thereby adjusting accurately the rate of heat loss to internal heat production, as happens in counter-current mechanisms (see Figure 5.13). Vigorous exercise is rarely necessary for feeding, because walruses eat mainly bottom-dwelling invertebrates, especially molluscs, and being so large (up to 1.5 tonnes), they have few predators except killer whales and, occasionally, polar bears. Adipose tissue has the advantage of being almost incompressible and, although fat is less dense than water, it contributes less to buoyancy than air trapped in the pelt.

However, restricted blood flow is incompatible with certain other functions of the superficial tissues. Walruses shed the outer layers of the skin each year, possibly as a means of getting rid of external parasites. To support regrowth of the skin, blood perfusion of the superficial tissues is plentiful throughout the moult, and walruses normally spend almost the entire period basking on beaches or ice-floes. Although the process takes place in mid-summer, walruses can die of cold if forced to spend too much time in the water while moulting. Cetaceans spend their entire life in water and moult less efficiently, enabling barnacles and ectoparasites to colonize their skin.

Thick layers of superficial adipose tissue also contribute to insulation in other species of seals, although the relative importance of fur and fat probably differs greatly between the seasons and in different species. The distribution of adipose tissue in most adult seals, dolphins and the small toothed whales suggests that it is adapted to contribute to thermal insulation: the superficial blubber forms an almost continuous layer, albeit of very variable thickness, and adipose tissue is almost absent from the abdomen and muscles.

All seals that have been investigated have surprisingly little superficial adipose tissue at birth, the superficial depots being only 2–4 mm thick in northern fur seal pups that weigh 5–6 kg at birth. Their thick natal coats keep them warm in dry weather, but although their BMR can increase to as much as $18 \, W \, kg^{-1}$, seal pups quickly become hypothermic if immersed in water or during heavy rain. Furthermore, the distribution of adipose tissue of neonates resembles that of typical terrestrial mammals: as well as several superficial depots, there are significant quantities of adipose tissue inside the abdomen, around the kidneys, and in the pericardium. Some of these internal depots contain adipocytes which appear under the electron microscope to have features in common with BAT (see Chapter 4): mitochondria are quite numerous but they lack cristae. However, although it may be thermogenic to some extent, the tissue is not true BAT in either structure or metabolism.

Birds replace old, worn feathers with new ones, usually one or twice a year, often just before breeding or migration. Moulting and replacement of the plumage impose heavy demands on the nutrient reserves because large quantities of energy and protein are used in the synthesis of new feathers. Foraging is also difficult or impossible: most large birds cannot fly (in the absence of primary wing feathers) and polar species do not swim because their insulation is so severely impaired that they would become too cold in water. The moult takes 2–5 weeks in emperor and king penguins (*Aptenodytes patagonica*), during which time they remain on land (or on ice-floes) and fast, losing up to 45% of their body mass and up to 50% of their protein reserves.

5.4.3 Humans in polar regions

Humans evolved in tropical Africa and gradually colonized colder climates during the Pleistocene Ice Age. There have been permanent populations in the Arctic for several thousand years: mostly Eskimos (Inuit) in what is now Canada, Alaska and Greenland, and several groups in northern Europe and Russia, such as the Lapps (Saami) in Scandinavia and the Chukchi in Siberia. Such people do not grow crops and keep only a few domestic animals, mostly for transport (e.g. husky dogs), not for food. Until very recently, they lived by hunting seals, fish and wild and semi-domesticated reindeer and, during the brief summer, gathering wild berries.

Adaptation to living in the Arctic has been more technological and cultural than physiological: Eskimos are shorter and stockier than Canadians of European ancestry, but comparisons of the distribution and abundance of their adipose tissue revealed that the native people have less, rather than more, superficial fat.

■   What does this comparison suggest about the function of superficial adipose tissue in humans?

It is not adapted to a role as thermal insulation. Frost damage to exposed parts such as the face and hands is prevented by efficient perfusion with warm blood (see Figure 5.13), rather than by any form of insulation. Human colonization of the Arctic was made possible by the effective use of animal skins as clothing.

Adaptations of digestion and metabolism have evolved among Eskimos: although their diet was very rich in fat and protein, and for 9 months of the year included almost no fruit or vegetables, diseases such as obesity, diabetes, scurvy, rickets, dental caries, constipation and colon cancer were rare. However, obesity, diabetes and dental caries have become much more common during the last 30–40 years since they adopted a western diet. Eskimos have never grown crops or stored grain, and so alcoholic (and caffeine-containing) drinks were never part of their diet: alcohol dehydrogenase, the enzyme that detoxifies alcohol, is present in very small quantities in their livers and it is not as readily induced as it is in people who have a long tradition of drinking fermented beverages. Consequently, grown men are easily intoxicated by as little as half a pint of beer.

The capacity of the human nose to conserve moisture by warming and hydrating inhaled air and reclaiming the heat and moisture of exhaled air (shown in the dog in Figure 3.13), is much less efficient than the long nasal turbinals of native arctic mammals such as bears, reindeer and wolves. The ability to breathe steadily through the nose rather than through the mouth improves with practice, but most inexperienced visitors to polar regions are bothered as much by thirst as by cold.

Living in such a severe climate is very tough: archaeological studies suggest that human habitation of arctic regions was often transient, with many settlements being abandoned when the climate worsened or food became scarce. Until very recently, resources were never abundant enough to support the development of large, dense cities or towns.

People from the temperate zone have only recently explored the polar regions. European expeditions, such those led by the Dutch sea captain, Willem Barents, in 1596–1597 and by the Russian-financed German explorer, Vitus Bering, in 1741, visited the Arctic Ocean and many of its islands, including the Svalbard Archipelago (see Section 5.1.1), but no permanent settlements of the Europeans were established in the high Arctic until the 20th century.

The voyage of Captain James Cook in 1772–1773 is the first known exploration of the southern oceans. Fisherman and hunters of whales and seals landed on many of the islands during the 18th and 19th centuries, but Antarctica itself was not explored until the first decade of the 20th century. Although research in and around Antarctica has been much expanded since the 1960s, there is still no permanent, breeding human population.

Summary of Section 5.4

Many arctic mammals and birds are obese because their food supply is highly seasonal or erratic. In large species, proportionately more adipose tissue accumulates in the superficial depots and less in the internal depots in tropical, temperate-zone and arctic animals. There is evidence for redistribution of adipose tissue as an adaptation to thermal insulation only in pinnipeds and smaller cetaceans. Unlike fur, adipose tissue is incompressible: its effectiveness as insulation depends upon rapid, efficient control of blood perfusion through it and the skin. Humans are basically tropical and have colonized arctic regions only very recently in evolutionary terms, so they have minimal anatomical and physiological adaptations to the environment and are capable of only limited acclimatization.

5.5 Polar ectotherms

The land and shallow water experience at least a brief summer at high latitudes, so terrestrial and freshwater ectotherms can be active during warm periods and hibernate when the temperature is below freezing (see Chapter 6). But the polar seas are never warmed significantly by the sun and so are continuously at between −1.9 and +6 °C: the inhabitants complete their entire life cycle at temperatures at which tropical ectotherms would die and most temperate-zone species would become torpid (see Section 6.3.6). There is much less mixing between warm and cold currents around Antarctica, so in the southern oceans temperature zones are sharply delimited and have distinctive faunas. However, movements of water currents in the North Atlantic and North Pacific cause quite large seasonal changes in water temperature around the Arctic and hence less clearly defined faunal zones.

The common arctic fish are closely related to species in north temperate-zone waters and include two salmonids, the capelin (*Mallotus villosus*) and the arctic char (*Salvelinus alpinus*), which breeds in rivers but spends part of its adult life

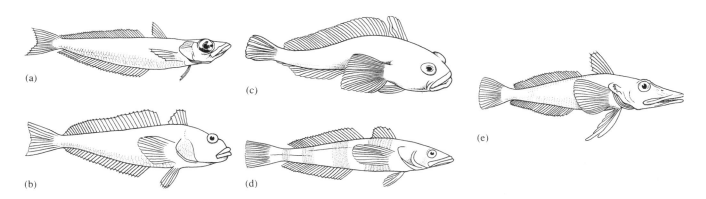

Figure 5.15 Some nototheniid fish native to the southern oceans that have been studied in the laboratory. (a) The antarctic silver fish (*Pleuragramma antarcticum*) 12–17 cm long; (b) *Notothenia neglecta* (25–40 cm long). (c) The emerald rockcod (*Trematomus bernacchii*) about 20 cm long. (d) The toothfish (*Dissostichus mawsoni*) up to 1.25 m long, the largest fish in antarctic coastal waters. (e) The icefish (*Chaenocephalus aceratus*) up to 1 m long.

in the sea, sculpins (family Cottidae), various flatfish such as polar halibut (*Reinhardtius hippoglossoides*) and flounder (*Pleuronectes americanus*) and members of the cod family, such as arctic cod (*Arctogadus glacialis*) and haddock. Many of the most abundant and widespread fish around Antarctica belong to a suborder Notothenioides of the order Perciformes (perches). Nototheniids (Figure 5.15) probably evolved in the oceans around Antarctica during the last 20–30 million years, and the living species are almost confined to that region. In contrast to the Arctic Ocean, there are very few species of the cod (Gadiformes), herring (Clupeiformes) and salmon (Salmoniformes) families in the Southern Ocean. Only a few chondrichthyan fish live in polar waters, among them the Greenland shark (*Somniosus microcephalus*).

5.5.1 Passive properties

Freezing is nearly always harmful to living cells because the tertiary structure of hydrophilic molecules such as proteins is disrupted and the permeability of membranes is drastically altered. The concentration of solutes in the blood of teleost fish is only about half that of seawater so, while seawater freezes at $-1.9\,°C$, fish blood would be expected to freeze at -1 to $-0.6\,°C$. One way in which fish living in very cold seawater avoid what seems like inevitable disaster is by **supercooling**: the body fluids can remain indefinitely below $-0.6\,°C$, provided they do not come into contact with any ice-crystals. The consequence of so doing were first demonstrated about 40 years ago by the Norwegian physiologist, Per Scholander (Figure 5.16).

■　What tissues are the likely route for entry of ice-crystals into the fish?

The gills, which present no effective barrier to ice-crystals, the gut when food is ingested, and the flow of urine from the excretory system.

Except during urination, the urethra is closed tightly by a muscular sphincter lined with large quantities of mucus, thereby minimizing the risk of ice-crystals forming in the relatively dilute urine. Ice floats in water and the deeper layers of the oceans are usually slightly warmer, $-1.8\,°C$, than the surface water. So one way of avoiding the fate described on Figure 5.16 is to remain in deeper water. However, some fish, notably the capelin, spawn on beaches where the air temperature can be much colder than that of the sea. The sticky secretions on the outside of the eggs both stick them to the rocks and promote supercooling down to $-5\,°C$, but if the shells are pierced, tiny ice-crystals quickly form and the embryos freeze at $-1.4\,°C$.

Freezing is also avoided by the presence of 'antifreezes' called **cryoprotectants** in the blood. Natural cryoprotectants are usually glycopeptides or peptides of molecular weight 2 400–36 000 that bind to ice-crystals and prevent them from growing larger than tiny nuclei. These cryoprotectants are present in almost all body fluids, including the blood, the cerebrospinal fluid, the peritoneal fluid, interstitial fluid of the muscles, and (via bile secretions) the lumen of the gut. Other body fluids, such as the ocular fluid in the eye, are protected from contact with ice-crystals by the surrounding tissues. Cryoprotectant molecules are not eliminated by the kidney because most polar fish that have them also have aglomerular kidneys: their urine is formed by secretion into the nephron rather than by filtration.

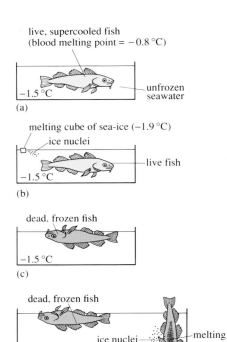

Figure 5.16 The effects of 'seeding' ice-crystals into water containing a supercooled fjord cod (*Boreogadus saida*). (a) The fish can remain indefinitely at $-1.5\,°C$, because its blood is supercooled, but if (b) a piece of frozen seawater at $-1.9\,°C$ is put near it, the supercooling is destroyed, and the fish freezes and dies (c) in a few minutes, although the seawater itself remains liquid at $-1.5\,°C$. Similar processes occur if the fish comes into contact with a dead conspecific that contains ice-crystals (d).

At least eight different cryoprotectant molecules have already been identified and almost all antarctic fish have some kind of antifreeze in their body fluids, usually throughout the year. Similar cryoprotectants have evolved in several kinds of arctic fish, but such adaptations are less widespread and cryoprotectants are present only during the winter in many species. In the northern oceans, most of the fish (and their mammalian and avian predators, see Section 5.3) stay in the highly productive waters at the edge of the iceshelf and avoid direct contact with frozen seawater. Other cryoprotectant agents have evolved in terrestrial arthropods, amphibians and reptiles that hibernate in sub-arctic areas of Canada and Russia (see Section 6.2).

Blood pigments

The solubility of oxygen (and of many other gases) in water increases with decreasing temperature: at 0 °C, seawater holds 1.6 times as much oxygen when saturated as at 20 °C. This fact, and continual disturbance by frequent storms, mean that the surface waters of arctic oceans are very well oxygenated. A family of 17 species of nototheniid fish, the Channichthyidae, have no erythrocytes, no haemoglobin and almost no myoglobin at all stages of the life cycle.

■   What would such fish look like?

Unless the skin is pigmented, they would be colourless. The most thoroughly studied species, the icefish (*Chaenocephalus aceratus*, Figure 5.15e), is almost transparent.

■   How could the absence of erythrocytes *improve* blood flow?

The viscosity of most fluids, including water, increases with decreasing temperature, so the heart must pump harder to maintain the circulation of the blood. However, cells make a major contribution to the viscosity of the blood and the elimination of erythrocytes would make the blood much less viscous and hence reduce the work of pumping.

As well as being large, icefish are active predators that swim in the surface waters and use oxygen at about the same rate as red-blooded antarctic fish such as *Notothenia* or *Pleuragramma* (see Figures 5.15a and b). Icefish blood contains solutes and a few white blood cells, so it is a yellowish, watery fluid similar to mammalian lymph. Large volumes of it flow in wide capillaries propelled by a heart that pumps out three to four times as much blood as that of a red-blooded fish of similar size and habits. The bulbus arteriosus on the anterior side of the heart is greatly expanded and is the only muscular tissue to contain any myoglobin. Measurements on the uptake and circulation of oxygen in captive icefish suggest that, as well as the gills, the thin, scaleless skin is important as a site of gas exchange, with up to 8% of the oxygen absorbed through the tail skin alone. At low temperatures, the blood of icefish circulates faster and takes up nearly as much oxygen from the water as red blood, although transfer of oxygen to tissues is less efficient. However, in even slightly warmer water, these advantages disappear and icefish suffocate.

■   What other aspect of energy metabolism is likely to be inferior in icefish?

Anaerobic metabolism. Without myoglobin, their muscles are unable to store oxygen so the fish quickly become anoxic during very fast swimming or in deoxygenated water. They tire quickly after a brief burst of swimming and cannot tolerate the build up of more than a very little lactic acid in the muscles and, of course, they do not survive in warmer, less oxygenated water.

5.5.2 Metabolism

Molecules diffuse more slowly at low temperature: measurements of the rates of diffusion of small molecules such as lactic acid, Ca^{2+} and analogues of glucose and ATP through fish muscles produced Q_{10} values of 1.75–2.04 between 5 and 25 °C. Nearly all enzyme reactions are slower at low temperatures (although sometimes whole pathways can be faster if an inhibitor is more inhibited by low temperature than the catalysts). So, in the absence of temperature compensation (see Section 2.8), most metabolic processes, including contraction and relaxation of muscle, digestion and growth, are slowed. The Q_{10} values (see Section 2.4) of most enzyme-mediated processes that have been studied directly are in the range of 1.5–3.0.

One of the fundamental cellular processes that has been most intensively studied is the maintenance of potential gradient across the cell membrane. This system is particularly relevant to cold adaptation because it is an almost universal property of cells and because ions leak into the cell passively but are actively extruded by an ATP-based pump. Inward movement of ions through ion channels is basically a physical process, for which the Q_{10} is about 1.2–1.4 in the range 0–10 °C, but, like other active, enzymatic mechanisms, the Q_{10} of ATP-producing pathways is 2–3. So as the temperature falls, extrusion cannot keep up with inflow, ions accumulate in the cells, and the membrane potential falls, with disastrous effects in nerve, muscle, kidney and many other kinds of cells. In theory, stable coupling between the two processes at low temperatures could be achieved either by increasing the capacity for active transport of ions or by decreasing membrane permeability.

■   What would be the implications of these adaptations for BMR and exercise habits?

ATP production and utilization are major components of BMR, so more active extrusion of ions would lead to higher BMR. Decreasing membrane permeability would reduce the need for ion pumping, leading to lower BMR and lower oxygen utilization, but also to diminished capacity for osmoregulation and sluggish movement.

Polar fish have recently been studied intensively both in the wild and in the laboratory. The resting metabolic rate of several antarctic fish at −2 °C proved to be at least twice as high as that expected from extrapolation of BMR data of temperate-zone or tropical fish to this temperature. However, if such warm water fish were cooled to this temperature, they would probably not be able to swim at all and would quickly die, so the comparison is not really valid. A more relevant comparison is with temperate-zone fish that live in the deep sea, where the water temperature is always 0–4 °C. When such species are compared at their normal physiological temperatures of about 0 °C, the few antarctic fish that have been studied are found to have relatively high BMR. Their respiratory capacity is also more efficient: at 0 °C, the isolated gills of the emerald rockcod (Figure 5.15c) take up oxygen at the same rate as those of goldfish at 15 °C.

Muscles

The rates of muscle contraction and relaxation, and the maximum force generated, are complex enzymatic processes that determine speed of swimming. Ian Johnston of St Andrews University has compared the maximum tension of muscle fibres isolated from several species of antarctic, temperate-zone and tropical fish (Figure 5.17).

■   Do the data on Figure 5.17 provide evidence for temperature compensation of the contractile mechanism?

Yes. Between 0 and 10 °C, muscles from antarctic fish generate forces five to ten times larger than those measured from muscles of tropical species.

However, these properties of isolated muscle fibres did not match well with studies of individual molecules and whole animals. Temperature compensation could not be demonstrated in the maximum activity of some key enzymes in muscle contraction (e.g. ATPase) and many mitochondrial enzymes (e.g. cytochrome oxidases) studied *in vitro*. When temperate-zone fish such as goldfish (*Carassius auratus*), eels (*Anguilla anguilla*) and carp (*Carassius carassius*) are acclimated to low temperatures, the proportion of the volume of red muscle fibres occupied by mitochondria increases from 14% at 28 °C to 25% at 2 °C, indicating that oxidative capacity is maintained by the presence of more mitochondria, rather than by temperature compensation of the enzymes. Antarctic fish also generally have more and/or larger mitochondria but the data are not very clear cut: the proportion of the volume of red muscle fibres occupied by mitochondria ranges from 13–56% in the five antarctic species studied, compared to 4–45% in temperate-zone fish. The muscle fibres of the icefish (*Chaenocephalus aceratus*, Figure 5.18a, *overleaf*) are more than half mitochondria, leaving little room for the contractile mechanism itself. Those of red-blooded antarctic fish, such as *Notothenia gibberifrons* (Figure 5.18b), contain a greater proportion of contractile myofibrils than the icefish, but mitochondria are still more abundant than in temperate-zone fish, particularly towards the edge of the muscle fibre near the blood vessel.

■   How could mitochondria arranged as in Figure 5.18 adapt the muscles to activity at low temperature?

Diffusion is slower in the cold. Delays in metabolites such as ATP reaching the contractile proteins are minimized if numerous mitochondria are interspersed between the muscle fibres, thereby shortening the mean distance between the mitochondria and the ATP-using enzymes.

Biologists from the University of Maine compared the maximum activities at 1 °C of several enzymes in the swimming muscles and the heart of two antarctic fish, *Notothenia gibberifrons* (similar to Figure 5.15b) and *Trematomus newnesi* (similar to Figure 5.15c), with those of two species of similar size and habits caught in the western Atlantic Ocean off the coast of Delaware, USA. They found that the activities of enzymes involved in lipid catabolism and aerobic respiration, such as carnitine palmitoyltransferase and 3-hydroxyacyl CoA dehydrogenase, were 1.3–27 times higher in the red muscles of the antarctic species than the temperate-zone species and the Q_{10} values were less than 2. However, the activities of phosphofructokinase, pyruvate kinase and lactate dehydrogenase that are essential to anaerobic utilization of carbohydrates were

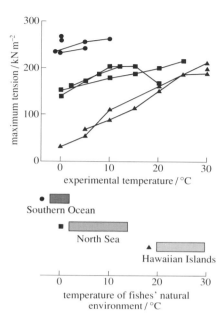

Figure 5.17   The effects of temperature on maximum tension generated by fast-contracting muscle fibres isolated from four species of antarctic fish (●), four temperate-zone species (■) and four species of tropical fish (▲). The outer membranes were removed to permit study of the intracellular contractile mechanism and the mitochondria in isolation.

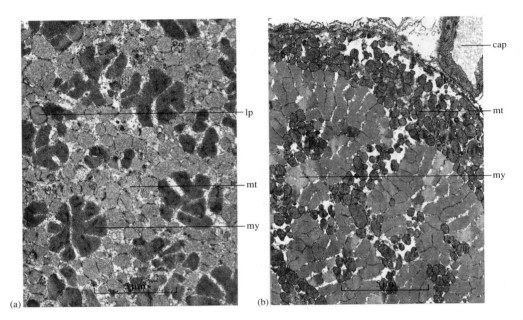

Figure 5.18 Electron micrographs of the slow swimming muscles of two antarctic fish. (a) The icefish (*Chaenocephalus aceratus*). The mitochondria are so large and numerous that they occupy more space within the muscle fibre than the contractile myofibrils. (b) *Notothenia gibberifrons*. The fibres contain fewer mitochondria and the myofibrils are more regularly arranged than in (a) my, myofibrils; mt, mitochondria; cap, capillary; lp, lipid droplet.

either not significantly different or were lower in the polar species. Thus these antarctic fish seem to be equipped to use lipid fuels more efficiently than carbohydrate fuels.

Maximum swimming speed during brief 'bursts' of activity (e.g. when escaping from a predator) has been measured accurately in only two species of antarctic fish, and was found to be at the lower end of the range found in temperate-zone fish of similar size and body shape. Clearly, the situation is complicated and further research on a greater range of species is necessary to understand adaptation to low temperatures. Nonetheless, even such limited information enables us to identify some principles of adaptation to polar conditions in ectotherms.

■ Which of the two mechanisms for maintaining ionic balance at low temperature are these data most consistent with?

Taken together, the observations suggest that antarctic fish living in surface waters achieve temperature compensation by increased activity of the ionic pump.

■ Why would this mechanism be better for antarctic fish living in surface waters?

Slow movement is unlikely to be adaptive where fast-swimming, endothermic predators such as penguins and seals are about. There are relatively few surface swimming fish in antarctic waters. Most fish live on or near the bottom, or in deep waters.

Pleuragramma antarcticum lives in in the surface layers of coastal waters and eats pelagic invertebrates. Around McMurdo Sound in Antarctica, it is known to be an important food for penguins, skuas and Weddell seals. Although its high density of mitochondria must increase its BMR and the energy cost of swimming, such adaptations to quick responses and fast escape are probably essential to avoiding predation. In contrast, most deep-sea fishes that have been investigated (and only a few species have been kept alive in surface laboratories for long enough to be studied) have lower BMR than expected and probably compensate for low temperature by reducing membrane permeability. Mammalian and avian predators are absent in the deep sea, and food (and probably also oxygen) is scarce, so the alternative mechanism for maintaining the potential gradient across the cell membranes is more efficient.

Another peculiar and consistent feature of nototheniid fish is that most species, including *P. antarcticum* (Figure 5.15a), *Dissostichus mawsoni* (Figure 5.15d) and species of *Notothenia* and *Trematomus*, have numerous sacs of lipid within and around their swimming muscles and between the muscles and the skin. Several functions have been suggested: energy stores, buoyancy (which could be important in fish that lack swim bladders) and more recently, oxygen diffusion. The solubility of oxygen in lipid is four times higher than in aqueous cytoplasm, and, particularly in fish in which blood pigments are reduced or absent, lipids closely associated with muscles may facilitate oxygenation of the tissues.

You may have noticed that in Figure 5.17 the contraction of muscles from tropical and temperate-zone fish were measured over a temperature range from 0 °C to 25–30 °C, but there are no data for the muscles of antarctic fish above 10 °C. Many polar fish tolerate only a very narrow range of temperatures and die within minutes if warmed more than a few degrees above the temperature of the water in which they normally live. Exactly why they die is not clear, but a likely cause is widely different Q_{10} values of enzymes in critical metabolic pathways, such as ion pumps or mitochondria: a small change of temperature puts the whole pathway 'out of kilter', causing metabolic intermediates to accumulate to toxic concentrations. In this respect, polar fish resemble non-hibernating homeotherms such as humans and rats: their metabolism is seriously, often irreversibly, disrupted by small departures from their normal body temperature. This property, of course, makes it much more difficult to transport such fish alive and to keep them in captivity for long enough to study habits such as breeding, growth and dietary preferences.

Summary of Section 5.5

Several anatomical and biochemical adaptations to living in very cold water have evolved in polar fish, particularly those of the southern oceans, which have evolved in isolation for many millions of years. Cold, turbulent water is rich in oxygen. One family of fairly large fish lacks blood pigments but its blood is less viscous and it has additional respiratory surfaces. Many fish have cryoprotectants in the blood and other body fluids, and the muscles of some contain numerous mitochondria and are adapted to use lipid as fuel in preference to carbohydrate. Many polar fish tolerate only a narrow range of temperatures and quickly die if exposed to water even slightly warmer than that in which they normally live.

5.6 Conclusion

There is much more to living in polar regions than withstanding the cold: food may be very scattered both in space and in time and breeding must be tightly synchronized to seasons and food availability. Some of the most spectacular examples of natural obesity and efficient regulation of appetite are found among polar animals. The study of such species not only demonstrates that it is possible to remain healthy and active when very obese and during prolonged fasting, it also helps us to identify the similarities and differences between natural and pathological or artificial obesity. Until recently, people were unable to remain in the Arctic and Antarctic for long enough to study the fauna and flora in detail, but as new techniques become available we can expect to find out more about these animals living at the extremes of climate.

Endothermic birds and mammals comprise a large part of the polar faunas and survive mainly by more efficient insulation and energy budgeting. Profound modifications of the circulation and muscles enable them to avoid excessive predation from marine mammals and birds, whose body temperature may be 40 °C warmer. Some teleost fish and numerous invertebrates (including crustaceans, molluscs and several phyla of worms) have also evolved ways of completing their entire life cycle in the cold. Reptiles and amphibians have failed to adapt to continuous cold and are absent from the arctic and antarctic fauna, although a few species occur in cold areas at lower latitudes where they hibernate during the winter and feed and reproduce during the brief warm summer (see Chapter 6).

Objectives for Chapter 5

When you have completed this chapter you should be able to:

5.1   Define and use, or recognize definitions and applications of each of the **bold** terms.

5.2   Outline the special features of the polar regions as a habitat and list some contrasts between the Arctic and the Antarctic.

5.3   Describe some effects of daylength on feeding, fat deposition and reproduction in arctic animals.

5.4   Explain why the environmental controls of appetite, activity level and fecundity are essential adaptations to living at high latitudes and describe some physiological mechanisms involved.

5.5   Describe some metabolic adaptations to prolonged fasting in penguins and bears.

5.6   Explain the use of comparative studies to identify anatomical and physiological adaptations to thermal insulation in aquatic and terrestrial endotherms.

5.7   Describe some adaptations of the blood, respiratory system and muscles of fish to the polar environment.

Questions for Chapter 5

(Answers to questions are at the end of the book.)

Question 5.1 (Objective 5.2)

Which of the factors (a)–(g) is/are a valid reason(s) for the fact that penguins are numerous and diverse around Antarctica but absent from the Arctic?

(a) The climate in the Arctic is too severe for penguins.

(b) There are not enough fish in Arctic waters to sustain a population of penguins.

(c) Penguins are excluded from the Arctic by the presence of bears.

(d) Penguins are excluded from the Arctic by the presence of seals.

(e) Penguins evolved in the Southern Hemisphere and have never occurred naturally in or around Europe, Asia or North America.

(f) In general, there are fewer birds in the Arctic than in the Antarctic.

(g) In general, there are fewer vertebrate animals in the Arctic than in the Antarctic.

Question 5.2 (Objectives 5.2 and 5.3)

What is the evidence that endogenous factors as well as daylength control food intake and breeding? Why are such dual control mechanisms adaptive for arctic animals?

Question 5.3 (Objective 5.4)

Which of the statements (a)–(g) about the food intake and metabolism of arctic mammals and birds is/are generally true?

(a) There are many more animals relative to the food supply in polar regions than in the tropics.

(b) The food supply in polar regions is highly seasonal and/or irregular.

(c) Being obese makes animals lethargic.

(d) Very lean animals are incapable of strenuous physical activity.

(e) Arctic animals have fewer predators than tropical animals so they can afford to be fat and lazy.

(f) The only food available in polar regions is less nutritious than that available in the tropics.

(g) Arctic animals have a higher metabolic rate and so need more food than those in the tropics.

Question 5.4 (Objective 5.5)

What information relevant to the metabolism of energy and/or proteins can be obtained from measurements of:

(a) Body temperature.

(b) RER.

(c) The composition of the blood.

Which of the statements (a)–(h) about the structure and arrangement of adipose tissue is/are true?

(a) All arctic mammals have thick subcutaneous adipose tissue.

(b) Birds, whether arctic or not, do not have thick subcutaneous adipose tissue.

(c) Polar bears have thick subcutaneous adipose tissue because they live in very cold climates and swim in the sea.

(d) In Carnivora, the partitioning of adipose tissue between superficial and intra-abdominal depots depends upon body size.

(e) In Carnivora, the partitioning of adipose tissue between superficial and intra-abdominal depots depends upon habits and habitat.

(f) In naturally obese mammals, fatter individuals always have more adipocytes than thinner individuals.

(g) In naturally obese mammals, as an individual gets fatter, its adipocytes enlarge.

(h) The number and size of adipocytes in relation to fatness is quite variable in naturally obese mammals and in humans.

Explain in a few sentences:

(a) The effects of the absence of red blood cells on delivery of oxygen to the muscles of *Chaenocephalus*.

(b) Why most fish living in very cold water remain on or very near the bottom, but there are plenty of invertebrates in mid- and surface waters.

CHAPTER 6 HIBERNATION

Prepared for the Course Team by Richard Holmes

6.1 Introduction

By now, having studied Chapters 1–5, you should have a clear idea as to how external temperature affects the physiological state of an animal, how particular species gain and lose heat, and how endotherms maintain T_b within a narrow range of usually little more than $\pm 2\,°C$ of their normal temperature.

Many endotherms, including the arctic fox and the emperor penguin, that experience sub-zero temperatures maintain their core T_b at $35\,°C$ at least. However, to do this requires both very good insulation and the availability of a plentiful food supply to sustain the increased thermogenesis needed to maintain a large difference between T_a and T_b. For many animals, the food supply in a cold environment will become extremely scarce or inaccessible beneath snow or ice.

■ What then are the possible options for surviving a very cold winter?

(1) If the animal is to remain *in situ* and active, it will require good and appropriate insulation, considerable energy reserves and a continuing food source; these requirements are met in the cases of the emperor penguin and the arctic fox.

(2) If the animal has sufficient mobility, it may be able to migrate seasonally out of the extreme latitudes as the available food dwindles; this applies particularly to birds and some bats.

(3) The animal could reduce the enormous metabolic cost by allowing T_b to fall; a very diverse group of birds and mammals can do this to varying extents.

Small homeotherms living at latitudes (or altitudes) at which they experience long periods of cold weather and lack of solar radiation have few options. A small animal has a relatively high surface area:volume ratio and therefore a high potential for heat loss: even at moderate ambient temperatures, it normally has a high metabolic rate and cannot carry enough really effective insulation, whether of fur, feather or fat. Some species can survive in burrows if they can emerge regularly and find enough plant material to eat beneath the snow, but even these animals are likely to have to find energy-conserving strategies for much of the time.

Thus, small rodents and insectivores, for example, are unlikely to survive except by exploiting option 3 above, and uncoupling their homeothermic mechanisms or re-setting the critical temperature (T_c): in other words **adaptive hypothermia**. In this chapter, we shall consider the energetic advantages of this adaptive hypothermia and its extreme manifestation, deep hibernation.

In common use, the term 'to hibernate' means to pass the winter in a lethargic or torpid state and it thus encompasses many diverse species of animals (vertebrate and invertebrate) and not a small number of plants. In mammals and birds, 'hibernation' has a rather more rigorous definition because these species allow their winter T_b to fall close to the ambient temperature and yet can, at any time, spontaneously re-warm without recourse to an external heat source.

The study of hibernation has a long history and over the years a confusing collection of terms has arisen. Before we begin, some definitions are important. **Euthermia**, as used here, describes the homeothermic state of an endothermic animal, be it awake or asleep, maintaining a body temperature close to normal. Adaptive hypothermia is a general term used to cover any manifestation of hypothermia that is not inadvertant, be it a fall of a few degrees overnight or a fall of 30 °C for several weeks. **Torpor** is used in this chapter to describe a state of hypothermic lethargy, either shallow or deep, prolonged or temporary. True deep seasonal hibernation is thus said to consist of bouts of torpor, the term **hibernation** referring to the seasonal process as a whole.

Although this chapter deals largely with hibernation and torpor in mammals and birds, Section 6.6 considers two other groups of vertebrates, the ectothermic amphibians and reptiles. These animals have another option, one not open to the mammals and birds. Provided they can find a place to 'hibernate' (in the wider sense of the word) where the T_a will not fall below −6 °C or so for sustained periods, they can allow their T_b to fall below 0 °C and recover when the T_a rises. Birds and mammals, however, cannot survive freezing under natural conditions.

This adaptive hypothermia pre-supposes that the effect of low temperature on body tissues is minimal. Brain temperatures a few degrees above normal are fatal, but there is a greater safety margin with subnormal temperature. Most mammals tolerate hypothermia down to a T_b of about 15 °C, though lack of muscular coordination can be seen when T_b falls just 5 °C below normal. For a small mammal inactive in a burrow, loss of muscle coordination may not present too many problems but loss of nervous coordination may do so. In addition, low temperatures slow the circulation, giving rise to the possibility of thrombosis, and reduce the kidney filtration rate, thus allowing possibly toxic wastes to accumulate. The tissues of those animals that hibernate must function across a wide range of temperatures.

6.2 The nature and extent of hibernation and torpor in endotherms

6.2.1 Degrees of torpor

Adaptive hypothermia occurs in at least six distantly related mammalian orders (Table 6.1) and in a several orders of birds. As we have implied, there is a spectrum running from those species which can tolerate a drop in T_b of 2 °C for a few hours to the seasonal deep hibernators, maintaining a T_b of perhaps 4 °C for weeks on end.

Table 6.1   Groups of mammals that contain species that routinely become torpid.

Group	Sub-group (and example)	Comments
Monotremes	Spiny anteater	seasonal
Marsupials	Didelphidae (American opossum)	occasional
	Dasyuridae (insectivorous mice)	occasional
	Phalangeridae (possums)	seasonal
Placentals	Rodentia* (see Table 6.2)	seasonal (and daily)
	Primates (dwarf lemurs)	seasonal
	Chiroptera* (temperate bats)	seasonal (and daily)
	Insectivora* (tenrec, African shrew, golden mole, hedgehog)	seasonal
	Carnivora (black bear, badger, polar bear)	seasonal lethargy — not deep hibernation

*Includes native British species.

■   From what we have said previously in this book, what characteristics would you expect to find in the deep hibernators?

They are likely to be small, and live in an environment where there may be a large difference between ambient and body temperature and where their food is absent or inaccessible for long periods, which in effect usually means that they are herbivorous or insectivorous.

As you saw in Section 5.4.1, *size* is a critical factor in the depth of torpor; for example, black and brown bears inhabit the same territory as several deep hibernators, but provided they have shelter they can manage on stored energy reserves, mainly of fat, for extended periods by lowering their T_b by only 2–6 °C. *The availability of food* is another factor; a number of small birds, for example the American goldfinch (*Carduelis tristis*, Plate 6.1), can survive in winter temperatures down to −60 °C, remaining active and defending its T_b with a huge (in excess of 500%) increase in thermogenesis. However, other species, such as the redpoll (*Carduelis flammea*, Plate 6.2) show, in addition, a nocturnal hypothermic torpor.

A strategy adopted by some larger animals when food becomes inaccessible is to remain 'active', in the sense that they are more mobile and alert than, for example, the black bear, but conserve their energy reserves by effectively standing still. A prime example of this approach, sometimes called 'arctic resignation', is shown by the Svalbard reindeer, mentioned in the previous chapter. Its appetite falls in the winter months, and during the periods when its food is under ice, it may stand still for 98% of the time but with no drop in T_b. The animal does not carry enough fat to see it right through the winter and it therefore feeds whenever food is accessible.

If an animal is very small, quite short periods without food may present a problem, and a nocturnal hypothermia and torpor can be important for energy conservation. This is true, for example, of several species of tropical humming-bird, even though the difference between T_a and T_b is not huge.

6.2.2 Species showing torpor or deep hibernation

Among the birds, torpor occurs in a number of species in the orders Apodiformes (humming-birds and swifts), Caprimulgiformes (nightjars, nighthawks, goatsuckers, poor-wills and the whip-poor-will) and Coliiformes (mousebirds). In all of the humming-birds (family Trochilidae) studied to date, torpor, if it occurs, takes place on a daily (or more usually nightly) basis. They are able to re-warm themselves independently of T_a and show an increased thermogenesis if T_a falls below 18 °C during the time when the bird is not searching for food (see Question 6.5). The tiny rufous humming-bird (*Selasphorus rufus*, weighing 3.0–5.5 g, Plate 6.3) has a summer range in North America that extends to Alaska, but it overwinters in Mexico. While undertaking this huge migration it undergoes overnight torpor, especially when breaking its journey for a few days at a time to rebuild its energy reserves with nectar.

There is no evidence for long periods of unbroken torpor in the humming-birds. The poor-will (*Phalaenoptilus nuttalli*, Figure 6.1a) is perhaps the only bird studied so far that shows bouts of torpor at all comparable to those of seasonally hibernating mammals. Poor-wills kept in the laboratory at a T_a of 1 °C without food go into torpor, with a T_b of 6 °C, from which they arouse spontaneously about once every 4 days, showing an exceptionally large rise in their metabolic rate in the process. The pattern of torpor, change in T_b, etc. that they undergo in the wild is not known.

Many birds, including doves and pigeons, enter shallow torpor (with the T_b falling to about 32 °C) when deprived of food; though, if food is available, the pigeon responds to low T_a by a large (up to 55%) increase in the basal metabolic rate. Indeed, a reduction in food supply seems to be a major factor in the induction of torpor in almost all the bird species studied. The white-throated swift (*Aeronautes saxatalis*) and the mousebird (*Colius* sp.) can tolerate a T_b of 20 °C and spontaneously re-warm at low ambient temperatures. In a survey of six small birds that wintered around Oslo (including the house sparrow and greenfinch), T_b was found to drop as low as 30 °C at night. So, many small birds may undergo a shallow torpor at night and even larger birds respond to food scarcity by allowing their T_b to fall and thus minimize energy consumption.

Among mammals, many groups contain species that undergo different degrees of adaptive hypothermia. Of the placental mammals, the largest number of hibernating species are found among rodents (see Table 6.2) and bats.

All temperate-zone bats, including the fifteen UK species, undergo daily torpor during certain seasons, and some species remain torpid for extended periods. The European hedgehog (*Erinaceus europeus*) and the fat or edible dormouse (*Glis glis*) native to Britain also hibernate. The most famous examples include this dormouse, which was much loved by the Roman palate because of its habit of storing fat prior to hibernation, and the sleepy guest of the Mad Hatter, the hazel mouse (*Muscardinus avellavarius*).

Most research on hibernating mammals has focused on bats, hedgehogs, hamsters and in particular, the sciurid rodents (squirrels). Figure 6.2 illustrates

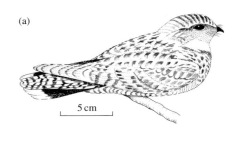

(a)

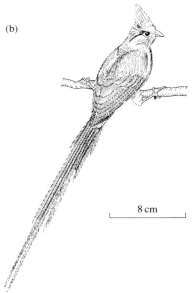

(b)

Figure 6.1 (a) The poor-will (*Phalaenoptilus nuttalli*), and (b) the mousebird (*Colius* sp.).

Table 6.2   The six (out of 30) families of rodents in which adaptive hypothermia is known to occur.

Family	Examples	Comments
Zapodidae	meadow jumping mouse, Scandinavian birch mouse	deep hibernation
Heteromyidae	pocket mice, kangaroo mice	erratic, seasonal hibernation
Gliridae	dormice (including native British species)	deep hibernation
Muridae	African fat mouse	daily torpor
Cricetidae	hamsters white-footed mice	deep hibernation daily torpor
Sciuridae	chipmunks, marmots (woodchuck), ground squirrels (at least a dozen species)	deep hibernation

some of the rodent species that we shall be discussing. However, it should be noted that little is known in the West about the habits of Asian mammals and the extent to which they have been researched.

6.2.3   Hibernators as eutherms

Hibernating endotherms are not the easiest animals to study, so perhaps it is not so surprising that, until the late 1960s, many biologists believed that mammalian hibernation was a process in which thermoregulation was simply 'switched off', following the receipt of a set of 'cues'. These cues included a declining T_a, a shortening daylength, the extent of body fat, a lack of food, etc. With this model, the hibernator essentially becomes an ectotherm whose T_b follows the T_a quite closely, and who is at great risk if the T_a in the hibernaculum (hibernatory winter retreat) falls below freezing. Indeed, prior to the 1960s, many workers assumed that a poor thermoregulatory ability was a prerequisite for hibernation.

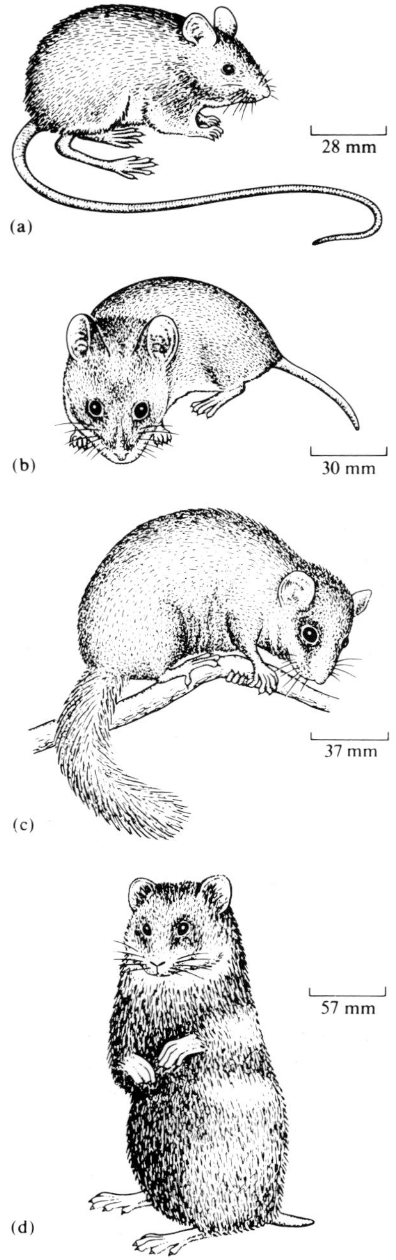

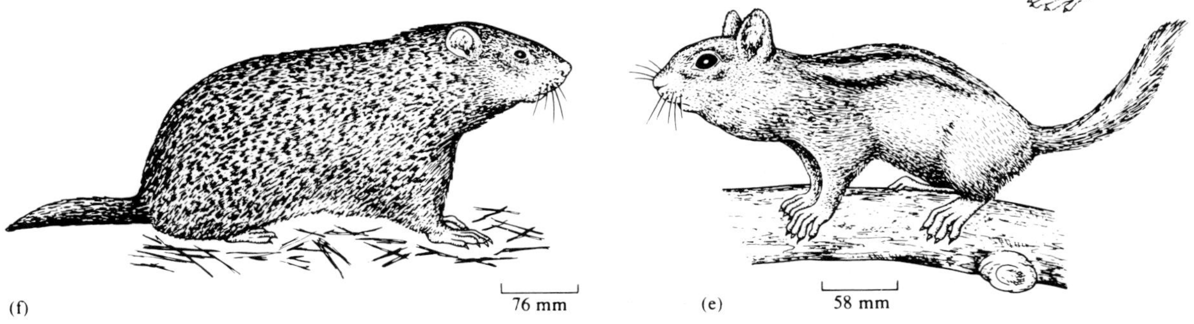

Figure 6.2   Some species of rodent that hibernate (note the scale bars, which indicate body size). (a) Jumping mouse (*Zapus* sp.); (b) African fat mouse (*Steatornys pratens*); (c) fat or edible dormouse (*Glis glis*); (d) black-bellied hamster (*Cricetus cricetus*); (e) golden-mantled ground squirrel (*Spermophilus lateralis*); (f) woodchuck (*Marmota monax*).

■   Do you know of evidence that casts doubt on these views?

You may be aware that many animals overwinter in hibernacula which are not very deep or well defended against cold. If they were entirely at the mercy of the T_a, a very high mortality rate would be expected. In addition, the ability to hibernate occurs in species very closely related to non-hibernators; it is unlikely that thermoregulatory ability would vary so widely between closely related genera of rodents such as the non-hibernating Djungarian hamster (*Phodopus* sp.) and the hibernating Turkish hamster (*Mesocricetus brandti*) and black-bellied or European hamsters (*Cricetus cricetus*).

It has been recognized for many years that hibernators were able to arouse in the middle of the hibernating season without an apparent rise in T_a, and that arousal could occur when animals were handled or disturbed in the cold (a fact noted as long ago as 1925 in work on the Columbian ground squirrel). Both of these observations imply a remarkably high degree of control by the animal. Indeed, regulation at very low body temperatures was recognized in 1938 (when Table 6.3 was published).

Table 6.3   Body temperature and heat production of a hibernating marmot at different environmental temperatures, derived from Benedict and Lee (1938).

temperature /°C		relative rate of heat production per day
environmental	rectal	
0.9	4.1	100
3.0	4.5	54
2.2	4.6	54
2.6	4.7	36

■   In what way does the table suggest that T_b is being controlled in the hibernating marmot?

The T_b in each experiment remain relatively constant, varying only between 4.1 °C and 4.7 °C, but the heat production varies, being very much higher when the T_a was held at the lowest temperature.

Nevertheless, it was not until manipulations of the hypothalamic temperatures of otherwise cold hibernating rodents that researchers began to consider that hibernating mammals might be exercising control similar to non-hibernating (normothermic) ones — a view that is now generally held.

Although, as we warned you in Section 6.1, variations in the processes of hibernation are numerous, some aspects of the mechanism appear to apply quite broadly, and we will concentrate on some of these in the next section in attempting to draw a picture of mammalian seasonal hibernation.

Summary of Section 6.2

Adaptive hypothermia occurs widely in both mammals and birds, but the ability is scattered throughout different families: even within a single family, some species show torpor and some not, suggesting that the ability may have evolved independently many times. Whereas a number of small birds show a daily, shallow torpor, so far only the poor-will has been described as showing extended bouts of torpor comparable to those seen in mammals. Species of birds and mammals that hibernate seem to have a highly advanced euthermic ability, and in most cases can control T_b closely down to 3–4 °C, contrary to earlier views which assumed that hibernation was a manifestation of poor thermoregulatory ability.

6.3 Seasonal hibernation

6.3.1 The general pattern

In this section we use the phrase 'seasonal hibernation' in the same sense as we use 'deep hibernation'; that is to say a process in which:

(1) T_b falls with T_a until quite close to freezing, at which point it is maintained independently of T_a,

(2) the bouts of hypothermia are extended, lasting days or weeks, and

(3) hypothermia is a response to seasonal hardships, usually food shortage, associated with a low T_a.

We will not therefore be considering the extended dormancy of large carnivores such as bears (Chapter 5), badgers or skunks in any detail, although, like many true hibernators, the last two species remain underground for long periods during winter, 70 consecutive days being common in the badger and much more in some skunks, but with a T_b reduced by only about 3–8 °C. We return to the possible significance of this form of dormancy in Section 6.4.

So far as is known, no hibernator remains hypothermic throughout the period of hibernation; all of them undergo bouts of torpor, followed by arousal, followed by re-entry into torpor. These bouts may last between a few days to a few weeks, depending on the species and, to some extent, other variables such as T_a, food reserves, etc. Figure 6.3 shows the T_b of a black-bellied hamster during a fairly typical bout of torpor lasting about 3 days.

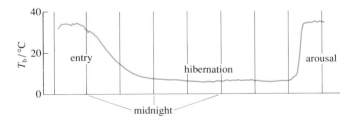

Figure 6.3   The body temperature of a black-bellied hamster during a hibernation bout.

6.3.2 Cues for entry into hibernation

Before we come to discuss the possible mechanisms for the whole remarkable process of entry into hibernation, we need to consider some of the cues the hibernator receives which can trigger it. You may not be surprised to find that different species of hibernator react rather differently to the same stimulus and that entry into an individual bout of torpor usually depends upon several stimuli, some from the environment and some from within the animal. Clearly, the external stimuli also exert an important effect on the internal stimuli themselves.

Exogeneous or environmental stimuli

The three most important environmental stimuli appear to be food supply, daylength and ambient temperature, though the order of importance differs between species and between seasonal hibernation and daily torpor.

Food supply is relevant in two ways: in the short term, a diminution of available food towards the beginning of the hibernation period may itself trigger hibernation, and in a laboratory cold room at constant temperatures torpor can be induced in several species by the removal of food, e.g. in some humming-birds and the poor-will, entry into torpor rapidly follows the removal of food. In the longer term, food supply determines the animal's ability to build fat reserves, and in some species, including some hamsters and ground squirrels, the presence of large fat reserves may be necessary for the animal's entry into hibernation. Others may not readily enter torpor in the absence of a store of food.

In several species in the wild, including hamsters and chipmunks, there is evidence that daylength is important. In general (and perhaps always), decreasing daylength is part of the stimulus, but the mechanism by which it acts may involve several separate routes. The first, which is not yet well understood, is that decreasing daylength causes an increase in the secretion of the peptide melatonin from the pineal gland in the brain, which appears to act via a number of routes to predispose the animal to torpor. The second route, with which you are already familiar, is via the hypothalamus and the gonads; in most hibernators, entry into hibernation does not take place if there are high levels of androgens in the blood, and in the Turkish hamster withdrawal of the testes into the body cavity is a prerequisite for hibernation in males. Likewise, an injection of androgen into a torpid male hamster provokes arousal. The situation in the female hamster is less well defined, but may be similar. It may also be that melatonin from the pineal gland acts to reduce gonadal secretions, as well as acting directly on the brain.

Once again, the importance of ambient temperature as a cue to entry into hibernation may vary between species, though no species will enter a bout of torpor unless the T_a is below its thermoneutral level.

Endogenous or internal stimuli

Animals such as the hamsters and chipmunks are sometimes called '**facultative hibernators**' because they hibernate in response to environmental conditions, in contrast with the so called '**obligative hibernators**', such as the ground squirrels and marmots, whose sequence of fattening, hibernating and arousing seems to be strongly driven by an endogenous circannual cycle. Figure 6.4 is drawn from data on the golden-mantled ground squirrel (*Spermophilus lateralis*), kept in the laboratory for 2 years under constant conditions of light (12 hours light and 12 hours dark) and at a constant temperature (22 °C).

■   What several conclusions on the triggers for hibernation can you draw from this figure?

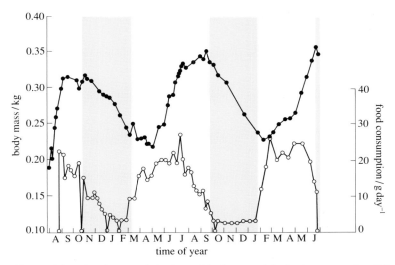

Figure 6.4   The circannual rhythms of body mass (●), food consumption (○) and hibernation in the golden-mantled ground squirrel (*Spermophilus lateralis*). The shaded grey bars indicate periods of hibernation.

As the sequence of food consumption, weight gain and hibernation continue as normal under constant environmental conditions, environmental triggers are not essential in this animal. However, it does appear that under these circumstances the cycle may be shortening: in the first year the animal entered hibernation in late October, in the second in late September, and at the end of the experiment it was just entering hibernation at the end of June.

Thus, this figure suggests that although the timing of the cycle may be primarily due to an endogenous circannual rhythm, in natural circumstances the timing may be re-set annually by environmental factors. Clearly, therefore, a sharp distinction between environmental and endogenous cues to entry cannot really be drawn: indeed, the importance of the state of gonad activity to hibernation in the hamster will already have alerted you to the interrelationship of these cues.

Many hibernators show a marked cycle in the production of thyroid hormones and decrease secretion of these at a time when a non-hibernator would be increasing secretion to increase thermogenesis. In some species at least, this cycle seems to be independent of the cycle of weight gain and hibernation. This and other hormonal changes, such as the secretion of serotonin (5-hydroxy-tryptamine), which exerts a depressant effect on the animal, clearly must involve the hypothalamus and quite possibly the action of a hypothalamic clock; we return to these issues in Section 6.5.1.

6.3.3   Entry into hibernation

Bouts of torpor are always entered from sleep (see Section 6.4.2) and are not induced when T_a is close to normal T_b. As you are aware from Chapter 3, under normal euthermic circumstances a rodent kept in an ambient temperature of $0\,°C$ would be expected to show a marked increase in metabolic rate and thermogenesis. However, the heart rate and oxygen consumption of a woodchuck (*Marmota monax*) about to enter torpor does not follow this pattern (Figure 6.5).

Following a period of 2 hours or so when the T_b is held more or less constant, but oxygen consumption and heart rate are highly irregular, the woodchuck lowers its oxygen consumption (a measure of its metabolic rate) and within 8 hours of the start of entry, metabolism appears to be at a minimal base-line, with the T_b subsiding smoothly to about 12 °C within 14 hours.

Entry into hibernation can take a great deal longer than the few hours it takes in the woodchuck. The Californian and arctic ground squirrels (*Spermophilus beecheyi* and *Spermophilus undulatus*) take 3–5 days to enter hibernation with increasingly steeper drops in nightly T_b. In the 1960s at Harvard University, Felix Strumwasser recorded the brain temperature (T_{brain}) of the Californian ground squirrel entering hibernation (see Figure 6.6). The brain temperature dropped during each dark period but rose again before the period of light. On the first, third and fifth 'nights' the drop was only 34 °C, but on the remaining 'nights' the drops were successively greater. Strumwasser argued that these *test drops* indicated metabolic and neuronal preparation for deep hibernation. Such test drops are quite common in mammals entering hibernation, but are by no means universal.

The blood pressure of ground squirrels entering hibernation has been measured by inserting a catheter into the aorta. At first, the mean blood pressure remains within the range of the active animal, but as hibernation deepens the blood pressure decreases. A mild peripheral vasoconstriction takes place and persists throughout the period of hibernation, which may be important in maintaining adequate blood pressure to the brain, given the huge reduction in heart rate.

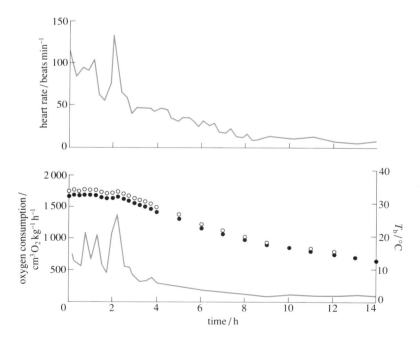

Figure 6.5   The heart rate, oxygen consumption and T_b of a woodchuck entering hibernation. (●) subcutaneous temperature, (○) mid-dorsum temperature.

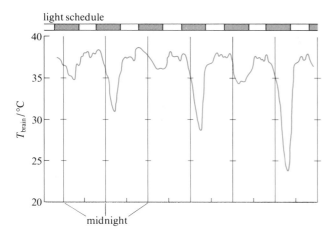

Figure 6.6 'Test drops' of brain temperature in the Californian ground squirrel.

However, during entry into hibernation, there are large fluctuations in vasomotor tone, and periods of superficial vasodilation occur, which may have the effect of accelerating heat loss. Indeed, it is quite likely that vasomotor control is largely responsible for the changes in T_b seen in test drops.

These fluctuations alternate with short periods of shivering, suggesting that the rate at which the T_b is allowed to drop is being carefully controlled. There is evidence that, in some instances, vigorous vasoconstriction, combined with a depression of the heart rate, may act to 'throttle' much of the metabolism. Thus, the animal is doing more than just ceasing to defend its T_b and allowing it to fall smoothly towards the T_a; it is hurrying the process by actively depressing its metabolism.

6.3.4 Deep torpor

Entering hibernation, as we have seen in Section 6.3.2, is not a passive process in response to falling ambient temperature. Nor is deep hibernation a passive process or indeed a uniform state. Figure 6.7 shows the pattern of hibernation (as measured by the heart rate) of an arctic marmot (*Marmota caligata*) kept in the laboratory at a T_a of 10 °C for 18 days in February. Every one or two days the heart rate rises abruptly, remains high for a number of days, and falls again. These records are from an animal under laboratory conditions, but are they relevant to the natural situation? All hibernating mammals show sporadic arousal during the winter sleep. The nature and possible function of these

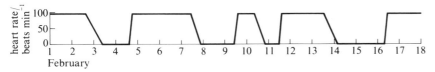

Figure 6.7 The heart rate of an arctic marmot (*Marmot caligata*) undergoing bouts of hibernation in the laboratory during early February.

awakenings are taken up in Section 6.4.2 but it is important to remember that they occur, even though the temperature of the animal's surroundings remains relatively constant during hibernation.

Most hibernators spend the winter in burrows or dens some feet below the ground surface. The importance of the behaviour involved in the selection and 'engineering' of these winter quarters is demonstrated in Figure 6.8, which shows the variation in external temperature in Alaska from September to May. Superimposed on these data are temperatures of the warmest and coolest burrows of arctic ground squirrels. You can see the burrow temperatures vary by less than 10 °C throughout these winter months, though for most of that time they are below zero.

An exception to the rule is the dormouse, which hibernates above ground, usually amongst the leaf litter (which provides some protection) on woodland floors. The dormouse hibernates curled up, as do all hibernating mammals, but with its bare hind feet exposed (the reasons for this are discussed further in Section 6.5.1).

The most obvious dramatic changes in deep hibernation (apart from the lowered T_b) are concerned with metabolism.

- Heart rates of over ten or under three beats per minute are rare. The major explanation for these extremely low rates is the lengthening of time between individual beats.

- Cardiac output is also reduced, to about 1.5% of normal (a mere 1 cm^3 blood min^{-1} in the ground squirrel).

- Respiration is greatly reduced. It may take place at quite evenly spaced intervals, or long periods of *apnoea* (cessation of breathing) may occur followed by several deep respirations (the record for holding a breath in torpor is 150 minutes in a hedgehog, though the average for this species is 60 minutes).

The lower T_b of hibernating animals and the changes in the respiratory and cardiovascular performance lead to a marked respiratory acidosis. The arterial pH falls by 0.24–0.48 and P_{CO_2} is increased by a factor of 2.5–4. Remember that the oxygen supply to the tissues is dependent upon cardiac output, haemoglobin concentration, and on the shape of the oxygen dissociation curves. Figure 6.9 illustrates the latter for euthermic (T_b of 38 °C) and hibernating (T_b of 6 °C) ground squirrels.

■ What do you conclude from Figure 6.9?

The curve for the hibernating individual has shifted markedly to the left. Half saturation (P_{50}) is therefore achieved at a much lower P_{O_2}, indicating a higher oxygen affinity. Other evidence suggests that there is also an increase in haemoglobin concentration as an animal enters hibernation. The hibernator's tissues therefore have a high tolerance towards hypoxia. These changes explain how a hibernating animal such as a hedgehog can survive the long period of apnoea that is characteristic of intermittent breathing; it draws on the increased oxygen stored in the arterial blood.

In addition to changes in respiration and in the cardiovascular system, there are marked changes in endocrine function. Endocrine gland atrophy is characteristic

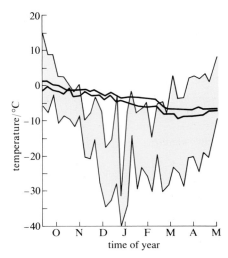

Figure 6.8 Temperatures of the burrows of arctic ground squirrels in Alaska (thick lines). Readings from the warmest and coldest burrow in the sample are shown. The shaded area shows fluctuations in maximum and minimum air temperature outside the squirrels' burrows.

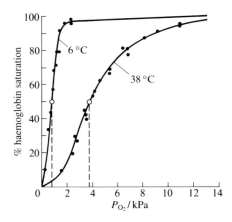

Figure 6.9 Oxyhaemoglobin dissociation curve of blood from euthermic and hibernating ground squirrels, determined at the corresponding T_b of 38 °C and 6 °C. Vertical dashed lines show the P_{O_2} of half saturation (P_{50}).

prior to the onset of hibernation, particularly atrophy of the pituitary, gonads, thyroid and adrenal glands. However, the study of endocrine functions in relation to hibernation is difficult. First, it takes time to follow annual changes; second, seasonal changes independent of hibernation, e.g. gonad development in some hamsters, must be taken into account; third, sampling blood from a hibernator is difficult; and finally, and most important, it must be recognized that not all hibernators are alike. From the few studies done, it seems that, prior to hibernation, there is a general reduction in the synthesis, transport and release of neurosecretory material.

The physiological state of an animal in deep hibernation is, however, dynamic (the physiological controls are still working), and not that of a passive animal *made* hypothermic. If, for example, there is a decline in the resistance of the peripheral blood vessels and a drop in blood pressure, there follows a compensatory increase in heart rate and cardiac output. The most graphic illustration of the fact that a hibernator retains physiological control mechanisms is in its response to the falling ambient temperature. If T_a drops below a particular level (which depends upon the species in question). there is *always* a compensatory increase in heart and respiratory rate, and a rise in metabolic rate, and therefore a tendency to raise or at least preserve T_b. If the carbon dioxide concentration of the inhaled air is increased, then hibernating mammals react by increasing their breathing rate. In the hedgehog, the CO_2 threshold is 0.7–1.7%, at which point the periods of apnoea become shorter. Continuous breathing replaces periodic breathing at 5–9% CO_2.

The evidence suggests, therefore, that the hibernator is sensitive to changes in its environment and that appropriate physiological responses can still be made. If the change or response is major, then the individual rapidly begins to arouse. It is this ability of hibernators to elevate T_b from 5–10 °C to the euthermic level, even at T_a values below zero, that puts them into a class of their own.

6.3.5   Energy sources in hibernation

Carbohydrate, in the form of glycogen stored in the liver and muscles, is the most important immediate energy reserve in a waking mammal, although lipids play a significant role, especially in sleeping mammals. Glycogen, however, does not play a major role in supplying the reduced energy needs of a hibernator, except perhaps in species that arouse frequently to feed from food caches in the hibernaculum. The reason for the relative lack of importance of glycogen is simply that the reserves are not great, and are used extremely quickly. It has been shown in marmots that carbohydrate metabolism is 'switched off' early in the hibernation phase, and the animal becomes insensitive to insulin. Later, during hibernation, this process is reversed, and carbohydrate usage returns. This switch may be important in fuelling shivering thermogenesis during arousal.

The proteins of the body represent a larger total reserve of energy, but contain fewer calories per gram than fat, and their maintenance is essential to life. Few animals can survive losses of body protein greater than 30–50%, and a much smaller reduction in the lean muscle mass would disadvantage the animal when it emerges from hibernation. Furthermore, the ability of the dormant black bear to recycle almost all the nitrogen released by the breakdown of proteins (see

Section 5.3.2) may well be unusual, and it is to be expected that problems could arise from the accumulation of nitrogen metabolites if protein was used extensively. In deep hibernators, proteins provide only about 6% of the energy used.

Fat therefore seems to be the major source of energy for the hibernator (about 90% in ground squirrels), and the ability of an individual to enter prolonged torpor, especially in facultative hibernators, depends on it having built up large fat stores. Arousal involves a large part of the total energy consumption throughout the whole period of hibernation and in many species arousal draws on BAT as a major source of energy.

It is, however, important to realize that the question of the fuels used in hibernation is complex: much is not yet known, and there are many differences between species. There are also quite often differences between the sexes within a species; in golden-mantled ground squirrels, the males emerge from hibernation with quite large fat stores, and with a high body mass, whereas the females emerge at their lowest body mass of the year. Thus, it is necessary to be wary of generalizations about the fuels used in the different stages of hibernation, given our present state of knowledge.

6.3.6 Arousal

We can identify three types of arousal during the hibernation period, on temporal rather than physiological grounds. The first is alarm arousal, in response to a major exogenous stimulus such as a sudden large drop in environmental temperature. The second is a periodic arousal when, in the absence of external cues, the animal spontaneously begins to re-warm. The third is the final arousal in the spring when the animal does not re-enter hibernation but emerges to a sustained euthermia. Physiologically, all three are similar.

Alarm arousal

As we mentioned in Section 6.2, a potentially life-threatening event, such as a fall in T_a to below zero, elicits a metabolic response in a hibernator. If the lowered temperature is maintained, the animal will respond not just with transient increases in metabolism, but with a dramatic rise in T_b and complete arousal.

Mechanical stimuli as well as temperature changes can evoke arousal. In animals fitted with electrodes just under the skin to monitor muscle action potentials, an externally applied stimulus results in a long-lasting burst of action potentials. The response in the fat dormouse is very striking. This species hibernates with its bushy tail curled over its back. If the erect hairs are gently displaced, a burst of muscle action potentials occur with a concurrent rise in respiratory and heart rates. Vibration, pressure, locally applied heat or cold, and the infusion of a variety of substances, all produce the muscle response. In fact, the responsiveness of receptors in hibernators appears to increase with decreasing temperatures, in marked contrast to that of non-hibernators made hypothermic.

The adaptive value of such a response is obvious. An animal torpid in a burrow seems quite defenceless. By retaining a high degree of surveillance, the animal can still perceive disturbances in air flow or collapse of the burrow and make the appropriate response.

Periodic arousal

All species of hibernators arouse periodically. The frequency of the arousal and the length of the euthermic periods between bouts of hibernation vary widely with species, within species, among individuals, and with the time of year (e.g. in deep hibernators, the larger species seem to have longer periods of wakefulness than the smaller ones; see Section 6.4.1). The marmot, whose heart rate recording is shown in Figure 6.7, aroused from hibernation every 2–3 days and remained euthermic for 3–4 days at a time. Figure 6.10a shows the average number of days between successive arousals of golden-mantled ground squirrels at various times in one hibernation season; Figure 6.10b shows the frequency of arousals in a Richardson's ground squirrel.

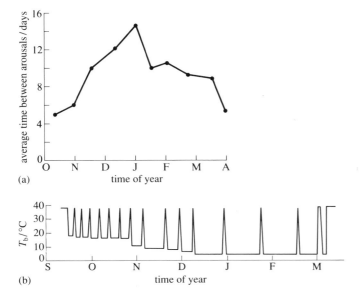

(a)

(b)

Figure. 6.10   (a) Average number of days between arousals in golden-mantled ground squirrels at various times in the hibernation season, and (b) arousals (as measured by body temperature) throughout the season in a Richardson's ground squirrel. Note the lower T_b in the torpid animal towards the end of the season.

■   What do you deduce from Figures 6.10a and b?

The frequency of arousal changes during hibernation. Early on, the arousals occur every 5 or 6 days. In December and January these arousals occur every 10–15 days in the golden-mantled ground squirrel, and nearer 30 days in Richardson's ground squirrel: as the time for emergence approaches the arousals become more frequent again.

What could be the function of periodic arousals? Some hibernators, such as hamsters, store food for the winter in their nests or burrows, and eat during the periods of arousal. Bats arouse to drink on mild nights. For those species that metabolize only fat from their stores during hibernation the reason for arousal is not so obvious, particularly as the energy expended in a single arousal lasting a few hours can equal that used in 10 days of hibernation (see Section 6.4.3).

In the arousing golden or Syrian hamster (*Mesocricetus auratus*), changes in oxygen consumption and temperature in various parts of the body are rapid and extensive (see Figure 6.11, *overleaf*). At the start of arousal at an ambient temperature of 5 °C, oxygen consumption is 60–80 cm³ kg⁻¹ h⁻¹. Within 3 hours this rate rises 100-fold, to a level comparable to that of violent exercise. At the start of arousal, cheek pouch temperature is virtually the same as that of the rectum but you can see that, as arousal progresses, the cheek pouch temperature

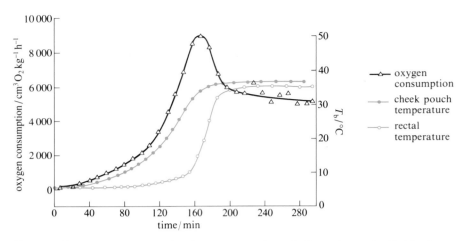

Figure 6.11 Oxygen consumption (as a measure of metabolic rate), anterior T_b (cheek pouch) and posterior T_b (rectal) in the golden hamster (*Mesocricetus auratus*) during arousal.

rises more rapidly and there is a difference of more than 20 °C by 160 minutes. A short time later, oxygen consumption reaches its peak and declines rapidly, whereas cheek pouch and rectal temperatures attain the euthermic level. In some species, for example many ground squirrels, the process of arousal may be much faster than in the hamster (see Figure 6.12).

A difference between anterior and posterior T_b during arousal is seen in virtually all hibernators, including bats. Since the end of the 19th century, it has been known that there are profound circulatory adjustments during hibernation. By using a radio-opaque dye and X-ray equipment it is possible to show that blood flow to the posterior region of the golden hamster is restricted during hibernation, but increases in the forelimbs, heart, diaphragm, thorax and deposits of BAT during the initial stages of arousal. Figure 6.13 shows various measures (blood pressure, heart rate, and rectal and heart temperatures) during arousal of a thirteen-lined ground squirrel. Peripheral vasoconstriction, and thus the resistance, appears to lessen at the start of arousal, indicating vasodilation, but then rises rapidly (arrow) while the heart is also accelerating: as a consequence the rapidly beating heart is working against a high blood pressure. In these circumstances, the heart may be an inefficient pump but it is a good source of heat as the animal warms up. As rectal temperature increases rapidly, the blood pressure starts to decline, associated with a decrease in peripheral resistance: a sudden vasodilation in the posterior regions of the body is thought to be responsible. Evidently, vasomotor changes are important in arousal as well as in entry to torpor.

Hibernators arouse without recourse to external heat, so what is the source of the heat required? The violent shivering that accompanies some stages of arousal suggests that contraction of skeletal muscle is important but even animals in which skeletal muscle activity has been inhibited by curare (which blocks transmission at neuromuscular junctions), can re-warm.

■ From what you read in Chapter 4, what alternatives to shivering would you look for as the source of heat?

The BAT in the interscapular region.

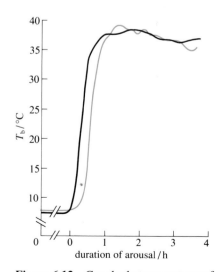

Figure 6.12 Core body temperatures of two ground squirrels during spontaneous arousal.

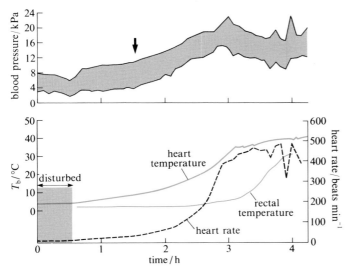

Figure 6.13   Blood pressure, heart rate, and rectal and heart temperatures in a thirteen-lined ground squirrel arousing from deep torpor after being disturbed, at a T_a of 3 °C.

We mentioned above that blood flow to the BAT is restored early in the arousal process, and recent work has shown that, while the uncoupling protein in the mitochondria is in a 'masked' or inactive form during hibernation, the amount of active uncoupling protein is rapidly increased during arousal.

The interscapular regions of all hibernating mammals are significantly warmer than other tissues (except possibly the heart) in the early stages of arousal. In big brown bats, the area of BAT is always warmer than the heart, and arousal is very fast (8 °C to 37 °C in less than 30 minutes). Completely curarized bats (maintained by artificial respiration as their respiratory muscles are paralyzed) can arouse from hibernation as rapidly as normal animals. Figure 6.14 shows the thermographic tracing of body heat (infrared radiation) in an arousing bat. The area of BAT is the warmest part, suggesting that it is the thermogenic source.

We should not infer that BAT is the major or only source of heat in all arousing hibernators. Many rodent hibernators, including golden-mantled and thirteen-lined ground squirrels, do not have IBAT, and in experiments on the Turkish hamster after IBAT has been surgically removed, arousal still takes place. However, the issue of the importance of BAT in arousal is still controversial. For example it has recently been shown in Richardson's ground squirrel that although, like the golden-mantled and thirteen-lined ground squirrels, it does not have IBAT, it does in fact have very large axillary BAT depots. This has lead some workers to question the interpretation of the data on the other two related species.

In the rodents which *do* lack BAT, and probably in the hedgehog, most of the heat in a normal arousal is generated by the shivering of skeletal muscle. There is no evidence that white adipose tissue contributes to arousal in any mammal. The heat from the heart must contribute some, as yet unknown, fraction to the process. Though BAT contributes to thermogenic arousal in the big brown bat, it does not follow that shivering thermogenesis is unimportant in daily arousal from shallow torpor in this species.

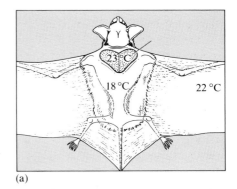

(a)

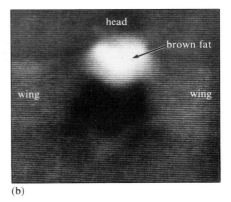

(b)

Figure 6.14   (a) A bat in position for thermography (dorsal side uppermost) showing the location of IBAT, and the major temperatures prevailing at the commencement of thermographic scannings. (b) Thermogram of the dorsal surface of a bat during its arousal from torpor. (The higher the temperature and intensity of infrared radiation from the skin, the brighter the image.)

It is not yet clear what energy source birds use for arousal; they do not seem to possess BAT, and yet are capable of non-shivering thermogenesis. This thermogenesis takes place in the muscles of cold-adapted ducklings and emperor penguin chicks, and there is evidence that it depends on free fatty acids liberated from white adipose tissue. However, it is not yet known what the relative importance of shivering and non-shivering thermogenesis is during arousal from daily (or more prolonged) torpor. Most birds can increase their basal metabolic rate (BMR) by a factor of four or five under extreme cold stress, but the arousing poor-will has been reported to reach rates of nearly nine times BMR. The bird in Figure 6.15 shows a metabolic increase of over five times its torpid metabolic rate.

Final arousal

Emergence can be viewed as the last in the series of periodic arousals. Instead of re-entering hibernation, the animal maintains the euthermic condition. The cue for maintaining this final arousal is probably not temperature, as some species emerge when T_a is well below zero. It is difficult to see how arousal could be affected by daylength, as the hibernating animal is usually underground in a cavity or a burrow. Perhaps fat or food stores reach a minimum or the timing of the final arousal is preprogrammed into the animal's activity cycle.

Summary of Section 6.3

The physiological details of deep or seasonal hibernation vary widely between species, but the general pattern is similar, involving controlled entry to torpor, with or without 'test drops', and periodic arousals, the intervals between these arousals depend on size, T_b and other factors. The frequency of the arousals falls off during the deepest part of the hibernation. Entry to hibernation may be triggered by temperature, day length and shortage of food, especially in facultative hibernators (e.g. hamsters, chipmunks), or by endogenous circannual rhythms, as in some obligative hibernators (e.g. marmots, ground squirrels). In spite of the very low T_b, physiological control is maintained, as is a low level of metabolic activity.

The three types of arousal — alarm, periodic and final — are physiologically similar. Alarm arousal is initiated by external stimulation. Periodic arousal is initiated by endogenous signals. Shivering is an important source of heat, as is to a lesser extent, the heart. BAT is certainly important for arousal in many species of mammals, though apparently not in birds. Final arousal occurs in spring, though it is not known what prevents the animal from re-entering hibernation.

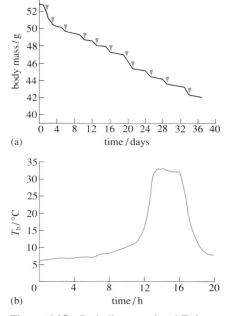

Figure 6.15 Periodic arousal and T_b in the poor-will. (a) Weight loss and arousals (marked by arrows) in a captive poor-will, at a T_a of 4–5 °C. (b) T_b and one spontaneous arousal in the same poor-will at a T_a of 1 °C.

6.4 The benefits of adaptive hypothermia

Throughout this chapter we have emphasized the importance of adaptive hypothermia to the conservation of energy under circumstances where the availability of food is critical, whether overnight in a very small animal or overwinter in a larger one. What we have not done is to look closely at measurements of the savings achieved, to see how important they really are to the survival of the animal in that environment.

Data on this topic are not so easy to obtain in practice, as metabolic surveillance of hibernating animals in the field is extremely difficult, and not particulary easy in the laboratory, where there is the additional problem of not knowing whether the results can be safely extrapolated to the natural situation.

A further complication is that, in a number of species, gestation must proceed across the winter in order that the young may be born early in what may be a short summer season. The extra energy required for fetal development is another factor in the animal's energy balance.

For example, it has been shown that, in the laboratory, pregnant pipistrelle bats (*Pipistrellus pipistrellus*) deprived of food in the cold become torpid, and that pregnancy is extended by a period which is similar in duration to the period of the induced torpor. If food is available, both captive and wild bats maintain a high T_b and gestation proceeds.

However, in spite of these difficulties, measurements have been made both on individual animals and whole colonies or groups of hibernators, enabling crude energy budgets to be calculated.

Some of the best designed studies, albeit on one species, were those by Lawrence Wang and colleagues at the University of Alberta in Edmonton, carried out in the early 1980s. Wang trapped Richardson's ground squirrels in early summer, implanted them with small radiotransmitters that responded to changes in T_b, and then released the animals again. The transmitters had a short range (a few metres) but by carefully tracking the individuals he could mark in which burrows they would spend the winter and place a receiver nearby. In addition, Wang measured the temperature of the burrow throughout the Canadian winter. These ground squirrels begin to show bouts of hibernation at the end of July, enter long periods of torpor in October and would emerge in the following March. Adult individuals start to hibernate before juveniles, probably because the latter take longer to accumulate sufficient fat deposits. By recording just T_b throughout the winter, Wang could build up an accurate daily picture, for each individual, of the depth of hibernation, time in hibernation, frequency and degree of arousal, and time taken to return to hibernation.

Meanwhile, in the laboratory accurate estimates of energy expenditure were made in captive ground squirrels at different T_b, and while entering and arousing from hibernation. In Wang's studies, therefore, laboratory hibernators provided the estimated costs which were then applied to what really happens in the wild.

The first observation was that Richardson's ground squirrels in natural hibernation spend longer periods between arousals than do those in the laboratory. Thus, a laboratory estimate would undervalue hibernation as an energy-saving strategy. The average time spent in a periodic arousal in the wild is about 10 hours and the frequency of arousal decreases during November–March, when animals are spending more than 90% of their time in torpor (recall Figure 6.10). Monthly total oxygen consumption in January is about 35% of that in August, and rises again in February and March. On average, between July and March, entry into hibernation accounts for 27% of total energy expenditure, torpor for 33% and arousal for 40%. However, if the time between periods of torpor is taken into account, the figures are 12% for entry, 17% for torpor, 19% for actual arousal, and 51% for the euthermic periods between arousals.

Entry into hibernation, it seems, costs little. Entry and the hibernation period together account for less than a third of total energy expenditure averaged over the whole 9-month period. Arousal in itself is not that expensive (less than 20%). It is the time between bouts of hibernation, when the animal is euthermic, that consumes more than 50% of the energy expended, though the amount varies between months. For example, in December and January, entry and torpor account for more than 35% and time in euthermia for about 40%.

We have estimates therefore of how hibernators apportion expenditure throughout the hibernating season. But how do the figures compare with similar individuals that are euthermic over the same period? Wang's estimates are given in Table 6.4. From August to February, the savings due to hibernation are over 80%. Even in July and March, months in which arousal frequency is high and time in torpor is short, the savings are significant. On average over 9 months, hibernation endows a small mammal, such as this ground squirrel, with an 88% saving. Over an entire year, the hibernating habit costs an animal 60% less in terms of energy than an individual of similar size that maintains the euthermic condition around the clock.

Table 6.4 The conservation of metabolic cost by hibernating, in Richardson's ground squirrel.

Month	Total energy expenditure with torpor/cm^3 O$_2$ per month	Total energy expenditure if animal remained homeothermic/cm^3 O$_2$ per month	% energy saved by exhibiting torpor
July	38 793	161 820	38.0*
August	59 689	323 640	81.6
September	45 704	313 200	85.4
October	37 692	372 744	89.9
November	31 577	432 000	92.7
December	26 782	542 004	95.1
January	22 222	555 768	96.0
February	33 596	501 984	93.3
March	76 611	394 416	51.2*
		Mean for 9 months	87.8

* For some of July and March the animal is not in hibernation, hence these values are low.

A study of a close relation of the golden-mantled ground squirrel showed that, during the hibernating season, energy expenditure in this species was also only 20% of what would be expected from the animal if it remained euthermic, and that energy consumption throughout the 7 months of the hibernating season was only 15% of the total annual consumption.

Both these species are what we described earlier as obligative, deep hibernators; the picture may be a little different in facultative hibernators, responding more directly to environmental cues. Using one such animal, the golden hamster (*Mesocricetus auratus*), the energy budgets of a whole population in the laboratory were estimated. The hibernating behaviour of individuals varied widely, and the average for the group was that only 18% of the 'hibernating season' was spent in torpor, though this might not have been the case in a wild population. However, when in torpor their energy consumption was only 9% of normal euthermic consumption at that temperature, and overall, the group saved 23% of the energy they would have used without torpor, still quite a significant figure.

When considering the extent to which torpor can promote survival, theoretically it has been calculated that a reasonably well insulated mammal weighing 100 g, at a T_a of 0 °C, should be able to survive without food for 4 days if awake but inactive, 5 days if sleeping with its T_b reduced by 2 °C (a fairly typical figure for a sleeping rodent), or 7 days if in a shallow torpor with a fall in T_b of 10 °C. If it entered deep hibernation with a fall in T_b of 33 °C, regulating its T_b at about 6–7 °C, it should survive for 65 days. However, this calculation did not consider any arousal costs.

Energy saving from nocturnal torpor is also significant in small birds. By allowing its T_b to fall by 10 °C for 10 hours, Gould's manakin (*Manacus vitellinus*, a small, fruit-eating South American bird weighing about 14 g) (Plate 6.4) can save nearly 50% of the energy it would spend at normal T_b, when in a T_a of 22 °C. Similarly, the willow tit (*Parus montanus*, with a weight of about 10 g) in a T_a of 20 °C can save 35% by allowing its T_b to fall by 8 °C. At a lower T_a, the *percentage* saving is less (the animal has to spend more energy defending a particular T_b), but even at a T_a of 0 °C, the willow tit's hypothermia allows it to survive at least 3 hours longer for a given amount of food reserve, a fact which could be crucial on a cold night.

Clearly then, the energy savings of torpor are very real and likely to be highly significant for the ability of the species to colonize a particular environment, especially in cases where the food supply is almost totally unavailable and the animal is not large. The same may be true for the ability of a small bird to change its environment; the rufous humming-bird mentioned in Section 6.2.2 weighs only 3.0–5.5 g, but migrates a thousand miles to overwinter. It starts the journey when its body weight is, on average, about 4.5–5.0 g, and undertakes 'fuel stops' of a few days duration in areas of abundant blossom when its body weight is down to about 3.3 g, moving on again when its weight has built up to about the previous 'start level'. Each night on these 'fuel stops', the humming-bird goes into torpor — its overnight weight loss is about 0.04 g, whereas it would be 0.37 g if it maintained its waking T_b in the same roost. This saving represents nearly as much weight as the bird might expect to put on in a day's feeding, so that, without torpor, the bird might not gain the necessary weight at all.

However, in some environments, such as high altitude forests, not all of the apparently similar species show torpor. Some of the humming-birds that can become torpid only do so if their food reserves at night fall below a certain level. This suggests that entering torpor may not be an unqualified benefit and that there is a price to pay; thus, whether or not to become torpid may be a question of balance of advantage.

■ Can you think of possible disadvantages to an animal in entering torpor, or full seasonal hibernation?

The animal becomes very vulnerable to predators — a deep hibernator may take quite a long time to respond even to an alarm arousal. Also, unless the 'cold alarm arousal' is efficient, the T_b may go below the point from which it can recover.

6.4.1 Hibernation and body mass

At several points in this chapter and the previous one, we have emphasized that the need to escape the consequences of a low T_a becomes more pressing as the size of the animal decreases. The smaller the animal the less insulation it can carry, the higher its metabolic rate per kilogram, the higher its surface area:body weight ratio, etc. Few, if any, deep hibernators are known to have a body weight over 5 kg. Larger animals do not *have* to show a deep torpor to survive, but we have not considered why they *never* seem to show it. After all, assuming food to be unavailable during the winter, a hibernator should not have to build up such large food reserves either of fat or food caches as does a euthermic animal, which should be advantageous. However, in larger animals with longer gestation periods there may be additional positive reasons for *not* hibernating.

■ Can you recall one such reason?

While bears are denning in shallow hypothermia their fetuses develop, are born, and then suckled. Compare this situation to that in the pipistrelle bat (Section 6.4).

In addition, however, there may be energetic reasons why it is not really helpful to larger animals to enter deep torpor. Because of the decline in metabolic rate per kilogram in larger animals, a lower proportion of energy has to be saved to see them through a winter. A theoretical calculation of the 'winter price' needed to see an animal through 100 days of fasting, at a thermoneutral T_a, is shown in Table 6.5.

Table 6.5 The effect of body size on the feasibility of winter euthermia.

body mass / kg	species	winter price / MJ	fat needed / kg	body mass / % extra
0.01	mouse	0.95	0.032	320
1.00	guinea-pig	29.00	0.961	96
1 000.0	large bear	5 134.00	171.00	17

Thus it is quite feasible for the bear to rest for 3 months, even at a T_a well below thermoneutral, given that it can amass a good deal more than 17% of its body weight as fat, without even taking into account the substantial savings from a shallow hypothermia. But would it actually be energetically disadvantageous for it to hibernate? A similar calculation on the cost of re-warming animals of different weights by 30 °C, from 7 °C to 37 °C, alongside a 're-warming equivalent', i.e. the number of hours the animal could have remained euthermic for the cost of its arousal, is shown in Table 6.6.

Table 6.6   Re-warming equivalent in relation in body size.

body mass / kg	species	metabolic rate / W	re-warming cost / kJ	re-warming equivalent / h
0.01	mouse	0.11	1.25	3
0.1	rat	0.59	12.5	6
1.0	guinea-pig	3.34	125.0	10
10.0	marmot	18.80	1 250.0	18
100.0	man	106.0	12 500.0	33
1 000.0	large bear	593.0	125 000.0	58

These 're-warming equivalents' are only theoretical and indicative, as in reality they vary with the T_a. However, it is clear that the *relative* cost of arousal will be higher in larger animals, and that a daily torpor and arousal is unrealistic for any animal over 1 kg — indeed the savings would be small for any animal much over 100 g, unless it was a long night! However, these figures do not provide evidence that a longer bout of torpor would not be energetically useful for a larger animal, other things being equal. A bear, if it could enter deep hibernation for at least 4 or 5 days per bout, would achieve a net saving. However, other things are not equal. Arousal would be very slow, partially abolishing the value of alarm arousal, gestation of the cubs would not proceed, and much would depend on the length of the period of wakefulness between bouts of torpor. This last point is interesting. In general among deep hibernators, the larger the species the longer the periods of wakefulness between bouts. The duration of euthermic wakefulness during the season is proportional to body mass$^{0.38}$. The reasons for this are not clear, but as you will recall from Section 6.4, the periods of euthermia between bouts of torpor may account for a large proportion of the energy consumed during the hibernating season (over 50% in some species). Thus, the periods of wakefulness are important, and might be expected to reduce the value of hibernation to an outsize hibernator.

6.4.2   Why is there periodic arousal?

It is obvious that there is a very high energetic cost to arousal, and an even higher one to the periods of euthermic wakefulness prior to re-entering torpor. If an animal could simply enter torpor once, and arouse 2, 4 or 6 months later, depending on the environment, it would represent a huge energy saving. Thus, it has been assumed that either prolonged torpor is physiologically impossible, or there is some strong selective value to the species in regular arousal.

In the case of some small species of mice, which cannot store very much energy as fat and therefore build up a cache of seeds in their hibernacula, periodic arousal to feed is explicable, as is arousal to forage in those species that do not make food stores. For most species, however, there is no such obvious rationale. Many species urinate when they arouse, and as kidney function is very low indeed in torpor it has been widely believed that arousal is important to clear the buildup of toxic nitrogenous wastes in the blood. However, work on the nitrogen metabolism of the dormant bear, discussed in Section 5.3.2, shows that urea does not accumulate in that species at least, and although it is rash to extrapolate from the bear to small seasonal deep hibernators, there is little evidence so far to support the 'nitrogen' theory. Likewise, there is little evidence to support similar arguments about the need to restore ionic or pH balance. There may be a metabolic connection nevertheless. Larger animals tend to have longer euthermic intervals, and body mass scales with metabolic rate in about the same proportion. Thus, if a specific amount of metabolic activity is required before the animal can re-enter torpor, the need for a longer interval is explicable.

There is good evidence that arousal is important to bats to allow them to drink as well as urinate, but in general terms, there is no real agreement on why deep hibernators show periodic arousal and euthermia.

John and Janet Twente (1965), at the University of Missouri in Columbia, made an interesting point that, across quite a wide range of hibernators, T_b relates inversely to the length of the bout of torpor, and that if the Q_{10} of their metabolism is taken into account, the length of the bout of torpor of each species relates closely to their ordinary sleep/wakefulness pattern when euthermic. Put more simply, the bout is a normal night's sleep, slowed down and extended in proportion to the decline in T_b. Such data would suggest a hypothalamic 'clock' or oscillator which was not temperature compensated. However, some other rhythms are known to persist in torpor (especially in obligate hibernators) and they must depend on a clock that *is* temperature compensated: like all the other hypotheses, Twente and Twente's view has been challenged.

Sleep, thermoregulation and hibernation

There has been a good deal of speculation about the relationship between sleep and hibernation. Sleep in homeothermic animals can be divided into several phases, each with distinct patterns of electrical activity in the brain, as measured by an electro-encephalogram (EEG).

The passage into sleep is a transition from wakefulness into the stage called *slow-wave sleep* (SWS). SWS and its characteristic electrical pattern are interrupted by periods of sleep characterized by, among other things, rapid eye movements, loss of muscle tone in the head and neck, and loss of a shivering response. These periods are known as Rapid Eye Movement (REM) sleep. Dreaming occurs mainly at this time, and blood flow to the brain is markedly increased; although the electrical patterns shown are very close to those of wakefulness, thermoregulation is largely abondoned, and T_b may fall. However, this fall during REM sleep does not appear to be very relevant to torpor or hibernation, which as we have emphasized, is a very *controlled* process; indeed, torpor is always entered from periods of SWS. (In normal SWS the T_b is often lowered by about 2 °C.) As torpor sets in, REM sleep is reduced or phased out altogether. Some human races, for example the Aborigines of Australia and the bushmen of the Kalahari desert can sleep unclothed through cold nights; shivering is reduced, T_b falls to about 35 °C, and there is a peripheral vasoconstriction which reduces heat loss through the skin. This vasoconstriction, and the fact that T_b does not appear to fall to dangerous levels, suggest that the process is a controlled one regulated during SWS, rather than a simple loss of thermoregulatory ability during REM sleep, though this has not been verified.

Workers other than Twente and Twente have argued that the drop in T_b in SWS, shallow torpor, and deep hibernation are different points in what is essentially the same phenomenon, all representing a form of sleep in which the regulation of body temperature is lowered in a controlled manner. This theory is attractive, but while so little is understood of the physiology of normal sleep (it is not clear for example what is the significance of the distinction between SWS and REM sleep), it is a theory that does not explain a great deal.

Summary of Section 6.4

Studies undertaken so far indicate that the energy savings achieved by hibernation differ between periods of the hibernating season, largely because the number of arousals and the euthermic periods between arousals vary across the hibernating season. Also, laboratory studies suggest that the obligate hibernators save more energy than the facultative ones. Taken right across the hibernating season, Richardson's ground squirrels saved at least 80% of what they would have used if they had remained euthermic, and roughly the same figure seems to apply some other ground squirrels. In the golden hamster in the laboratory, the saving was only 23%, owing mainly to the longer periods of wakefulness. Larger animals not only gain less advantage from undergoing a deep hypothermia but are also less efficient at it. A large animal can carry enough additional fat to survive for long periods with only a small drop in T_b and a lethargic or dormant habit; also, the cost of re-warming on arousal becomes high, equivalent to many hours of euthermic wakefulness.

There is, as yet, no generally accepted and compelling evidence for the reason for periodic arousal, although all hibernators do arouse at intervals. The relationship between arousal and normal sleep cycles is not fully understood, nor is the relationship between torpor and normal SWS.

6.5 Control of body temperature in endotherms

While the emphasis in the earlier chapters has been on temperature regulation, so far we have not paid much attention, in endotherms at least, to what controls and coordinates the regulatory mechanisms. A study of hibernation in endotherms is not only fascinating in that hibernators appear superficially to be breaking many of the physiological 'rules', but also because it brings new research and thinking to bear on normal euthermic processes, and some of the assumptions about them which have been rather taken for granted for many years.

6.5.1 Neuronal control

Thermosensitive receptors are distributed in deep tissues and over the body surface. Currently it is thought that inputs from 'cold' and 'warm' sensors interface centrally in the nervous system and that a *set-point* mechanism exists. Input signals from the temperature sensors do not activate effectors of heat production and heat loss until their temperature-linked activities exceed some *threshold level*.

The *hypothalamus* plays a major role in the regulation of T_b in mammals. This part of the brain is itself temperature-sensitive in mammals, and receives inputs from the core and peripheral thermosensors. In some classic experiments started in the 1970s, Craig Heller and colleagues at Stanford University in California used *thermodes* to change the temperature of specific areas of the brain during the hibernating cycle of the marmot and ground squirrel. The thermode assembly is illustrated in Figure 6.16. Three stainless steel tubes, sealed at one end, are mounted perpendicularly on a perspex block and positioned so that the sealed ends may be lowered into the brain. Two of the tubes (1 mm in diameter) are the thermodes. Each contains a smaller tube through which water is pumped at a controlled temperature and returned to a reservoir via the surrounding, larger tube. The third and thinner tube receives a thermocouple for measuring brain temperature. The assembly is mounted so that the sealed ends of the thermodes straddle the pre-optic anterior hypothalamic area (Figure 6.17).

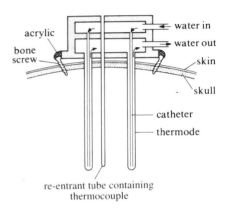

Figure 6.16 Schematic diagram of the thermode assembly used to heat and cool the pre-optic hypothalamic area.

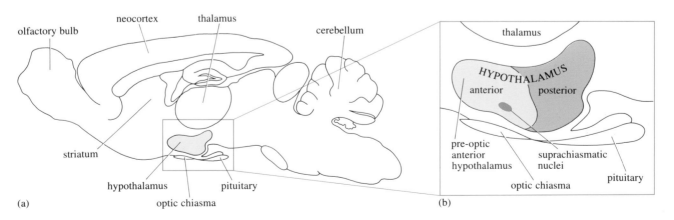

(a)

(b)

Figure 6.17 The rodent hypothalamus (shaded blue), showing the location of the anterior hypothalamus and its pre-optic area.

If the animal is then placed inside a metabolism chamber, it is possible to monitor metabolic rate while varying hypothalamic or ambient temperature.

In euthermic mammals, we would predict that lowering or elevating the temperature of the hypothalamus (T_{hy}) would elicit heat-production and heat–loss responses. Figure 6.18 illustrates this process in the dog at an ambient temperature of 25 °C. The hypothalamic threshold for the metabolic heat response is 36 °C and that for the evaporative heat loss response is 40 °C. From the slopes of the curves, Heller suggests that the intensity of each response is proportional to the difference between the actual temperature of the hypothalamus and the threshold temperature at which that particular response is initiated.

Is this ratio true for hibernating species during their euthermic 'summer' phase? Figure 6.19a shows a similar experiment with a marmot in its euthermic phase. When T_{hy} is lowered below 36.5 °C, metabolic rate increases, again with an intensity proportional to the difference between T_{hy} and the threshold temperature. Figure 6.19b is the response in another marmot which is in hibernation at a T_a of 5 °C.

■ What do you deduce from Figure 6.19b?

The shape of the curve is identical to that in Figure 6.19a, suggesting that here also there is a threshold temperature. However, there are two striking differences. First, the threshold temperature in the hibernating marmot is about 7 °C, compared with 36.5 °C in the euthermic marmot. Second, the metabolic rate is much lower (10% of that in the euthermic marmot) though the response to lowered T_{hy} (a fourfold increase) is about the same.

These experiments indicate that, in marmots and in ground squirrels:

- the hypothalamus is a thermosensitive centre;
- the hypothalamus is linked to effector systems that raise the metabolic rate (and produce heat);
- a temperature set-point exists in the hypothalamus of both euthermic and hibernating mammals;
- the absolute value of the set-point is much lower in a hibernating individual;
- the proportionate metabolic response to lowering the temperature below the threshold is the same in euthermic and hibernating species.

So it seems that the hypothalamus retains thermoregulatory control even at the very low T_b of hibernating animals. If the T_{hy} is held above the ambient temperature at which a metabolic response is normally elicited, we would predict that the animal should not respond, as shown in Figure 6.20 (*overleaf*). In this hibernating marmot, the interscapular temperature (T_{is}), hypothalamic temperature (T_{hy}) and ambient temperature (T_a) are being recorded over a number of hours. Note that T_{hy} remains consistently 3 °C above T_a (except when manipulated experimentally), and that this difference is maintained by cyclical bursts of metabolic heat production. Each momentary increase in metabolic rate is associated with a rise in T_{is}. Over the period of heating marked by the bar, the T_{hy} is artificially raised by 3 °C.

■ What is the consequence of raising T_{hy}?

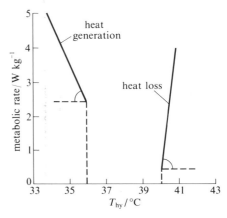

Figure 6.18 Threshold temperatures (dashed lines) in a dog with an optimal T_b of 37 °C at a T_a of 25 °C. Above and below the threshold temperature, heat loss and heat generating mechanisms are turned on, reflected in the altered metabolic rate (solid lines)

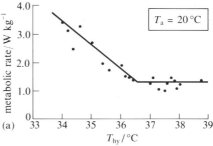

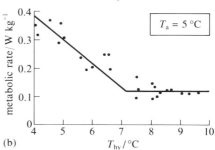

Figure 6.19 Metabolic responses in (a) a euthermic marmot, and (b) a hibernating marmot, to the lowering of hypothalamic temperature (T_{hy}).

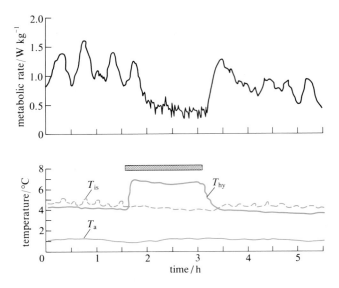

Figure 6.20   The metabolic response of a hibernating marmot to an artificially raised T_{hy}. The bar indicates the period of heating.

The marmot responds to a *rise* in T_{hy} by *reducing* its metabolic rate in much the same way it would if T_b were elevated above T_a. In fact, T_{is} falls slightly over this period (indicating a general body cooling) and, when T_{hy} is no longer elevated artificially, there is a rebound effect, metabolic responses are prolonged and T_{is} is elevated.

This story is true of ground squirrels and marmots but the dormouse is different. The dormouse (unlike other hibernators) hibernates on its back with hind legs exposed. In this study, double-layered, jacketed half-boots (wellingtons) were slipped over the dormouse's feet so that a temperature-controlled liquid could be pumped between the two layers of the boot. With this device the temperature of the hind feet could be altered without affecting deep-body or brain temperature and it was found that, irrespective of T_{hy}, cooling the hind feet stimulated an increase in the metabolic heat response. This observation implies that the mechanism governing the set-point may not always reside in the pre-optic area of the anterior hypothalamus (POAH) as had been supposed. In fact, in pigeons, Adélie penguins, geese and eiderducks, an area of the spinal cord is critical in this respect.

As yet, we have not answered the major question about thermoregulation in hibernators. What happens to re-set the threshold temperature at a level lower than 35 °C as the animal enters hibernation?

One possibility is that, just before the animal enters into hibernation, the thermoregulatory centre 'is turned off' by inhibitor neurons, and then turned on again at the new, lower set-point.

■   Can you think of other possibilites?

It might be that the set-point remains in operation, but is steadily shifted downwards. The following experiments, again performed by Craig Heller, explore these possibilities. By manipulating T_{hy} of marmots entering a bout of torpor, he was able to determine absolute values for the T_{hy} threshold (T_{set}), and see how these changed with time. Figure 6.21 shows such an experiment in two marmots.

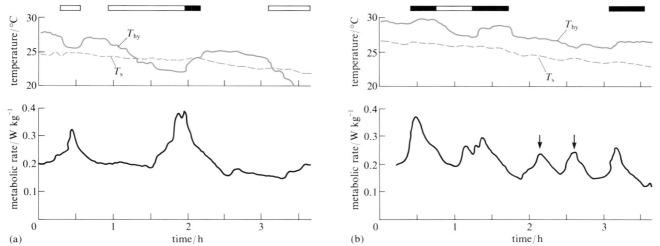

Figure 6.21   Entrance into hibernation of two marmots: (a) a smooth entry, and (b) an irregular entry. The white and black bars indicate periods of hypothalamic cooling and heating, respectively. T_s is the skin temperature. The arrows in (b) indicate irregular bursts of metabolism.

T_{hy} is varied, using the thermode arrangement and T_s (the skin temperature) is measured. The metabolic response is indicated on the lower traces. The marmot in Figure 6.21a is entering hibernation fairly smoothly, whereas, as judged by the frequent bursts of high metabolic rate (see arrows), the marmot in Figure 6.21b is progressing into hibernation rather irregularly. The white and black bars above each figure indicate the periods during which T_{hy} was being manipulated (lowered and raised, respectively). Take the left-hand trace (a) first. Depressing T_{hy} in the early stages effects a metabolic response, but 30 minutes later, the same decrease in T_{hy} has no effect on metabolic rate, suggesting that the threshold temperature has fallen from 22–27 °C to 23–24 °C in half an hour. At 3 hours into hibernation, lowering the T_{hy} even below 23 °C has little effect initially on metabolic rate. In the right-hand trace (b), T_{set} also declines with time but is consistently above the manipulated T_{hy}, as indicated by the bursts of metabolic activity. Therefore, at any one time, the threshold may be above or below the actual T_{hy}. If the threshold is above it, then the entrance is irregular, interrupted by bursts of metabolic heat production which slow the fall in T_b. Heller concluded that the rate of entry into hibernation is limited by the rate at which threshold T_{hy} falls. It seems, therefore, that entrance into hibernation and the lowering of T_b are controlled events.

Using experimental data such as those gained from Figure 6.21, it is possible to plot the declining threshold temperature. Figure 6.22 (*overleaf*) shows such a plot for a golden-mantled ground squirrel entering hibernation. The filled circles represent actual hypothalamic temperatures at specific times during entry. Manipulation of T_{hy} reveals that the threshold for metabolic heat production is somewhere in the range indicated by the vertical line below each dot. As Craig Heller states, 'entrance into hibernation involves a progressive and continuous resetting of the thermostat'.

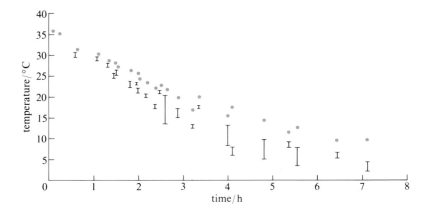

Figure 6.22 T_{hy} (●), and T_{set} (bars indicate range of values) during entrance into hibernation of the golden-mantled ground squirrel.

Rheostasis

This process of continuously varying the controlled level of a feedback system has been called *rheostasis*, to distinguish it from homeostasis, which has implications of a fixed level or point. Nick Mrosovsky (1990) has defined rheostasis as the condition or state in which at any one instant homeostatic defences are still present, but in which over a span of time there is a change in the regulated level. Rheostasis is probably quite an important and often overlooked physiological principle, with a far wider significance than just temperature regulation in hibernators. For example, there appears to be a re-setting of the levels at which the hypothalamic control of hunger operates that is involved in the fattening process prior to hibernation (working to a circannual cycle). In the previous chapter we saw that food intake and appetite diminished in the winter months in both Svalbard reindeer and Svalbard ptarmigan, despite being given food *ad libitum*. In the latter, the body weight that the animal defends gradually declines across the winter, even with unlimited food. Furthermore, if the ptarmigan are deprived of food altogether for a few days, they eat more when it is restored, but only until their weight is roughly 'normal' for the date (Figure 6.23).

Similar phenomena are seen in body weight regulation in incubating jungle fowl and domestic hens, and in the level at which feedback responses are triggered in a number of endocrine systems.

However, it seems that the elegant sliding rheostasis shown by the ground squirrel entering hibernation — Heller's 'progressive and continuous re-setting of the thermostat' — may not represent a universal phenomenon. Indeed, even in the ground squirrel, alarm arousal, as we have seen, can be an almost explosive metabolic event, suggesting that the raising of the T_{set} is itself very sudden. In the eastern chipmunk (*Tamias striatus*), a facultative hibernator, a gradual, controlled decline in T_{set} on entering hibernation is often absent. Manipulating the PAOH temperature may have no effect in chipmunks hibernating with a T_b of about 4 °C, until about 2.1 °C is reached (which is T_{alarm} for this animal), when there is full arousal (Figure 6.24). Thus, the animal has the ability to increase thermogenesis when cold as a result of T_{hy} falling too low, but does not normally control and defend T_b above the T_{alarm} level — at least not as a result of changes in hypothalamic temperature. Perhaps the tight control of T_b shown by the ground squirrel is confined to sophisticated obligate seasonal hibernators.

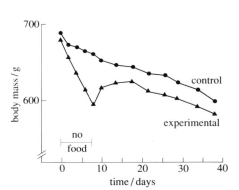

Figure 6.23 Body weights of Svalbard ptarmigan deprived of food. The experimental group (▲) were starved for 8 days at the start of the experiment, and the control group (●) were fed *ad libitum*.

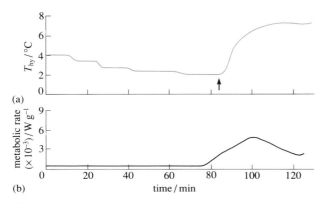

(a)

(b)

Figure 6.24 Metabolic responses of a hibernating eastern chipmunk (*Tamias striatus*), with a T_b of 4.2 °C, to stepwise cooling of the POAH. Cooling of the POAH to about 2.1 °C (T_{alarm}) precipitated arousal, but earlier steps produced no effect. Warming the POAH (indicated by the arrow) at the start of arousal suppressed it within 20 minutes or so.

6.5.2 Chemical control

Research into the part played by various chemicals in the induction and control of hibernation has been very active since the mid-1980s, but the wealth of information becoming available is not easily integrated into a single convincing pattern.

■ From what we have said so far in this chapter, can you think of at least one reason why there might be some confusion?

A very obvious reason is that different experiments are performed on different species in different laboratories. As there is unlikely to be a single universal physiological and biochemical answer to the questions, many of the results appear initially to be contradictory.

However, it is clear that chemical factors play an important part in the whole process. We have already mentioned that serotonin (5-hydroxytryptamine), which is important in normal sleep, also appears to be involved, and that melatonin from the pineal gland may be important in inducing torpor.

However, pineal melatonin is *not* very important for the induction of the *daily* torpor shown by the Siberian hamster. Pinealectomized Siberian hamsters continue to show daily torpor, whereas torpor is abolished by damage to certain areas (suprachiasmatic nuclei) in the hypothalamus. Thus, in this animal, daily torpor appears to result from a lowering of T_{set} induced by a 'clock' or oscillator in the suprachiasmatic nucleus, directly, and not via a chemical circulating in the blood.

As long ago as 1969 at Loyola University in Illinois, Albert Dawe and Wilma Spurrier demonstrated that in hibernating thirteen-lined ground squirrels there appeared to be a fraction in the blood which, when extracted and injected into summer non-hibernating ground squirrels, induced immediate hibernation. This unidentified fraction was called Hibernation Induction Trigger (HIT). This finding aroused some scepticism among many physiologists, prominent among whom was Lawrence Wang. In 1988, Wang and others showed that although the 'HIT' fraction of the blood of hibernating thirteen-lined ground squirrels would induce hibernation in summer specimens, so would almost everything else, including injections of warm saline! However, injection of this blood fraction into summer juveniles of Richardson's ground squirrels had no effect, so Wang and co-workers concluded that any effect might be specific to thirteen-lined ground squirrels, and that they were unsuitable experimental animals as they could be induced to hibernate with very non-specific stimuli. However, extracts from the blood of hibernating ground squirrels, woodchucks and even dormant bears have since been shown to induce a degree of hypothermia and 'sleepiness' in a wide variety of both hibernators and non-hibernators (including primates), so there is undoubtedly at least one factor present in the blood of a hibernating mammal which is not present when it is euthermic, and which is relevant to torpor.

There is good evidence for the involvement of naturally occurring opiates in the brains of hibernating mammals. There are a variety of substances, for example the enkephalins which are produced in the brain, that act centrally on the brain, and play a part in, among other things, the suppression of pain in a manner very similar to opiates such as morphine. Some of these enkephalins are found in unusually high quantities in specific areas of the hypothalamus of hibernating mammals. Indirect evidence that most of the opiate receptor sites in the brain may be already taken up by endogenous opiates during hibernation comes from the fact that, during torpor, the thirteen-lined ground squirrel does not become addicted to exogenous morphine when given experimentally, whereas when euthermic it does, suggesting that an opiate produced in the animal's brain is occupying the receptor sites.

Attempts to discover whether there is a endogenous opiate that constitutes HIT have, so far, produced conflicting results both within and between species, so once again a clear integrated picture is still lacking, if indeed there *is* such a picture to be found!

Summary of Section 6.5

Certain areas of the hypothalamus, especially around the pre-optic area of the anterior hypothalamus (POAH) and suprachiasmatic nuclei, are important in maintaining normal T_b in most mammals by controlling thermogenesis and heat loss mechanisms. The PAOH operates a 'set-point' system, and if the temperature of the anterior hypothalamus (T_{hy}) rises above the set-point, cooling responses are triggered; if it falls below it, thermogenesis results. In marmots and ground squirrels entering hibernation, this set-point is lowered, allowing the animal to cool down towards T_a in a controlled manner; this variation of the set-points is called rheostasis. This highly controlled process also occurs in some birds and the dormouse, but the mechanism is not driven from the hypothalamus. Other hibernators may allow T_b to fall in a less regulated way, until the T_{alarm} operates. A variety of chemicals play important but different roles in hibernation, including peptides such as melatonin, serotonin (5-hydroxytryptamine) and naturally occurring opiates such as the enkephalins. However, the exact part played by these substances appears to differ in different species, and there is as yet no clear overview of their action, or their relationship to the so-called Hibernation Induction Trigger (HIT).

6.6 Hibernation in ectothermic vertebrates

In the physiological sense that we have used the term in this chapter so far, hibernation does not occur in ectotherms. As you saw in Chapter 2, temperature regulation in amphibians and reptiles is largely behavioural, and they lack the insulation and control of metabolic rate necessary to raise T_b significantly above T_a so as to protect themselves from freezing in a low T_a. They have, nevertheless, successfully colonized temperate climatic regions where the winters are too cold to allow them either mobility or an adequate food supply. In this section, therefore, we are using the term 'hibernation' in its more colloquial sense of the animal passing a winter inactive, without feeding and out of sight in a hibernaculum or under water, emerging only when the T_a rises sufficiently to restore activity.

6.6.1 Hibernation strategies

Amphibians and reptiles living in seasonally cold regions face essentially the same problems as the mammals we have considered — a short summer season for reproduction, long periods where food is unavailable, and periods in which T_a is often below the freezing point of their body fluids. Many of them are terrestrial and air-breathing, and are therefore potentially exposed to much greater extremes of temperature than their aquatic relatives (see Sections 5.1 and 5.5).

The majority of species can resist seasonal cold by finding or creating hibernacula deep underground, or in ponds or rivers, where the immediate T_a does not drop below the freezing point of their body fluids. So long as they do not freeze, they can remain like this for very long periods, immobile and with an extremely low metabolism, until they are passively re-warmed by a rise in T_a. Some species cannot rely on these conditions, however; for example several species of frog hibernate in the leaves of the forest floor, and a number of terrapins overwinter as adults in shallow pools or burrows or as hatchlings in shallow nests. These animals are insufficiently protected to avoid a T_a which may fall to $-6\,°C$ to $-8\,°C$ for periods of time, especially overnight. Their body fluids are likely to freeze at about $-0.5\,°C$ (see Section 5.5.1), so such conditions would potentially be fatal for most species.

■ Can you recall from the previous chapter why the freezing of their body fluids would be fatal?

The structure of cell membranes would become disrupted, as would the tertiary structure of large hydrophilic molecules such as proteins.

Additionally, as larger ice-crystals expand they do a great deal of crude mechanical damage, tearing tissues apart, and if they form within the cells, they irreversibly disrupt the delicate intracellular structure.

■ From what you know of the situation in fish (Section 5.1), can you think of a reason why supercooling might not be a good solution?

Two reasons spring to mind; the first is that there must be a very high risk of the animal, in frozen leaves, touching ice-crystals which would seed a sudden freezing of the blood. Second, the T_a may well fall below that of polar oceans, too cold for supercooling to provide an answer.

Thus, although supercooling may give some protection against moderate frost, and indeed may be the only protection for many species in hibernacula which occasionally fall below 0.5 °C, it is not adequate in all cases. In such animals, freeze avoidance — by good hibernaculum selection or supercooling — must give way to *freeze tolerance*.

6.6.2 Freeze tolerance

Since many ectotherms can recover after brief periods in which some ice formation takes place in the body, it has been suggested that the description 'freeze tolerant' be confined to those species in which there is 'an ecologically relevant strategy of hibernation that includes the ability to survive long-term freezing with a stable maximum ice content, at subzero temperatures naturally encountered within the hibernaculum'. It has been known that, as a practical yardstick, all the species found so far in which freeze tolerance is a necessary component of hibernation survive after 24 hours at −2.5 °C, with a stable ice content of 45–64% of total body water. Thus it has been suggested that these criteria be used to define freeze tolerance.

Table 6.6 gives a selection of those amphibians and reptiles which meet the definition, compared to the garter snake (*Thamnophis sirtalis*), which does not quite do so. However, this degree of tolerance may be precisely what is required within the garter snake's actual habitat, that is, saving the snakes from a short sharp frost within their hibernaculum. Probably also, individuals in the middle of an intertwined mass of hibernating snakes would seldom have such a low T_a, and not even know that they had failed to achieve the criteria!

Table 6.6 Freeze tolerance in some amphibians and reptiles.

animal	time of year	% survival	conditions		% body water as ice
Amphibians					
Rana sylvatica (wood frog)	autumn	100	3–13 days	at −2.5 to −3.0 °C	−
	autumn	100	4 days	at −4.0 °C	47.8 (±2.5)
	spring	73–100	7 days	at −2.5 °C	−
	spring	95	48 h	at −2.0 to −3.0 °C	65.3 (±1.4)
Pseudacris crucifer (spring peeper)	autumn	100	5 days	at −6.0 °C	35.6 (±1.1)
Reptiles					
Trachemys picta marginata (painted terrapin/turtle)	autumn	100	3 days	at −2.5 °C	43.5 (±1.0)
	spring	100	11 days	at −2.5 °C	50 (±1.2)
Thamnophis sirtalis (garter snake)	autumn	100	3–5 h	at −2.5 °C	40
	autumn	93	6 h	at −3.3 °C	18–36
	autumn	0	24 h	at −2.5 °C	60–70

6.6.3   Mechanism of freeze tolerance

In view of the effects of ice-crystals on the tissues, it is remarkable that animals can develop such freeze tolerance, and some generalizations can be made. No vertebrate is known to survive the formation of intracellular ice-crystals, and the limits of freeze tolerance, as confirmed in the laboratory, is about −6 °C, though there is evidence of hibernacula falling to −8 °C for sustained periods in the wild. Most of the species studied were more tolerant after having a period of acclimatization at about 5 °C, and in several species (e.g. the wood frog) spring animals were less tolerant than autumn ones. The cells of a freeze-tolerant animal are rather more resistant than normal to ischaemia (shortage of oxygen due to interrupted blood supply) and to elevated levels of the breakdown products of metabolism. The cells also have to be relatively resistant to shrinkage, as they lose water to the extracellular fluids due to the increased osmotic pressure of these fluids.

■   Why should the osmotic pressure of the body fluids rise?

As the water freezes out of solution, the remaining solutes increase in concentration. There are other reasons as well, discussed below.

However, important though they are, all these factors fail to explain the critical difference between the tolerant species and the great majority. This critical difference lies in the control of ice-crystal formation.

Ice formation in the tissue

Water changes into its solid phase, ice, at or below 0 °C, because of the formation of crystals; crystal formation can only occur in a pure solution when water molecules cluster together to form a transient grouping or 'nucleus' which appears 'ice-like' to other water molecules. Molecules are then transferred from the liquid phase around it to build an ice-crystal, losing energy in the process.

The statistical probability of a sufficiently large and long-lived nucleus existing at 0 °C is remote, and in pure water it does not become probable until about −38 °C—hence supercooling to this temperature is theoretically possible. However, some very small particles may show enough similarities to an ice-crystal to hasten this process—most especially, of course, an actual ice-crystal! The lower the temperature is when freezing starts around a nucleus, particle or crystal, the more sudden is the crystallization and the larger the crystals.

Animal body fluids have a lower freezing point (below −0.5 °C) than water because of the dissolved salts present and, as you have seen in Chapter 5, some fish may have an antifreeze in solution that lowers the freezing point still more. However, none of these factors keep the body fluids from freezing at, say, −2.5 °C. Thus, it is critical for a freeze-tolerant animal to form only very small ice-crystals, which do the minimum damage. The presence of *cryoprotectants*, as mentioned in the previous chapter, and of *ice-nucleating proteins*, prevents the formation of larger ice-crystals. Living organisms produce a number of cryoprotectants, usually quite small molecules such as glycerol, alcohol or glucose. While the presence of such substances, in the levels at which they can be tolerated in blood, lowers the freezing point of the body fluids slightly, their major action is to act as the focus or nucleus for the formation of very small ice-crystals. In some frogs, for example the wood frog and the spring peeper, the cryoprotectant is glucose, and is released from the liver to raise the blood level to as much as 300 μmol g^{-1} wet weight, a level which would normally be considered highly hyperglycaemic. Glucose is produced by a massive and rapid breakdown of liver glycogen, stored prior to hibernation, but this breakdown does not begin until freezing has actually started (this may, however, be peculiar to glucose-protected frogs). Freezing begins in the skin, and spreads inwards. (Supercooling is less than in non-tolerant ectotherms, ranging from −1 °C to −3 °C.) In the wood frogs, maximum ice formation at −2.5 °C is quite slow, and takes up to 24 hours. Within minutes of the first crystals forming in the skin, the glucose level of the blood begins to rise from 3 or 4 μmol g^{-1} (see Figure 6.25), to about 70 μmol g^{-1} after 4 hours, and continues to rise for 2 or 3 days. The rising concentration of the active form of the enzyme, glycogen phosphorylase *a*, which breaks down the glycogen in the liver, is even more spectacular, doubling within 2 minutes of the first ice-crystal formation in the skin. Clearly, all the normal glucose homeostatic mechanisms are over-ridden in some manner.

The painted terrapin (*Trachemyspicta marginata*) appears to use a mixture of lactate and glucose as cryoprotectant, but the picture is not yet as well known in reptiles as in amphibians.

In 1990, the presence of an *ice-nucleating protein* was demonstrated in the wood frog. The protein has not been identified at the time of writing (1993), but it is quite different from an anti-freeze protein such as that described for arctic fish, and it functions, like the cryoprotectant molecules mentioned, to bring about the early formation of small crystals. It is a very effective 'nucleating' agent, being active in dilutions of 1:1 000 frog plasma. It is present in frogs in both the spring and autumn, but in painted terrapins only during the autumn. It is present before hibernation, but only in freeze-tolerant species.

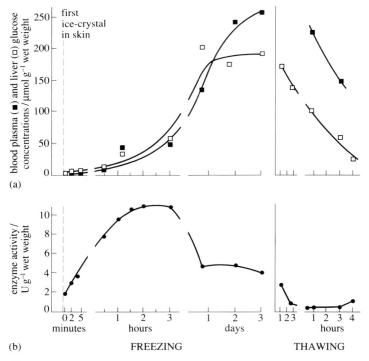

Figure 6.25 Changes in (a) glucose concentrations in the blood plasma (■) and liver (□), and (b) glycogen phosphorylase activity in wood frogs (*Rana sylvatica*) over a period of 3 days at −3 °C.

These adaptations allow ice formation to begin close to the freezing point of the body fluids, as soon as the skin makes contact with an ice-crystal, and with the minimum of supercooling. The process is therefore fairly slow, the crystals are small, and the main mass of them are found in the abdominal cavity and in the veins around the heart. If T_a falls too low, and more than about 65% of the body water freezes, there is too much shrinkage of the cells and the animal dies. On the other hand, if freezing proceeds too quickly, *not enough* of the slightly supercooled cellular fluids can escape into the blood, and although there is not excessive cell shrinkage, crystals form within the cells, and the animal dies.

Summary of Section 6.6

Ectothermic vertebrates are not hibernators in the endothermic sense of the word, in that they regulate their T_b just above freezing and are able to arouse at will, independently of T_a. They do, however, hibernate in the colloquial sense of the word, and for those species that are not able to depend on the T_a remaining close to or above the freezing point of their body fluids, special mechanisms have evolved to protect them from ice-damage, including a higher than normal resistance to cell shrinkage and osmotic stress, and cryoprotectants to keep ice-crystal size to a mimimum. Freeze damage is avoided by starting the process of crystallization at a higher temperatures than would be anticipated, thus keeping the process slow and the crystals small. These effects are brought about by the production of ice-nucleating proteins (INP) and cryoprotectants (small molecules such as alcohol and sugar). Different cryoprotectants are produced in different species; in the wood frog the cryoprotectant is glucose, and its very rapid release from the liver begins only after the first ice-crystals form in the skin.

6.7 Conclusion

Ectotherms colonizing temperate habitats face rather different challenges than do homeotherms; for an ectotherm the problem is not one of energy conservation while food is unavailable, but rather one of resisting frost damage while inert. For most species in cool climates, the key lies in the selection of hibernacula in which the T_a will not stay too low for too long, but the various mechanisms of freeze tolerance known to date will clearly extend the variety of hibernacula in which survival is possible, and thus by implication, the number of habitats which can be successfully exploited. This outcome is of course the same one as may be achieved by homeothermic torpor.

Among homeotherms full scale seasonal hibernation, whether obligative and timed by an annual rhythm, or facultative and dependent on various cues such as day length, T_a, and the extent of body fat reserves, is quite a widespread phenomenon among mammals. Bouts of torpor of more limited duration also occur quite widely, especially among groups of small mammals and small birds. This ability to undergo adaptive hypothermia has arisen apparently independently in different groups; the physiological processes involved vary considerably and even among closely related species there may be some which can become torpid and then re-warm at will, and some which cannot.

The key to this ability appears to lie in the rheostatic control of thermogenesis and temperature loss; the lowering of the set point (T_{set}) at which T_b is defended in a controlled manner such that the T_b is allowed to fall so far and no further, and also the ability to raise T_{set} again independently of T_a, to produce arousal. In the case of a 'deep torpor', the T_b may be allowed to follow the T_a down to quite low temperatures, perhaps only a little above freezing, whereas in 'shallow torpor' the permitted drop in T_b may be only a few degrees. When this shallow torpor is included in the category of adaptive hypothermia, it is probably the case that the phenomenon is far more widespread then was realized until a few years ago. For example, although shallow torpor used to be thought of typically as being the 'dormancy' of large carnivores, it is now known to be important in many small birds, such as some North American tits and finches, and in several species of mice, not normally thought of as hibernators. Thus, in addition to the importance of what might be described as 'classic" seasonal hibernation to animal survival in harsh conditions, it appears that shallow torpor may also be critical for the survival of animals ranging in weight from a tonne of denning bear to 5 g of migrating humming-bird.

Objectives for Chapter 6

When you have completed this chapter you should be able to:

6.1   Define and use, or recognize definitions and applications of each of the **bold** terms.

6.2   Give examples of the diversity of the major groups of mammals and birds that contain hibernating species.

6.3   Describe the physiological changes occurring during entry to hibernation, and at least three of the cues which may trigger entry.

6.4   Present evidence to show that hibernating mammals and birds retain physiological control of their T_b.

6.5   Critically describe experiments designed to evaluate the energy cost of hibernation as compared with euthermia, and suggest at least two reasons why large mammals do not hibernate.

6.6   Present experimental evidence for the view that control of T_b depends upon temperature-sensitive neurons, and suggest where they may be located.

6.7   Suggest why periodic arousals occur, and offer a mechanism for them.

6.8   Describe why freeze tolerance is important in some reptiles and amphibians, and give an account of how it is achieved in at least one species of reptile and one frog.

Questions for Chapter 6

(Answers to questions are at the end of the book.)

Question 6.1 (Objectives 6.1 and 6.2)
Categorize the following species as showing either shallow torpor or deep hibernation, daily or seasonal hibernation, or as non-hibernators.

(a) Pipistrelle bat

(b) Black bear

(c) Poor-will

(d) Guinea-pig

(e) Golden hamster

(f) Humming-bird

(g) Pigeon

(h) African fat mouse

Question 6.2 (Objective 6.2)
What reasons might you advance to support the argument that the ability to hibernate may have arisen several times quite independently?

Question 6.3 (Objective 6.3)
Based on the information you have so far, indicate whether the following statements are *true* or *false*, and, if false, explain briefly why.

(a) The increase in photoperiod in spring stimulates renewed activity in the testes of the ground squirrel.

(b) The laying down of fat deposits is a criterion for identifying an animal as a hibernator.

(c) The decline in heart rate on entry into hibernation is due to an increase in the number of skipped beats and a lengthening of the period between beats.

(d) The effects of atropine on heart rate suggests that the parasympathetic system is responsible for the low heart rate throughout the hibernation phase.

(e) Although blood pressure is lowered during entry, there is evidence for vasoconstriction.

Question 6.4 (Objective 6.3 and 6.4)
What evidence is there for the persistence of physiological regulation during hibernation? Give two examples.

Question 6.5 (*Objective 6.4*)
Figure 6.26 shows the oxygen consumption in the purple carib, a West Indian humming-bird (*Eulampis jugularis*, Plate 6.5), in the active (but resting) state (●) and when torpid (○). Using these data and information from Section 6.5, categorize the following statements relating to the humming-bird as either *probably true* or *probably false*.

(a) In the active state (i.e. resting, but not torpid; clearly when flying there is an enormous increase in oxygen consumption), the humming-bird's metabolic rate increases linearly with a decline in T_a below 36 °C, in order to maintain T_b.

(b) When torpid, the humming-bird's T_b fluctuates more or less with T_a between 36 °C and 5 °C.

(c) When T_a falls below 10 °C, the humming-bird arouses from torpor.

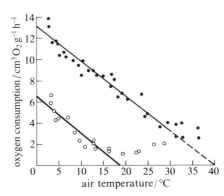

Figure 6.26 Oxygen consumption in a humming-bird (*Eulampis jugularis*) at different ambient temperatures.
(●) O$_2$ consumption in active specimens, (○) O$_2$ consumption in torpid specimens.

(d) The humming-bird's pattern of thermoregulation in torpor has similarities with that of the hibernating hedgehog.

What is the role of BAT in arousal from hibernation?

Give two possible explanations for the occurrence of periodic arousal.

What are the major pieces of evidence suggesting that hihernators retain thermoregulatory control, albeit at lower threshold temperatures?

What piece of evidence would you cite to counter the statement that 'on entry into hibernation the body thermostat is turned off and then turned on again at a lower set-point in deep hibernation'?

Characterize the following statements as either *true* or *false*, on the basis of what you know from this chapter.

(a) Freeze tolerance has developed in several species of frogs, and some mammals can undergo deep hibernation at a T_a below 0 °C.

(b) Cryoprotectants in ectotherms act to protect the tissue, mainly by lowering the freezing point of the blood.

(c) Ice-nucleating proteins produce a similar effect to cryoprotectants such as glucose on ice formation in the body fluids.

(d) Glucose is secreted into the blood in unusually high concentrations in the wood frog early in the autumn to prevent freezing in subsequent severe weather.

Why should some hibernating ectotherms adopt protective measures against ice formation when the majority do not?

CHAPTER 7 SHORTAGE OF OXYGEN

Prepared for the Course Team by E. W. Taylor and N. M. Whiteley

7.1 Introduction

In this chapter we consider the responses of animals to a specific environmental stress — the shortage of oxygen, also called **hypoxia**. Oxygen is essential for the maintenance of aerobic metabolism in tissues. It acts as the terminal electron acceptor (oxidizing agent) on the cytochrome chain in the mitochondria responsible for the production of ATP, the source of energy for biochemical work. When an animal's demand for energy outstrips its ability to supply tissues with oxygen, it may resort to anaerobic metabolism, but this yields less ATP per mole of glucose than aerobic metabolism and typically results in rapid fatigue of exercising muscles. Thus, when the supply of oxygen from the environment is restricted, most animals compensate and try to maintain aerobic metabolism. Here we examine the behavioural and physiological responses enabling animals to sustain levels of aerobic activity commensurate with survival during hypoxia.

Hypoxia is a relative term and refers to environments that contain less oxygen than is present in air at sea-level. For air-breathers this condition is encountered only at high altitude or in the stagnant air of burrows. In aquatic environments, oxygen partial pressures are often low and so the environments are hypoxic. Oxygen utilization by the respiratory activity of organisms rapidly depletes the relatively low oxygen concentration in the water and, in the absence of mixing, replacement from the surface is relatively slow, because oxygen diffuses at least 20 000 times more slowly through water than it does through air (Table 7.1).

■ In what types of environment might animals regularly experience hypoxia?

Table 7.1 A comparison of the physical properties of oxygen in air and water.

			Air	Water	Ratio air:water
1	Availability / $cm^3 \, l^{-1}$	O_2	210	6	35
		CO_2	0.3	0	–
2	Solubility or absorption coefficient $(\beta) / \mu mol \, l^{-1} \, kPa^{-1}$	O_2	7.15	0.23	30
		CO_2	7.15	6.78	1
3	Diffusion or Krogh's constant (K) / $nmol \, s^{-1} \, cm^{-1} \, kPa^{-1}$	O_2	1.35	0.000 006	230×10^3
		CO_2	1.09	0.000 12	9000
4	Density / $kg \, l^{-1}$		0.001	1.0	$\frac{1}{1000}$
5	Viscosity / $Pa \, s$		0.000 02	0.001	$\frac{1}{50}$
6	Specific heat / $J \, l^{-1}$		1.3	4 200	$\frac{1}{4000}$

Hypoxia commonly occurs in aquatic environments when rates of oxygen consumption are high relative to the rate of re-aeration of the water. For example, hypoxia is typical of small, stagnant pools; sea trenches and lakes (particularly those where vertical mixing of water is limited as, for example, below a thermocline or beneath ice); grossly polluted or slow-flowing rivers; and burrows or tubes in substrates where the mud may be completely free of oxygen due to respiration of micro-organisms. Parasitic animals resident in the gut of their hosts may encounter a virtual absence of oxygen called **anoxia**.

Internal or **systemic hypoxia** may be encountered by animals in environments where oxygen is relatively plentiful, but their ability to *extract* it is temporarily impaired. Such examples are considered in Sections 7.3 and 7.4 in relation to air-breathing animals diving into water and to water-breathers exposed in air.

This account of hypoxia takes a comparative approach, considering the overall responses of selected animals to problems of oxygen supply versus demand, and emphasizing the control and integration of the total response. We explore some respiratory, cardiovascular and metabolic responses of animals exposed to submersion, hypoxic water, aquatic pollutants, and emersion from water into air. In the next chapter, the responses of humans to hypoxia at altitude will be examined.

7.2 The oxygen cascade

However, before we look at how various animals cope with hypoxia, we will discuss oxygen transfer in more detail. The exchange of respiratory gases obeys the laws of physical diffusion, and in order for the oxygen requirements of deep body tissues to be provided from the environment, a diffusion gradient must be maintained. This gradient has been referred to as the **oxygen cascade** (see Figure 7.1), and in large, active animals it is separable into steps that describe gradients of:

Diffusive conductance, where oxygen transfer is by physical diffusion, being directly proportional to exchange area and the oxygen partial pressure (P_{O_2}) gradient, and inversely proportional to diffusion distance (e.g. lungs/gills to blood; blood to tissues).

Convective conductance, where oxygen transfer is by mechanical movement of the surrounding fluid (e.g. lung/gill ventilation with air/water, and perfusion of lung/gill and tissue capillaries by blood carrying oxygen, typically reversibly bound to a respiratory blood pigment).

In animals with specialized respiratory and cardiovascular systems an oxygen cascade with four major steps from environment to tissues may be identified. The first step is delivery of the external fluid (water/air) containing oxygen to the respiratory gas exchange surfaces of the animal. This process of external convection is termed **ventilation.** The second step is the passage of oxygen from the air/water presented to the respiratory gas exchange surfaces (gills/lungs) across the epithelium by diffusion into the body fluids. The third step is the transport of the oxygen (often combined with a respiratory pigment) to the metabolizing tissues by internal convection or perfusion through the cardiovascular system. The fourth and final stage is the passage of oxygen from the circulating body fluids to the metabolizing mitochondria by diffusion through tissues. Thus the steps in the cascade (Figure 7.1) are alternately convection, diffusion, convection, then diffusion.

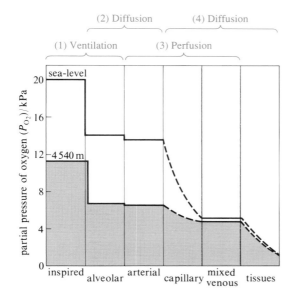

Figure 7.1 Mean P_{O_2} gradients from inspired air to tissues in human subjects native to sea-level, and in subjects native to 4 540 m. Although the P_{O_2} in the atmosphere at high altitude is greatly reduced and the P_{O_2} gradient down the oxygen cascade is much less steep than in sea-level residents, the venous P_{O_2} is not greatly diminished, so the P_{O_2} gradient for oxygen transfer to the mitochondria is maintained. Note that the dashed portions of the gradients represent estimations of P_{O_2} changes, rather then precise measurements. The labels identify the four steps in the cascade described in the text, where oxygen transfer is governed either by diffusive conductance (obeying Fick's law of diffusion, see Section 7.2.1) or convective conductance (where oxygen transfer is by mechanical movement of fluid, i.e. ventilation or perfusion).

7.2.1 Fick's law of diffusion

Transfer of oxygen down the oxygen cascade is governed by Fick's First Law of diffusion, which can be expressed by the following equation:

$$\dot{M}_{O_2} = \frac{K . A . \Delta P_{O_2}}{x} \tag{1}$$

$\dot{M}_{O_2}$ = rate of oxygen uptake / mmol O_2 min^{-1} kg^{-1}

K = Krogh's diffusion constant for tissue / nmol s^{-1} cm^{-1} kPa^{-1}

A = area of respiratory gas exchanger (gills or lungs or capillary bed) / cm^2

x = diffusion distance over respiratory gas exchanger / cm

ΔP_{O_2} = partial pressure gradient for oxygen over the respiratory gas exchanger / kPa.

(The dot over the M refers to the rate, so that $\dot{M}_{O_2}$ is the number of moles of gas consumed per unit time.)

Acceptance of this relationship, the so-called Fick principle, enables us to describe how rates of oxygen uptake are directly related to rates of ventilation or perfusion. When ventilation ($\dot{V}$) rates are taken into account the oxygen uptake, measured as volumes of oxygen, $\dot{V}_{O_2}$ (i.e. cm^3 O_2 kg^{-1} h^{-1} at STP), is given by:

$$\dot{V}_{O_2} = \dot{V}_{w} . \beta_{wO_2}(P_{IO_2} - P_{EO_2}) \text{ for water/gill breathers or,}$$

$$\dot{V}_{O_2} = \dot{V}_{A} . \beta_{AO_2}(P_{IO_2} - P_{EO_2}) \text{ for air/lung breathers,} \tag{2}$$

where $\dot{V}_{w}$ and $\dot{V}_{A}$ = ventilation rates in water and air, respectively,

β_{wO_2} and β_{AO_2} = absorption coefficients for oxygen in water and air, respectively (because β_{AO_2} is 30 times higher than β_{wO_2} (see Table 7.1), a water breather with a similar $\dot{V}_{O_2}$ to an air-breather would require its $\dot{V}_{w}$ to be 30 times higher than the air-breather's $\dot{V}_{A}$),

P_{IO_2} and P_{EO_2} = partial pressures of oxygen in inspired and expired air/water, respectively.

Considering perfusion provides the relationship:

$$\dot{V}_{O_2} = \dot{V}_b \cdot \beta_{bO_2}(P_{aO_2} - P_{vO_2}) \tag{3}$$

where $\dot{V}_b$ = perfusion rate of blood,

β_{bO_2} = absorption coefficient for oxygen in the blood,

P_{aO_2} and P_{vO_2} = partial pressures of oxygen in the arteries and veins, respectively.

As β_{bO_2} varies in a complex way with the oxygen binding curve of the respiratory blood pigment, this relationship is more often expressed as the arterial–venous oxygen content difference:

$$\dot{V}_{O_2} = \dot{V}_b \, (C_{aO_2} - C_{vO_2}) \tag{4}$$

where C_{aO_2} and C_{vO_2} = concentrations of oxygen in arteries and veins, respectively.

7.2.2   Indices for oxygen transfer

In order to discuss the factors governing diffusive oxygen transfer over respiratory gas exchange surfaces we need to establish an index for the relative effectiveness of oxygen transfer. Many have been suggested but the one giving a useful measure of relative diffusional capacity is **Transfer Factor (T_{O_2})**.

T_{O_2} was suggested as a useful index of respiratory gas exchange in gill breathers, being based on theoretical considerations derived from descriptions of heat exchangers by engineers. It quantifies diffusive conductance of the exchange surfaces, which depends on the morphological characteristics that limit physical diffusion, i.e. the area (A) and thickness (x) of the exchange surfaces and on the value for Krogh's diffusion constant, K:

$$T_{O_2} = \frac{K \cdot A}{x} \tag{5}$$

The transfer factor is more commonly derived from the other factors in Fick's equation; namely, the gradient of oxygen partial pressure between blood and water ($P_{wO_2} - P_{bO_2}$) and the rate of oxygen consumption ($\dot{M}_{O_2}$ in μmol min^{-1} kg^{-1}):

$$T_{O_2} = \frac{\dot{M}_{O_2}}{P_{wO_2} - P_{bO_2}} \tag{6}$$

$$\text{where } P_{wO_2} = \frac{P_{IO_2} + P_{EO_2}}{2} \tag{7}$$

$$\text{and } P_{bO_2} = \frac{P_{aO_2} + P_{vO_2}}{2} \tag{8}$$

7.2.3 Circulatory oxygen conductance

In animals with a circulatory system, the transfer of oxygen to the tissues is governed by blood flow and by the difference in oxygen content between arterial and venous blood. The oxygen combining properties of the blood are a product of oxygen capacity, which is dependent upon haemoglobin concentration and the degree of saturation of the blood with oxygen. This oxygen saturation is itself dependent upon the affinity of haemoglobin for oxygen. The oxygen binding properties of the blood can be shown using oxygen equilibrium curves, which plot either the oxygen content of the blood or the percentage saturation of the respiratory blood pigment against oxygen partial pressure. You should now remind yourself of the molecular basis and functional advantages of the sigmoid oxygen dissociation curves typical of respiratory pigments, and the reduction in oxygen affinity induced by increased carbon dioxide or reduced pH levels, known as the **Bohr shift**. Generalized curves illustrating the effects on oxygen transport of changes in oxygen capacity and oxygen affinity of a respiratory pigment are provided in Figure 7.2.

Figure 7.2a shows some of the factors which can modulate the relative affinity for oxygen of a respiratory pigment. Increased proton concentration ([H$^+$], usually expressed as a reduced pH), which may result from an increase in P_{CO_2}, typically reduces oxygen affinity by binding to the respiratory protein and stabilizing its deoxygenated molecular configuration. This results in a right-ward Bohr shift (R) and a consequent increase in P_{50} (from 8 to 12 kPa). Conversely, increased pH

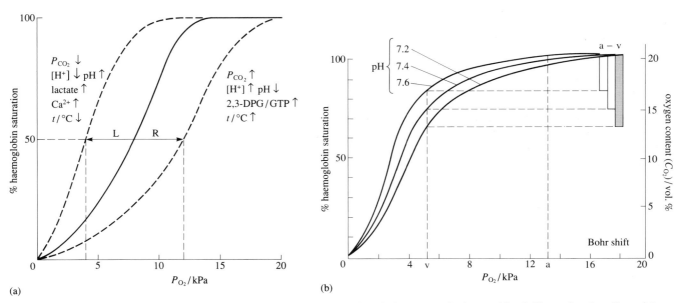

Figure 7.2   (a) A generalized oxygen dissociation curve. (b) Oxygen dissociation curves for human blood, illustrating the effect of the Bohr shift.

typically causes a left-ward Bohr shift (L), reducing P_{50} (from 8 to 4 kPa). Specific modulators of oxygen affinity are the organic phosphates 2,3-diphosphoglycerate (2,3-DPG) and guanosine triphosphate (GTP) found in vertebrate red blood cells which, like protons, reduce the oxygen affinity of haemoglobin, and calcium and lactate ions which increase the affinity of crustacean haemocyanins to oxygen, again giving a left-ward Bohr shift. Temperature can also affect oxygen affinity, which typically is reduced by increased temperature, due partly to direct disruption of oxygen binding and partly to a consequent reduction in pH.

The significance of the Bohr shift for oxygen transport in human blood is shown in Figure 7.2b, at the normal arterial (a) and venous (v) P_{O_2} values. The arterial–venous oxygen difference ($C_{aO_2} - C_{vO_2}$) is about 3 vol. % at pH 7.6 but is about 7 vol. % if a Bohr shift to pH 7.2 is taken into account. The *in vivo* arterial–venous pH shift is less (from about 7.4 to 7.3).

7.3 Systemic hypoxia in diving vertebrates

Many air-breathing vertebrates exploit the aquatic environment, particularly as a rich source of food. The lungs remain the primary site of gas exchange, though amphibians and some reptiles may exchange a significant proportion of carbon dioxide and some oxygen over the skin when in water. As returning (in evolutionary terms) to an aquatic existence has not involved any major redevelopment of aquatic gas-exchange organs and as submergence enforces breath-holding (apnoea), there is a subsequent limitation of oxygen supply, resulting in internal or systemic hypoxia.

7.3.1 Diving behaviour

The depth and duration of dives varies between species. In amphibians and reptiles, mean dive duration is related to the temperature and P_{O_2} level in the water (Figure 7.3). Many dives are fairly long and there is the possibility of exchange of gases, particularly carbon dioxide, over the skin.

■ What other factors might allow amphibians or reptiles to dive for long periods?

Ectothermic amphibians and reptiles often have relatively low metabolic rates, which are less at low temperatures. A low metabolic rate reduces their requirements for oxygen. In winter, amphibians and reptiles may stay submerged for many weeks. For example, the common frog in Britain (*Rana temporaria*) can overwinter at the bottom of a pond while the freshwater turtle (*Chrysemys picta bellii*) in the USA can survive submergence for up to 6 months in a virtually anoxic state at 3 °C. Both animals can survive beneath the ice in winter without surfacing and without freezing because water is at its most dense at 4 °C and thus presents a safe haven at the bottom of the pool.

As homeothermic birds and mammals maintain a high metabolic rate, and gas exchange over the skin is negligible, the smaller mammals and birds characteristically dive for short periods, typically less than 30 seconds. However,

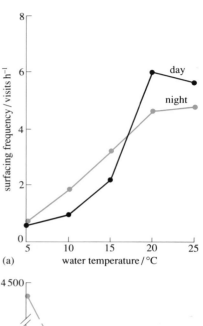

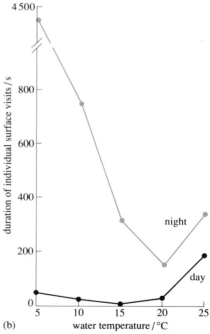

Figure 7.3 Surfacing behaviour of the African clawed toad (*Xenopus laevis*) at water temperatures between 5 and 25 °C. At 5 °C, they surfaced to breathe less than once per hour. This rose to a breath every 10 minutes at 20 °C. Although surfacing frequencies were the same in toads held in the dark, the mean duration of periods at the surface was over 1 hour at 5 °C, which resulted in them spending up to 50% of their time at the surface compared with less than 5% when they were held in the light. Thus diving may also serve to avoid predators such as birds which hunt by day.

the larger marine mammals can dive for much longer periods because they have relatively large oxygen stores in the blood and muscle. Weddell seals (*Leptonychotes weddelli*) are able to dive to a depth of 600 m and for as long as 70 minutes, after which they may sleep for several hours before diving again. Sperm whales (*Physeter catodon*) can dive for one hour or more; individuals have been caught in cables at a depth of 1 000 m and some are thought to dive to 3 000 m or more. Bottom-dwelling sharks, which usually live at these depths, have been found in their stomachs.

7.3.2 The classic diving response

Diving animals can be characterized by a number of biochemical, physiological and behavioural adaptations which increase their ability to survive and function effectively under water. At the biochemical level, the capacity to metabolize anaerobically is enhanced, as the enzymes that are involved in substrate level phosphorylation are present in high concentrations that favour the anaerobic production of ATP. In addition, the skeletal muscles in diving mammals often contain very high concentrations of myoglobin, and circulating haemoglobin levels are also high, so there is a large capacity for storing oxygen which may be used during dives.

One well documented response to head immersion (you can try it yourself) is a marked reduction in heart rate or **reflex bradycardia**. In 1870, the pioneer physiologist Paul Bert first observed reflex bradycardia during experimental dives, when he placed a duck's head under water and felt a reduction in its pulse rate. This reduction in heart rate is not accompanied by any marked change in cardiac stroke volume, so that cardiac output may fall to very low levels during a dive. This observation typifies the classic diving response, which has been described by many authors but is properly attributed to Peter Scholander and his co-workers, whose work on seals published in 1940 first clearly defined the response and suggested its possible physiological significance. Some of Scholander's original data are shown in Figure 7.4.

The marked bradycardia observed during experimental submersion of mammals or birds is accompanied by peripheral vasoconstriction of the vascular beds in the major skeletal muscles and the viscera (abdominal organs), including the gut, liver and the kidneys: the kidneys do not function during a dive. This vasoconstriction results in the maintenance of systemic arterial blood pressure

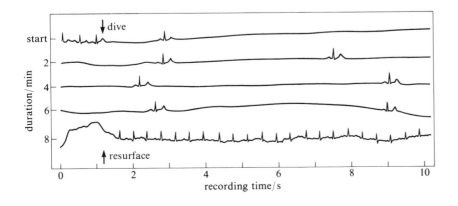

Figure 7.4 An electrocardiogram (ECG) during a forced dive in a seal (*Halichoerus grypus*) that was submerged during the period shown by the small arrows. The trace is discontinuous, showing representative 10-s recording periods during a total 'dive' of about 7 minutes, during which the seal maintained a marked bradycardia that was released immediately upon resurfacing.

close to pre-dive levels, despite the decreased cardiac output, and this ensures adequate perfusion of the brain, heart and lungs to which the blood is preferentially shunted.

■   If a drug that abolished peripheral vasoconstriction was injected into a mammal during a dive, what would you expect to happen to the oxygen partial pressure of the arterial blood?

Abolition of the peripheral vasoconstriction or of the bradycardia, by injection of appropriate drugs, causes a rapid decline in arterial oxygen partial pressure and an even more rapid increase in cerebral NADH levels. Aerobic metabolism in the brain, which normally converts NADH to NAD^+, is prevented. These experiments suggest that the primary role of the classic diving response is to conserve oxygen and supply it preferentially to the brain and heart, which both metabolize aerobically. It is interesting that pregnant seals also maintain blood flow to the placenta during a dive. During these typical experimental dives the muscles metabolize anaerobically, and on surfacing large quantities of lactic acid are flushed out into the circulatory system to be re-oxidized in tissues such as the liver. The resultant increase in oxygen uptake after a dive is referred to as **recovery oxygen**. How are these interrelated physiological changes that make up the classic diving response regulated?

Control of the classic diving response, which occurs in amphibians, reptiles, birds and mammals, is complex, involving the interaction of a number of reflexes.

· Diving bradycardia is due predominantly to inhibitory input via the parasympathetic vagus nerve, and may be abolished by the injection of atropine, which blocks the cholinergic synapses involved.

· Peripheral blood flow is controlled by arterial smooth muscle cells whose activity may be modulated by local concentration of metabolites (**autoregulation**), or by nervous input from the autonomic nervous system. Stimulation of α-adrenergic receptors (part of the sympathetic innervation of the blood vessels) causes vasoconstriction.

The onset of the diving apnoea in mammals and birds is initiated by water receptors in the nose and glottis, respectively.

· The reduction in heart rate and the accompanying cardiovascular adjustments seem dependent upon cessation of ventilatory movements, which abolishes afferent input from pulmonary receptors.

· In addition, activity in central respiratory neurons may decrease or cease altogether, which may in some way enhance the cardiovascular adjustments.

· Restriction of gas exchange causes oxygen levels in the blood to fall and carbon dioxide levels in the blood to rise.

· These changes stimulate central and peripheral chemoreceptors whose output, unable now to influence breathing, may retard circulation, and may cause changes in mean arterial or venous pressure, stimulating cardiovascular mechano-receptors, which affect cardiovascular performance (e.g. the baroreceptor reflexes).

These various inputs may occur sequentially or almost simultaneously and interact to produce the characteristic cardiovascular response to diving.

The classic diving response has been described in a large and diverse collection of air-breathing animals, including species that do not normally dive. In humans, immersion of the face in cold water increases activity in the vagal nerve to the heart, causing a diving bradycardia. Laboratory studies of 'diving' have used dogs, sheep and rabbits as experimental subjects. In all mammals during birth, immediately after the placenta ceases to function in providing oxygen and removing carbon dioxide, there is a short period before the first breath when asphyxia may occur. In humans, during the second stage of labour, as the fetus is delivered along the birth canal, it characteristically ceases fetal breathing and shows a pronounced bradycardia. Under these circumstances the onset of a 'diving response' may have a functional role in averting brain damage (i.e. the baby dives into air). Once in air, the baby's first breath is stimulated by its hypoxic and acidotic state, which results in a profound respiratory drive, mediated by the chemoreceptors.

In many naturally diving animals. the sensory inputs initiating the classic diving response can be overruled, as for example during feeding under water, showing that higher centres in the central nervous system (CNS) must play a role in the conscious adjustments to diving that typify natural dives.

7.3.3   Natural dives

A study of the comparative physiology of the diving response should properly consider species that naturally dive and should aim to study their diving behaviour under 'natural' conditions. Recent studies on diving birds, using telemetry from implanted radiotransmitters, have sought to fulfill these criteria. Pat Butler and his co-workers in Birmingham have studied the spontaneous diving behaviour of ducks and penguins, and have related this to physiological variables measured by radiotelemetry. The natural feeding dives differ from those described in the laboratory in several important ways. Laboratory dives were accomplished by submerging the head of a restrained and inactive duck in a small volume of water, often for several minutes, which is longer than most feeding dives. The animal appeared untroubled by this procedure but was unable to anticipate the 'dive'. Under these circumstances, the duck experienced a progressive reduction in heart rate down to very low levels accompanied by increased blood pressure and peripheral resistance, followed by a brief increase in heart rate (tachycardia) during recovery. Cardiovascular responses during involuntary submergence are shown in Figure 7.5.

For comparison, Figure 7.6 (*overleaf*) shows the events of a natural, spontaneous dive in the tufted duck (*Aythya fuligula*). Figure 7.6a shows the behaviour of the duck at points corresponding to the time periods shown in Figure 7.6b; the periods of submersion (C, D, E) are shown as a grey tone. Figure 7.6e gives the frequency of the heart beat, with the individual beats given on the ECG in Figure 7.6c. When diving freely the duck anticipates each feeding dive with a marked increase in heart rate (Figure 7.6e). Upon diving, the duck swims vigorously to the bottom, having to work against its considerable positive bouyancy due to the air contained internally in its lungs and airsacs, and externally in its plumage (period C). Heart rate during the dive falls initially and then rises to a rate similar to that recorded when the birds are casually swimming on the surface (Figure 7.6e).

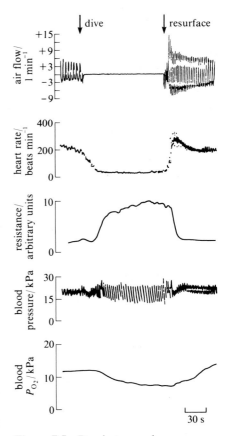

Figure 7.5 Respiratory and cardiovascular responses to involuntary submergence of a domestic duck (*Anas platyrhynchos*). Resistance refers to the peripheral resistance to blood flow, measured in an artery of one leg, and the units are arbitrary.

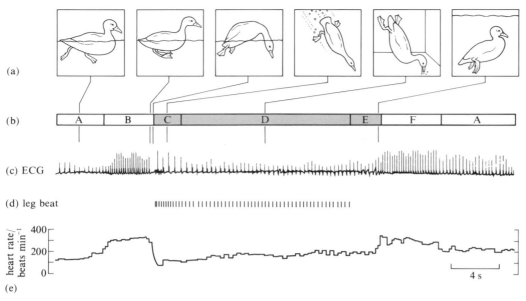

(a)

(b)

(c) ECG

(d) leg beat

(e)

Figure 7.6 Changes in heart rate (e) of a tufted duck (*Aythya fuligula*) during a spontaneous natural dive recorded telemetrically. In (a) the behaviour of the duck is traced from cine film and shows from left to right: swimming, preparing to dive, moment of submersion, swimming to bottom of tank, feeding on bottom, surfacing. (b) shows the time periods for A, swimming on surface; B, cardiac acceleration before submersion; C, descent; D, feeding on bottom; E, surfacing; F, cardiac acceleration following surfacing. The lines between the drawings of the duck and the time boxes join coincident points in time.

The differences between the respiratory and cardiovascular responses to involuntary and spontaneous dives in ducks are shown clearly in Figure 7.7, which reveals that the anticipatory increase in heart rate prior to the dive is associated with several rapid breaths, possibly serving to raise oxygen levels and reduce carbon dioxide in the airways. Heart rate during the natural dive is about five times greater than that measured after a similar period of involuntary submersion in the laboratory.

Calculations based on knowledge of the oxygen stores present in the respiratory system and bloodstream indicate that ducks metabolize aerobically throughout the short duration of typical feeding dives. They may dive repeatedly for extended periods without exhaustion and without having to invoke the intense oxygen conserving mechanisms that constitute the classic diving response. If, at the end of a feeding dive, their access to the surface is temporarily denied, they immediately switch to a pattern of response reminiscent of an involuntary dive with heart rate decreasing to very low levels. This response may be important if the birds become trapped under ice in the winter.

Figure 7.7 Changes in heart rate and respiratory frequency of a pochard (*Aythya ferina*) during (a) involuntary submersion in the laboratory, and (b) natural submersion while swimming gently on an outside pond. Each trace shows the ECG and changes in air temperature in the trachea, which indicate inspiration by an upward deflection.

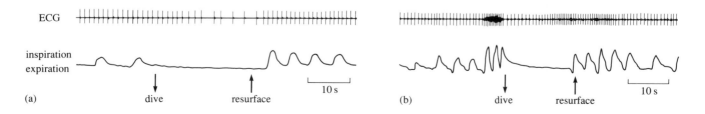

ECG

inspiration
expiration

(a)   dive   resurface   10 s

(b)   dive   resurface   10 s

These recent studies on freely diving birds have substantially altered our views on the cardiovascular and metabolic adjustments that occur during normal diving. In ducks, natural dives appear to be supported by aerobic metabolism with blood flow increasing to the exercising muscles. The same may be true of Weddell seals; in a recent study carried out in the Antarctic, it was found that nearly all voluntary dives were shorter than 20 minutes, with no increase in the level of blood lactate during recovery at the surface. Cardiovascular adjustments and the switch to anaerobic metabolism are evident only in forced dives of 10–15 minutes, or during the comparatively rare, prolonged, natural dives (more than 20 minutes), when the lactate level in the blood at the end of the dive can increase more than tenfold. It seems likely, therefore, that the most accomplished diving mammals (e.g. Weddell seal, sperm whale) rely on anaerobic mechanisms and widespread peripheral vasoconstriction, but only during prolonged dives. The relatively large stores of oxygen in the blood are used sparingly by many temporarily inactive organs (non-exercising muscles, kidneys and gut), which can delay the switch to anaerobic metabolism, necessary because prolonged anaerobic dives produced intense fatigue and a period of enforced inactivity at the surface as recovery oxygen is consumed. After a 45-minute natural dive, when anaerobic mechanisms are dominant, a Weddell seal needs about 70 minutes recovery before blood lactate and pH return to pre-dive levels. Thus, from a total of 115 minutes, only about 40% of the time is spent diving. If the seal were to dive in a succession of six 15-minute dives, similar to the natural pattern of feeding, recovery periods of only 4 minutes would be required between dives, and almost 80% of the time could therefore be spent underwater. Most dives in birds and mammals are for food, and a succession of brief, aerobic dives may indeed be the usual pattern. Most probably, the anaerobic potential is held in reserve for emergencies, such as escaping from predators (killer whales in the case of the Weddell seal), when trapped under ice, or for deep diving in search of food. Only under these circumstances do their responses resemble the classic diving response.

Summary of Section 7.3

During involuntary dives under experimental conditions, both birds and mammals display a profound bradycardia on submersion, together with widespread peripheral vasoconstriction, which results in the maintenance of systemic blood pressure. Oxidative metabolism in the brain, and perhaps the heart, is maintained but elsewhere there is anaerobic production of lactate. The bradycardia is maintained by increased parasympathetic activity, and the peripheral vasoconstriction is supported by increased sympathetic activity and changes in the levels of circulating catecholamines. Stimulation by water and cold receptors inhibit breathing.

By contrast, most freely diving birds and mammals usually undertake relatively short, aerobic excursions, with little cardiovascular adjustment. The exercising muscles, as well as the heart and brain, are supplied with sufficient oxygen to maintain aerobic metabolism. Higher voluntary centres in the CNS can stop breathing and influence changes in heart rate. The majority of voluntary dives terminate before the oxygen stores are exhausted, and another dive can commence after a brief replenishment of the stores. Anaerobic metabolism, together with profound cardiovascular adjustments, is probably used extensively only during prolonged dives, for adventurous hunting, escape from predators, or during long bouts of underwater exploration.

7.4 Respiratory gas exchange in aquatic animals

Water differs from air as a respiratory medium in several important respects: these differences are listed in Table 7.1. You are not expected to remember the precise values but you should appreciate the physiological significance of the values in the far right column. The oxygen content of water is determined by the partial pressure of the gas mixture with which it is equilibrated (usually this is air) and the absorption coefficient for oxygen (β_{wO_2}), which varies inversely with temperature and salinity. In general terms, the oxygen content of aerated water is approximately 30 times lower than air, and warm, salty water is a particularly difficult environment in which to maintain aerobic metabolism as its limited capacity for oxygen may soon be depleted.

Because of water's low oxygen content per unit volume, water-breathing animals have to move large volumes over the respiratory organs in order to obtain sufficient oxygen, and as water is both relatively viscous and dense, the metabolic or respiratory cost of ventilation is high. Water is, however, an excellent sink for the excretion of carbon dioxide because of its high absorption coefficient: carbon dioxide combines with water to yield protons and bicarbonate ions:

$$CO_2 + H_2O \rightleftharpoons H^+ + HCO_3^- \qquad (9)$$

The absorption coefficient is 30 times higher for carbon dioxide than for oxygen. Thus carbon dioxide never accumulates to high levels in submerged gill-breathers because they ventilate at relatively high rates that are determined by the reduced oxygen availability, and levels of carbon dioxide are driven down to very low partial pressures. These differences are best illustrated by a CO_2/O_2 exchange diagram (Figure 7.8). This diagram illustrates the relationship between oxygen and carbon dioxide levels at the respiratory gas exchange organs (e.g. alveolar gas volume in the lung) or in the arterialized blood of a typical lung-breather (e.g. human) and a typical gill-breather (e.g. fish). Oxygen uptake fuels aerobic metabolism and results in the excretion of carbon dioxide in approximately equal volumes to oxygen consumed. The **respiratory exchange ratio (RER)** will be unity if metabolism was completely carbohydrate based. The lipid and protein components reduce it to about 0.8. If we assume unity for simplicity then as an air-breather consumes oxygen it reduces oxygen partial pressure in the lung (P_{AO_2}) from the inspired level (approximately 21 kPa) to about 14 kPa. Then P_{CO_2} will rise from zero to about 7 kPa along a line for RER = 1. Removing or adding volumes of gas in the gaseous phase causes a directly related change in partial pressure (Daltons Law). However, when the gases are in solution, consuming oxygen and excreting carbon dioxide at equal volumes has unequal effects on their partial pressures which vary in reciprocal proportion to their absorption (solubility) coefficients in water (30:1 for $CO_2:O_2$). Thus a reduction in oxygen partial pressure from 21 kPa to 14 kPa is accompanied by an increase in P_{CO_2} of only about 0.2 kPa and consequently carbon dioxide never increases above about 0.4 kPa in the blood of fish even when they hypoventilate.

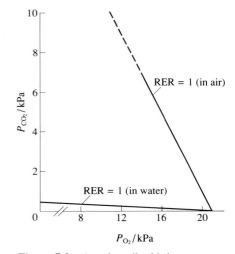

Figure 7.8   A carbon dioxide/oxygen diagram describing the changes in partial pressure of the respiratory gases at the exchange surfaces of an air-breather and a water-breather when equal volumes of oxygen are consumed and carbon dioxide excreted (i.e. RER = 1). As water-breathers in normoxic water ventilate their gills at rates determined by oxygen availability, which is relatively low and variable, then they effectively hyperventilate with respect to carbon dioxide which as a consequence is driven down to 0.2 kPa at a blood P_{O_2} of about 14 kPa.

7.4.1 Hypoxic aquatic environments

Rock pools on the sea-shore that contain algae and a substantial fauna may become supersaturated with oxygen (hyperoxic) in bright sunlight due to oxygen production by photosynthesis, and may be markedly hypoxic at night due to plant and animal respiration (Figure 7.9). Excretion of carbon dioxide at night can cause pH to fall, whereas carbon dioxide absorption for photosynthesis in bright sunlight causes pH to rise. Temperature is also very variable and salinity may vary due to evaporation, rainfall or freshwater run-off down the shore.

Oxygen levels often fall when replenishment of oxygen is restricted, e.g. beneath the thermocline or in the abyssal regions of deep lakes or sea trenches. Even running water may become virtually anoxic when it receives a grossly polluting organic load such as sewage. The action of micro-organisms in oxidizing this organic matter may totally deplete the water of dissolved oxygen, causing progressive changes in fauna and flora in the river, an environment which we examine in Section 7.4.5. Animals inhabiting water-filled burrows in hypoxic or anoxic substrata or on the sea-shore where they are regularly exposed by the tide often experience locally hypoxic conditions.

7.4.2 Behavioural responses to aquatic hypoxia

Many aquatic animals are active and free to move within their environment. When they detect a body of hypoxic water they may show an avoidance reaction (i.e. move into water with a higher P_{O_2}), indicating that they have oxygen receptors. Some species, particularly freshwater fishes, have been shown to identify gradients of partial pressure of oxygen and move along them, usually preferring well-aerated water. Some recent observations by John Steffenson in Copenhagen have revealed that fish may select water of lower temperature when it is hypoxic, possibly in order to reduce their metabolic rate and consequent demands for oxygen. Tube-dwelling animals, such as some marine worms and freshwater insect larvae, show patterns of alternate feeding/resting behaviour and active irrigation of the tube, with the proportion of total time devoted to irrigation rising during hypoxia. Other primarily aquatic species, when confronted by environmental hypoxia, exploit the high oxygen availability in air by either gulping air to aerate the water surrounding their gills, ventilating accessory air-breathing organs, or moving temporarily from water into air. These behavioural patterns are referred to either as bimodal respiration or facultative air breathing.

7.4.3 Physiological responses of fish to hypoxia

The transfer of oxygen from the environment to the tissues of water-breathing animals is via an oxygen cascade (Figure 7.10, *overleaf*) similar to that described in Section 7.2 for air-breathers. Relatively large and active species generally possess discrete respiratory organs, usually described as gills, perfused with body fluids and held in chambers that are actively ventilated with water. The majority of physiological studies have concentrated on respiratory gas exchange over the gills of fish.

■ What are the three major factors that influence oxygen uptake over fish gills?

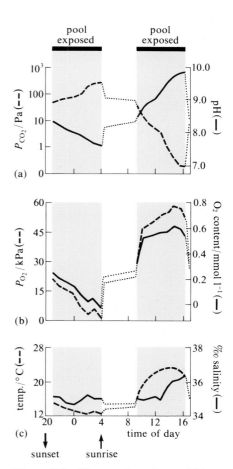

Figure 7.9 Changes throughout a 22-hour period in a rock pool during the summer. The axes to the left show partial pressures of (a) carbon dioxide and (b) oxygen, and (c) shows pool temperature. To the right the axes represent (a) pH, (b) oxygen content, and (c) salinity expressed as parts per 1 000 (‰). The pool was periodically exposed by ebb tide and covered by full tide, causing substantial changes in the physico-chemical conditions. The dotted lines in each case, therefore, show values typical of the advancing tidal sea-water.

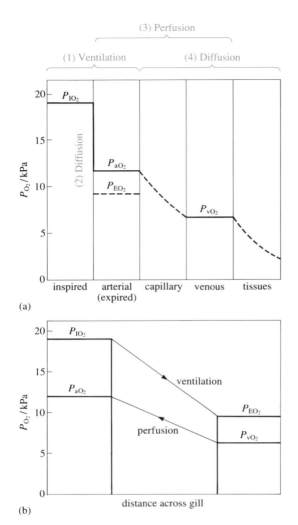

(a)

(b)

Figure 7.10 (a) Mean P_{O_2} gradients from normoxic water to tissues in a typical fish. P_{aO_2} is greatly reduced relative to P_{IO_2} because the gills present a considerable barrier to diffusion. However, P_{aO_2} is often higher than P_{EO_2} due to the counter current of blood and water at the gill lamellae. The oxygen cascade consists of both convective and diffusional oxygen transfer as described for air-breathers in Figure 7.1. (b) Diagram of counter-current showing how P_{aO_2} may exceed P_{EO_2}, as shown in (a).

The factors governing respiratory gas exchange over fish gills are: ventilation rate, blood perfusion rate, and diffusive conductance. Because of the relatively low oxygen capacity of water, ventilation rates are high, relative to oxygen consumption, in fish. In contrast, fish blood by virtue of its haemoglobin content has a relatively high oxygen capacity. The rates of flow of water ($\dot{V}_w$) and blood ($\dot{V}_b$) are matched according to their relative oxygen capacities. In fish, the $\dot{V}_w:\dot{V}_b$ ratio ranges from 10 to 20. This is in contrast to a value of 1 for the equivalent ratio ($\dot{V}_A:\dot{V}_b$) in air-breathers, where the oxygen capacities of air and blood are similar. It is significant that the antarctic icefish (*Chaenocephalus aceratus*) has a $\dot{V}_w:\dot{V}_b$ of less than 3 (see Section 5.5.1).

■ What might explain the low value for $\dot{V}_w:\dot{V}_b$ in icefish?

The blood of icefish contains no pigment, so its oxygen-carrying capacity is similar to that of seawater. It is not identical to seawater, however, because the blood has a lower osmolarity than seawater, so its oxygen content is a little higher (hence the $\dot{V}_w : \dot{V}_b$ ratio of 3). This is high enough to satisfy the oxygen requirements of the fish because at low temperatures the blood plasma has a higher absorption coefficient for oxygen.

Water flowing over the surfaces of the secondary lamellae on fish gills exchanges oxygen and carbon dioxide with blood flowing through each lamella in the opposite direction. Thus, a functional **counter-current** operates over the gills, enabling arterialized blood to leave the gills in equilibrium with inspired water, so that P_{aO_2} may exceed P_{EO_2} and up to 80% of the available oxygen may be extracted from the water, giving a potentially high level for oxygen extraction (Figure 7.10b). The effectiveness of oxygen transfer over the gills of fish may be further enhanced by synchrony between heart beat and ventilation which ensures that the periods of maximum blood and water flow in each beat are concurrent. Long periods of synchrony have been observed in resting normoxic dogfish. Synchrony was abolished by injection of the drug atropine, suggesting that synchrony is controlled from the CNS via the vagus nerve. In trout, synchrony only becomes apparent during hypoxia, indicating that it is an important factor promoting oxygen uptake.

The matching of flows across the counter-current over the gill lamellae ensures that blood, at least in normoxic environments, leaves the gills saturated with oxygen without unnecessary work being done in either hyperventilating or over-perfusing the gills. The relative ability of the gills to transfer oxygen from the environment to the blood is measured as their diffusion capacity or Transfer Factor (T_{O_2}), which was defined in Section 7.2. The level of T_{O_2} varies with effective gill area and diffusion distance, which may be more complex than simple morphological characteristics imply. First. the number of lamellae perfused with blood, and therefore the functional exchange area, may vary and there is some evidence that a variable proportion of total blood flow to the gill arches may travel via blood-shunts that do not contact the exchange surfaces. Second, because the rate of gas diffusion through water is relatively slow it represents a major barrier to effective exchange. Water flow between the gill lamellae is relatively non-turbulent so that maximum flows are present at the middle of each water channel and flow decreases towards the lamellar surface. Consequently, water in contact with the gill surface may become depleted of oxygen and so increase the effective diffusion distance from the oxygen-containing water to the blood. Third, patterns of blood and water flow may affect the functional diffusive conductance of the gills and a rate-limiting step may be the oxygenation reaction of the haemoglobin in the large, nucleated corpuscles.

Fish pump water over their gills at rates controlled with respect to oxygen supply or demand. When exposed to hypoxic water, fish may maintain oxygen uptake at normoxic levels until a critical P_{O_2} (characterized as P_c), by showing a characteristic hypoxic response that includes increased rates of ventilation and a reflex bradycardia. In teleost fish, ventilation increases when oxygen supply is reduced by environmental hypoxia, or when transport in the blood is reduced, either directly by anaemia or indirectly by hypercapnia (the resultant acidosis may cause an exaggerated Bohr shift known as the Root effect on their haemoglobin, reducing oxygen carrying capacity). Similarly, an increase in oxygen demand during vigorous swimming or following the stress of experimental manipulation results in an increase in ventilation rate.

The onset and degree of cardiac slowing during progressive hypoxia varies with temperature (Figure 7.11). The effect of temperature may be to alter the P_{O_2} threshold for the stimulation of peripherally placed oxygen receptors. These receptors have been identified on the first gill arch of teleost fish but are more generally distributed in the branchial (gill) chambers of elasmobranch fishes and decapodan crustaceans.

Mark Burleson, working in North America, has recorded afferent (sensory) nervous activity from oxygen receptors on isolated gill arches of trout. The low levels of activity recorded from the preparation in normoxia increased progressively as P_{O_2} levels were reduced, reaching a maximum at a P_{O_2} of about 4 kPa. Below this level activity was sharply reduced. Other receptors, apparently sited in the arterial blood system draining the gills, respond to reduced blood oxygen content and flow (i.e. oxygen delivery) and induce a hypoxic ventilatory response. Some evidence has emerged for the existence of P_{O_2} receptors in the venous system of elasmobranch fish that may cause a reflex tachycardia when the oxygen level of the venous blood is reduced, thereby increasing its rate of delivery to the gills from the tissues for re-oxygenation. The possession of a series of oxygen receptors in the arterial and in the venous blood, monitoring P_{O_2} at the gills, may enable relative flow rates of blood and water over the counter-current exchanger on the secondary lamellae of the gills to be controlled with reference to the P_{O_2} gradient at the exchange surfaces, in order to maximize the effectiveness of gas exchange. Both the ventilatory and cardiac responses to sudden exposure to hypoxia or exercise are rapid in onset, indicating that nervous pathways are involved.

■ What is the functional significance of changes in ventilation and heart rate on respiratory gas exchange, during exposure to hypoxia?

At first sight, the significance of an increase in ventilation accompanied by a reflex bradycardia in response to hypoxia may seem obvious: an increase in $\dot{V}_w$ will present more dissolved oxygen per unit time to the exchange surfaces, whereas a decrease in $\dot{V}_b$ will give the blood a greater diffusion time in the gills in order to reach the maximum level of oxygen saturation of the haemoglobin. Together they effect an increase in the $\dot{V}_w : \dot{V}_b$ ratio. The story is a little more complex than this, however, because as well as improving the rate of oxygen delivery, hyperventilation may stir stationary layers between the gill lamellae, providing turbulent rather than laminar flow, which could reduce the barrier to diffusion presented by interlamellar water. In addition, hyperventilation (by definition) causes a small reduction in P_{aCO_2} and a consequent respiratory alkalosis which may increase the oxygen affinity of haemoglobin (refer to Figure 7.2).

However, the hypoxic bradycardia is often accompanied by an increase in cardiac stroke volume (Figure 7.12), which may compensate, at least partially, for the bradycardia so that total cardiac output is not much changed during moderate hypoxia. This raises doubts over the significance of the hypoxic bradycardia, though it may serve to reduce power output of the heart and therefore lower the heart's requirement for oxygen.

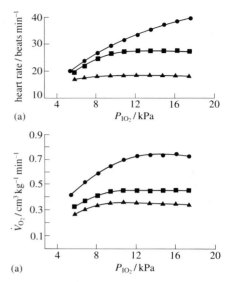

Figure 7.11   Mean changes in (a) heart rate, and (b) oxygen uptake in dogfish (*Scyliorhinus canicula*) during progressive hypoxia at 7 °C (▲), 12 °C (■), and 17 °C (●). Both are little affected by hypoxia in fish acclimated to 7 °C but are markedly reduced at 17 °C.

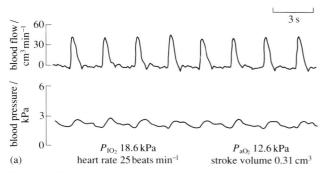
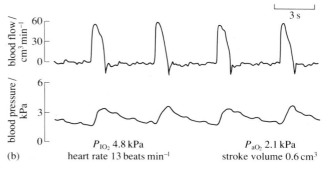

(a)	P_{IO_2} 18.6 kPa heart rate 25 beats min⁻¹ P_{aO_2} 12.6 kPa stroke volume 0.31 cm³
(b)	P_{IO_2} 4.8 kPa heart rate 13 beats min⁻¹ P_{aO_2} 2.1 kPa stroke volume 0.6 cm³

Figure 7.12   A dogfish was exposed to (a) normoxia, and (b) hypoxia at 12 °C. In each case, the traces show blood flow to the first two pairs of branchial blood vessels, and the ventral aortic blood pressure. Values for the partial pressure of oxygen in the inspired water (P_{IO_2}) and in the arterial blood (P_{aO_2}) are given, together with stroke volume and heart rate. During hypoxia, a reduction in heart rate to 50% of the normoxic rate was accompanied by a doubling in cardiac stroke volume.

Injection of atropine into hypoxic dogfish, by removing the influence of the vagus nerve on the heart, abolished the bradycardia and caused a reduction in diffusive conductance and effectiveness of oxygen transfer to the blood, demonstrating the role of the bradycardia in increasing the effectiveness of respiratory gas exchange, despite an unchanging cardiac output. The bradycardia, because it is associated with increased stroke volume and systolic pressure (Figure 7.12), may result in improved perfusion of the gill lamellae, resulting in an increase in T_{O_2}.

During long-term exposure to hypoxia some fish show an increased oxygen affinity of the haemoglobin due to a reduction in concentration of organic phosphates in the red blood cells (Figure 7.13). (In the nucleated red blood cells of fish, the principal effector is GTP, which is generated by their high rates of aerobic metabolism, rather than 2,3-DPG which is produced anaerobically in mammalian red blood cells.) This causes a left-ward shift of the haemoglobin oxygen equilibrium curve.

■   What would be the effect of such a left-ward movement of the haemoglobin oxygen curve?

The effect of the shift in the curve is to increase oxygen affinity during hypoxia (refer to Figure 7.2). This response is due to a reduction of a direct allosteric affect of GTP on the binding of oxygen to haemoglobin plus an increase in intracellular pH due to the influence of GTP on the distribution of H⁺ across the red blood cell membrane, as shown in the red blood cells of eels (Figure 7.13).

7.4.4   Catecholamines and oxygen delivery in fish

The concentrations of catecholamines (adrenalin and noradrenalin) in the blood of fish are elevated during periods when oxygen delivery to the tissues may be compromised, for example during hypoxia, anaemia or following severe exercise. Elevation of circulating catecholamines mimics some of the controlling effects of the sympathetic nervous system and influences the passage of oxygen down the oxygen cascade at all levels in fish. We shall consider these influences in turn.

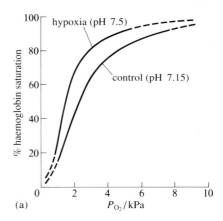

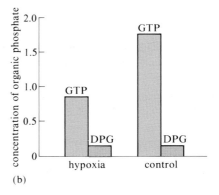

Figure 7.13   (a) The oxygen dissociation curves of whole blood from control (normoxic) and hypoxic eels (the pH inside the red blood cells is given for each curve). (b) The concentration of the two organic phosphates GTP and DPG in red blood cells from the blood of hypoxic and control eels, expressed as a proportion of their haemoglobin content.

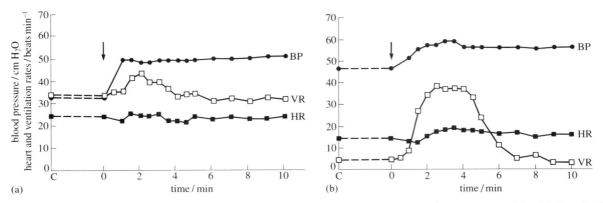

(a)

time / min

(b)

time / min

Figure 7.14 Changes in blood pressure (BP), heart rate (HR) and ventilation rate (VR) in two groups of dogfish ($n = 9$), (a) from dogfish with a high ventilation rate when resting, and (b) with a low ventilation rate when resting, following intra-arterial injection (indicated by the arrow) of 10^{-5} M adrenalin. Adrenalin injection caused an increase in blood pressure in all fish, but ventilation rate increased markedly only in fish having low initial ventilation rates (C, the mean control values prior to adrenalin injection).

Injection of catecholamines into the blood of fish can result in an increase in gill ventilation (Figure 7.14), but the degree of response depends on the initial ventilation rate.

Studies on trout have shown that the gill oxygen chemoreceptors increase discharge in response to falling oxygen levels but are insensitive to changes in circulating catecholamines. Thus, progressive increases in ventilation during hypoxia are largely the result of stimulation of peripheral chemoreceptors, and during mild hypoxia are *independent* of catecholamines. This work suggests that catecholamines do not exert an effect on gill ventilation in fish by stimulation of peripheral chemoreceptors. Interestingly, below a P_{O_2} of about 4 kPa, trout chemoreceptors show a marked inhibition of activity (see Section 7.4.3) and it is at about this P_{aO_2} that their haemoglobin no longer saturates with oxygen during its passage through the gills and catecholamines are released into the blood (Figure 7.15). So, in trout, increased ventilation in extreme hypoxia, with an associated hypoxaemia, is maintained by increased circulating catecholamines levels, via a pathway other than the gill chemoreceptive reflex.

In fish, the blood–brain barrier allows the passage of catecholamines, especially noradrenalin, and the action of catecholamines could be due to a direct stimulation of the central respiratory pattern generator or respiratory motor neurons in the medulla. Noradrenalin has a more potent effect than adrenalin on ventilation in trout and crosses the blood–brain barrier more easily, providing circumstantial evidence for a central action of noradrenalin in stimulating ventilation in trout.

Our work on dogfish has monitored the central respiratory drive in the form of bursts of action potentials recorded from the central cut ends of branchial branches of the vagus nerve, which innervate respiratory muscles in the gill arches. In the dogfish, infusion of catecholamines into the medulla in the brain stimulated activity in branchial branches of the vagus nerve, innervating the gill arches. The onset of stimulation occurred 40–120 seconds after injection (Figure 7.16), a lag which was consistent with the time taken for the adrenalin to reach cell bodies of the vagal respiratory neurons, which lie in the dorsal motor nucleus.

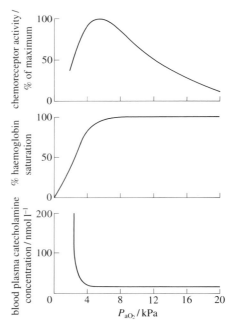

Figure 7.15 The effect of progressive hypoxia on trout. Activity recorded from oxygen receptors on the gills increased with hypoxia down to a P_{O_2} of about 4 kPa, when activity fell. Below this P_{O_2}, haemoglobin was no longer saturated as red blood cells passed through the gills, and hypoxaemia stimulated the release of catecholamines.

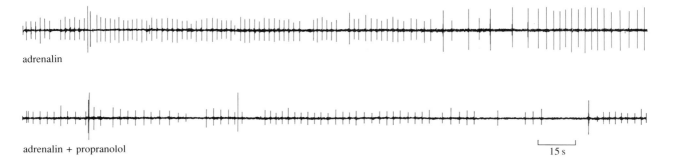

adrenalin

adrenalin + propranolol

15 s

In adult mammals, the development of a tight blood–brain barrier prevents the central action of elevated circulating catecholamines, but a peripheral action may have evolved, retaining a role for catecholamines in matching ventilation to metabolic requirements. Carotid body chemoreceptors in mammals are sensitive to changing levels of circulating catecholamines. These differences in ventilatory control between water- and air-breathing animals are, to some degree, reflected in mammalian development. Fetal mammals, like fish, have a more leaky blood–brain barrier and a reduced central carbon dioxide drive compared with adult mammals, and it is possible that central stimulation of breathing via changing catecholamine levels is important here. The transition from water to air-breathing at birth may involve a change in control systems, from aquatic breathing regulated via peripheral oxygen chemoreceptors and central effects of catecholamines, to air-breathing dominated by central CO_2/H^+ responses plus peripheral chemoreceptor reflexes, modulated by circulating catecholamines.

In fish, catecholamines affect oxygen transfer at all other steps of the oxygen cascade.

- The permeability of the respiratory epithelium is increased.

- Transport of oxygen by the fish cardiovascular system is improved by catecholamines because stimulation of β-adrenergic receptors on the heart increases cardiac contractility (causing an increase in stroke volume) and may accelerate heart rate, resulting in an overall increase in cardiac output or blood flow which will improve oxygen delivery.

- Stimulation of α-adrenergic receptors in the peripheral circulation can cause vasoconstriction, resulting in increased peripheral resistance and a rise in blood pressure, with blood diverted to highly aerobic tissues (e.g. heart and brain).

- Catecholamines increase haematocrit (the volume of red blood cells per unit volume of blood) by causing red blood cells to be released from the spleen, in addition to some red blood cell swelling. This will increase the capacity for oxygen transport by the blood during hypoxia, acting together with the other effects of catecholamines. In addition, catecholamines cause pH in the red blood cells to increase due to stimulation of H^+/Na^+ exchange across their membranes. This improves oxygen affinity.

- Finally, catecholamines induce greatly increased rates of glycogen utilization by anaerobic metabolism in the exercising muscles.

Figure 7.16 The effect of adrenalin, injected into the fourth ventricle of a dogfish, upon bursting efferent activity recorded from the central cut end of the third branchial branch of the vagus nerve. Injection of 20 μl of 10^{-1} M adrenalin, after a delay of about 100 s, induced slow bursts of increased amplitude, which progressively increased in rate. Injections of adrenalin together with propranolol abolished this stimulatory response.

7.4.5 Fish in polluted environments

When a mixed pollutant load, such as that produced by an industrial city, is discharged into a river, it causes a reduction in oxygen availability below the outfall due to breakdown of organic material by micro-organisms (the typical sag curve, Figure 7.17). In addition, the water may become polluted by organic (e.g. phenols) and inorganic (e.g. copper, lead, chromium, zinc, cyanide) industrial waste products. These can cause gill damage to fish, affecting respiratory gas exchange, so that fish potentially have to cope with *two* sources of hypoxia, environmental and systemic. Naturally, they exhibit a range of responses to this problem, including behavioural avoidance, i.e. they swim away from the source of pollution. However, it is common to find fish that are tolerant of hypoxia, such as roach and chubb, in large numbers and often of large size around sewage outfalls that are not heavily contaminated with industrial waste. The fish appear to be benefiting from this source of food and warmth, and present us with an interesting example of the adaptive value of hypoxia tolerance. In the last 10 years, physiologists have begun to study the specific effects of pollutants on fish.

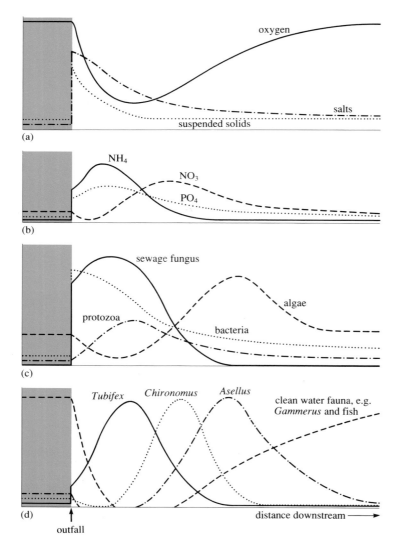

Figure 7.17   A diagrammatic representation of the effects of a mixed sewage effluent on a river and the progressive changes downstream from the outfall. (a), (b) Physical and chemical changes (the salts may include toxic metals). (c) Changes in micro-organisms. (d) Changes in fauna, indicated by marker species that indicate pollution. The freshwater annelid worm *Tubifex* and the larval insect *Chironomus* both thrive in the anoxic organic material that forms mud banks. The pond louse *Asellus* lives in mildly hypoxic conditions, but the pond shrimp *Gammerus* prefers cool, well-aerated waters and so its appearance indicates complete recovery of the river from the polluting discharge.

Copper in freshwater is toxic to trout and other fish: in experimental conditions mimicking pollution in the Tees estuary, fish died during the first 24 hours of exposure to abnormal levels of copper. The physiological changes occurring during this period were observed in our laboratory and they gave clues to the physiological effects of the toxic metal ion. The fish's ability to osmoregulate broke down so that sodium and chloride levels in blood plasma fell progressively (Figure 7.18a). Potassium levels increased progressively indicating leakage from damaged tissues. Plasma calcium levels were regulated at first, but rose precipitately at the point of death (Figure 7.18b). Breakdown in ion regulation signifies gill damage, and examination of gill lamellae from these

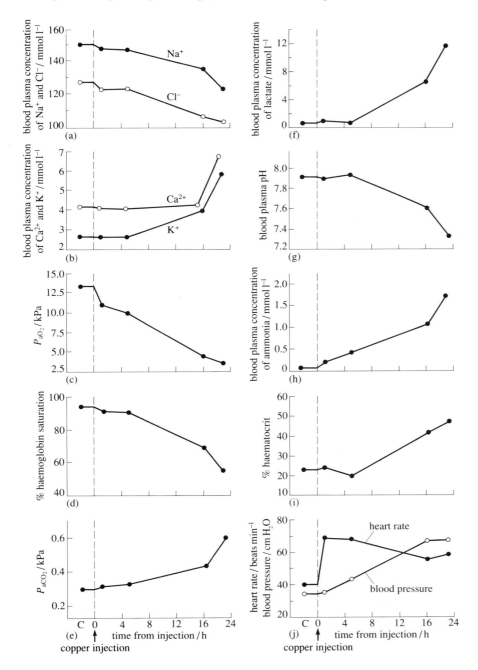

Figure 7.18 The toxic effects of exposure to 4.9 μM copper on trout: changes in (a) concentration of sodium and chloride ions in blood plasma, (b) concentration of calcium and potassium ions in blood plasma, (c) P_{aO_2}, (d) percentage saturation of haemoglobin, (e) P_{aCO_2}, (f) concentration of lactate in blood plasma, (g) blood plasma pH, (h) ammonia accumulation in blood plasma, (i) haematocrit, and (j) heart rate and blood pressure (C, the mean control values prior to copper injection).

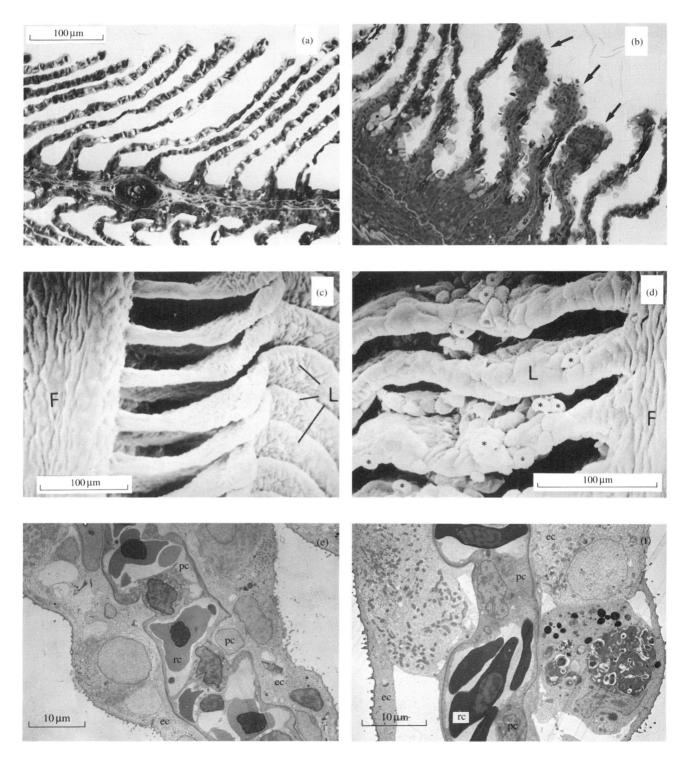

Figure 7.19

fish revealed that the gill epithelial layers were badly disrupted, with cell adhesion failure and red blood cells pooling in regions of the lamellae due to cells detaching (Figure 7.19, *opposite*). These effects are likely to arise from disruption of calcium regulation, as calcium is important in the maintenance of epithelia.

Experimental work on isolated gills has revealed that metal ions such as copper compete for calcium channels in the cell membranes and reduce the activity of the sodium/potassium exchanger on the basolateral membranes of the ion-transporting cells on the gills, causing a reduction in transepithelial potential. The physical damage to the gill epithelium, together with the disruption of ion transport, may account for the progressive accumulation of ammonia during copper exposure (Figure 7.18h).

Structural and functional disruption of the gill epithelium has drastic effects on respiratory gas exchange. The fish become progressively hypoxic (Figure 7.18c) and, as a consequence, haemoglobin oxygenation is reduced so that oxygen supply to tissues is reduced (Figure 7.18d). Carbon dioxide accumulates (Figure 7.18e), and the fish switches to anaerobic metabolism so that lactic acid levels in the blood rise (Figure 7.18f). The blood becomes progressively acidotic (Figure 7.18g) due to a combined respiratory (carbon dioxide) and metabolic (lactic acid) acidosis; this in turn causes a right-ward Bohr shift on the fish's haemoglobin, and oxygen uptake and transport are further curtailed.

As part of an attempt to compensate for these changes, the fish exhibits an increase in haematocrit to values as high as 50% (Figure 7.18i). This is partially due to a reduced plasma volume, partly due to increased red blood cell numbers (probably squeezed from the spleen), and partly due to red blood cell swelling. These changes are likely to result in an increase in apparent blood viscosity. Simultaneously, the fish show increased heart rate and blood pressure (Figure 7.18j), and together with the changes in haematocrit, these indicate that circulating catecholamines are elevated (see Section 7.4.4). The combined effect of these responses is cardiac failure, and the fish dies. Similar trauma have been described from fish exposed to very acid waters (the product of acid rain). The fish is killed because its integrated physiological responses to the toxic environment culminate in its destruction.

← **Figure 7.19** Changes in gill structure following damage by exposure to copper in freshwater trout.
Light micrographs of gills from (a) control fish, and (b) trout exposed to 4.9 µM copper. In the control fish, lamellae are thin and uniform with a minimal blood–water diffusion distance. However, cells on the surface of lamellae appear swollen after exposure to copper (b), causing a thickening of the respiratory epithelium and hence an increase in the blood–water diffusion distance. Arrows indicate lamellae where curling has occurred, leading to a further reduction in the effective surface area for gas exchange.
Scanning electron micrographs of gills from (c) control fish, and (d) trout exposed to 4.9 µM copper. Asterisks in (d) mark respiratory pavement cells (as indicated by their microridged surface under higher magnification) which have become almost completely detached from the surrounding lamellar epithelium on exposure to copper. L, lamellae; F, filament.
Transmission electron micrographs of gills lamellae from brown trout in (e) unpolluted water, and (f) after exposure to low levels (0.7 µM) of dissolved copper. Exposure to copper has caused epithelial and pillar cells to become detached, causing increased diffusion distances, together with red blood cells aggregating in the disrupted blood spaces. ec, epithelial cell; pc, pillar cell; rc, red blood cell.

7.4.6 Physiological responses of crustaceans to hypoxia

Crustaceans have several features of their respiratory and circulatory systems that differ from the vertebrate plan. They have an *exoskeleton* of chitin, which is strengthened by calcium carbonate except where it extends over the respiratory surfaces and joints on the body and appendages, an open circulatory system or *haemocoel*, and a respiratory pigment in the **haemolymph** called **haemocyanin.** This pigment contains copper instead of the iron in haemoglobin, and is blue when oxygenated and colourless when deoxygenated. It is held in colloidal suspension in the haemolymph; crustaceans do not possess the equivalent of the vertebrate red blood cell, so there are no blue cells! In decapodan crustaceans, such as the lobster, the gills are contained in paired branchial (or gill) chambers ventilated by a paddle-shaped structure (the scaphognathite), which oscillates to pump water through the chambers and past the gills. Deoxygenated haemolymph (pre-branchial/venous) enters the gills from the systemic circulation and returns to the heart as post-branchial/arterial haemolymph.

The calcified exoskeleton is relatively impermeable to respiratory gases, water and ions. Oxygen uptake in water-breathing crustaceans is therefore restricted to the respiratory surfaces of the gills. Actively ventilating crustaceans can extract as much of the available oxygen from the ventilated water-stream as can fish, typically 30–40%, and in the freshwater crayfish up to 80% of available oxygen. When the shore crab (*Carcinus maenus*) is actively ventilating its gills with aerated water, P_{aO_2} levels rise to 12.5 kPa, similar to the value obtained in fish. Measurements of the diffusion constant of oxygen (K) through the chitin covering freshly moulted crabs showed that crustacean chitin has a permeability to oxygen similar to the epithelial cells it covers. Therefore, it is likely that the chitin covering the gills does not present as substantial a barrier to oxygen diffusion as previously thought. The ultrastructure of the gill lamellae is shown in Figure 7.20.

Active crustaceans are effectively 'supersaturating' their respiratory blood pigment in normoxic water and a large proportion of the oxygen transported to the metabolizing tissues is carried in solution in the haemolymph rather than combined with the haemocyanin. In these circumstances, the pigment remains almost fully saturated with oxygen during its passage through the tissues back to

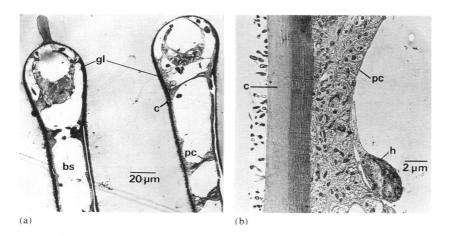

(a)

(b)

Figure 7.20   Ultrastructure of the gill lamellae of the shore crab (*Carcinus maenus*). (a) A transverse section through two gill lamellae (gl) to show the interlamellar distance and the relationship of supporting pillar cells (pc) to haemocoelic (blood) spaces (bs). (b) A transverse section (at a higher magnification) through the processes of two pillar cells (pc) and enveloping chitin (c) to show the pathway for diffusion of gases between air or water and haemolymph; h, blood cell or haemocyteal (remember though that in crustaceans the pigment haemocyanin is not contained within cells).

the gills, and is effectively a venous reserve of oxygen. This would appear to be metabolically very wasteful because of the high energy cost of ventilating the gills with water, but the answer to this apparent paradox is that many crustaceans maximally ventilate both of the branchial chambers for relatively short periods of time. For prolonged periods when resting in normoxic water they may ventilate on one side only or cease to ventilate altogether. During these *respiratory pauses*, haemolymph P_{O_2} levels rapidly fall to the functional range of the haemocyanin (see Figure 7.21), which then operates as the major supplier of oxygen to the tissues (Figure 7.25). However, in response to hypoxia and to the increased demand for oxygen associated with activity, both the gill chambers may be ventilated for extended periods, and respiratory pauses become very infrequent (Figure 7.22).

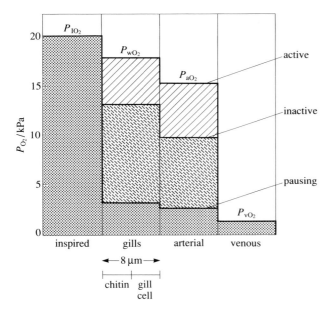

Figure 7.21   Gradients of P_{O_2} across the gills of the shore crab when it is actively ventilating its branchial chambers (active), undisturbed and showing reduced rates of ventilation (inactive) and during a respiratory pause (pausing).

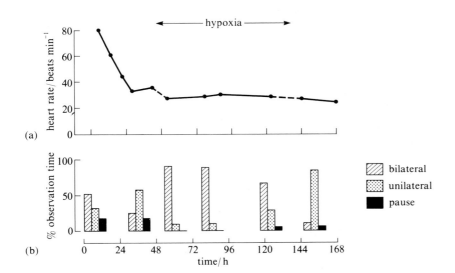

Figure 7.22   Changes in heart rate and ventilatory activity in lobsters allowed to settle initially in normoxic water for about 48 hours, then exposed to hypoxia for 90 hours (blue shaded area), and then subsequently returned to normoxia.
(a) The mean heart rate, with the trace broken by dashed lines when the animal is transferred between media. (b) Ventilatory activity from a single lobster is given as the percentage of total observation time the lobster ventilated both gill chambers (bilateral), the period of ventilation of only one gill chamber (unilateral) and the period when there was no ventilation (pause). The lobster ventilated both gill chambers for more than 70% of the time during hypoxia (measurements were taken over 75–150-minute periods).

Water-breathing decapod crustaceans may encounter both external hypoxia due to a reduction in environmental oxygen levels or internal hypoxia, despite environmental availability of oxygen, during the transition from water onto land, and during moulting when the respiratory surfaces of the gills may become impaired and oxygen uptake restricted.

7.4.7 Responses to external hypoxia

The pattern of physiological responses to progressive hypoxia have been described in some detail in the freshwater crayfish (*Austropotamobius pallipes*). Figure 7.23 shows the compensatory responses that occur at 15 °C when the partial pressure of oxygen in the ambient water is reduced progressively from 20 to 4 kPa. The top graph (a) shows the rate of oxygen consumption, expressed here as the amount of gas (in μmol) consumed per unit time ($\dot{M}_{O_2}$) rather than the volume ($\dot{V}_{O_2}$). The remaining curves show: (b) ventilation volume, i.e. the volume of water ventilated per unit time ($\dot{V}_w$); (c) heart rate; (d) haemolymph lactate concentration. The values for oxygen and carbon dioxide levels quoted are for both pre-branchial (○) and post-branchial (●) haemolymph, showing:

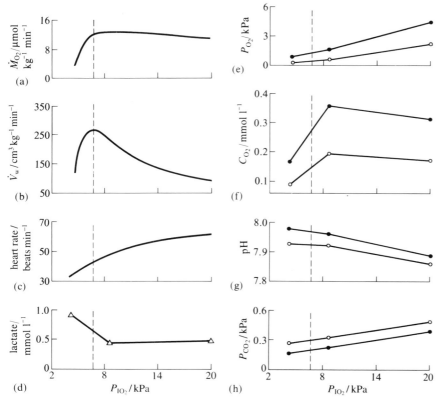

Figure 7.23 Response of the freshwater crayfish (*Austropotamobius pallipes*) to an increasing degree of hypoxia at 15 °C. The critical partial pressure of oxygen (P_c) is marked by the dashed line. Hypoxia was produced by progressively lowering the P_{O_2} of the inspired water from 20 to 4 kPa (horizontal axis). The responses of the animal to varying degrees of hypoxia are shown on the vertical axes (a)–(h). See text for details.

(e) oxygen partial pressure (P_{O_2}); (f) oxygen content (C_{O_2}); (g) pH; (h) carbon dioxide partial pressure (P_{CO_2}). The first point of interest to emerge from these data is that oxygen uptake is maintained independent of environmental P_{O_2} to a critical level (P_c). Second, as the P_{O_2} of the inspired water (P_{IO_2}) decreases to 6.7 kPa, the rate of ventilation of the gills ($\dot{V}_w$) (b) increases to 2.8 times the normoxic value, partly because of a doubling in respiratory frequency, and heart rate slows during hypoxia (c), although blood flow is maintained by an increase in cardiac stroke volume.

This hyperventilation has the effect of enhancing carbon dioxide elimination, with the result that carbon dioxide partial pressures are almost halved (h) and a respiratory alkalosis occurs in the haemolymph (g). Because of the Bohr shift this has the effect of increasing the affinity of the blood pigment for oxygen. Thus, the 'arterio-venous' oxygen content difference is maintained (f) in moderately hypoxic water, despite reductions in pre- and post-branchial oxygen partial pressures of 50% (e). As a result of these compensatory responses, the crayfish at 15 °C maintains an unchanging rate of oxygen uptake during a progressive reduction in ambient partial pressure of oxygen down to a P_c of about 6.7 kPa (a). This is achieved in part by an increase in T_{O_2}. At levels below 6.7 kPa, crayfish are unable to sustain the hyperventilation. Haemolymph oxygen content decreases so that the haemocyanin is no longer saturated on its passage through the gills (f), and the rate of oxygen consumption falls (a). Under these conditions a partial switch to anaerobic metabolism occurs, with lactic acid accumulating in the haemolymph (d); a potential metabolic acidosis is offset by the respiratory alkalosis, caused by increased carbon dioxide elimination.

Unlike the crayfish, many invertebrates merely tolerate progressive hypoxia, experiencing a gradual reduction in the rate of oxygen consumption ($\dot{V}_{O_2}$), i.e. they are **oxygen conformers**. The crayfish, on the other hand, regulate their $\dot{V}_{O_2}$ down to a critical partial pressure of oxygen (P_c), the precise value of which has been shown to vary with temperature, salinity, disturbance, diurnal and seasonal variations, and other factors that affect activity levels and consequently $\dot{V}_{O_2}$.

Below the P_c, $\dot{V}_{O_2}$ varies with P_{O_2}, and for an active animal P_c may be close to air-saturation levels, so that on exposure to mild hypoxia, active or disturbed animals would behave as conformers. At markedly reduced P_{O_2} levels animals may either show reduced levels of activity, often involving the cessation of hyperventilation (as in the crayfish), and/or it may switch to anaerobic metabolism to either partly or completely replace aerobic energy production, thus maintaining activity levels close to those at normoxia. Under these circumstances, $\dot{V}_{O_2}$ is clearly not a reliable measure of activity or metabolic rate.

7.4.8 Bimodal respiration in crustaceans

The shore crab shows a typical set of compensatory responses to progressive hypoxia resembling those described for the crayfish, resulting in the maintenance of a constant rate of oxygen consumption down to P_c levels that vary with temperature and salinity. Below P_c, it resorts to anaerobiosis, maintaining unchanged levels of activity and accumulating lactic acid.

However, if the crab is exposed to hypoxia in shallow water, it raises the front of its carapace above the water surface and, by a maintained reversal of the normal direction of ventilation, draws bubbles of air back into the branchial chambers to aerate the water surrounding the gills (Figure 7.24). This 'emersion behaviour' serves to raise the P_{O_2} level in the post-branchial haemolymph. Because the gills retain their contact with aerated water, metabolism remains aerobic and no carbon dioxide or lactate accumulates, and the pH of the haemolymph is unchanged. Emersion is accompanied by a recovery tachycardia, with the crab's heart rate rising to its normoxic level, presumably due to stimulation of oxygen receptors in the branchial chambers, and this ensures adequate delivery of oxygen to the metabolizing tissues.

The crab is able to maintain oxygen consumption following emersion, by taking advantage of the characteristics of the oxygen dissociation curve for haemocyanin (Figure 7.25). When the animal is in normoxic water, the P_{O_2} of the haemolymph is such that the pigment is fully saturated, on the plateau of the curve. When the crab is submerged in hypoxic water the pigment is not saturated with oxygen during its passage through the gills. However, when the animal emerges from shallow water and aerates the branchial chambers, the P_{O_2} of the haemolymph increases. In fact, the increase in P_{O_2} is modest but because it occurs over the steep part of the oxygen dissociation curve, its effect on oxygen content is considerable. So even at these relatively low post-branchial P_{O_2} levels, the pigment is at least 50% saturated and oxygen delivery to the tissues is ensured.

Water temperature markedly affects the emersion response. The shore crab emerges from shallow hypoxic water at relatively high P_{O_2} levels, when the ambient temperature is raised. At 25 °C it emerges from virtually normoxic water and its behaviour cannot contribute to oxygen supply because the haemolymph is already saturated with oxygen. It is probable that emersion at high temperatures is thermoregulatory, since air temperatures will be lower than surface rock and rock-pool temperatures on a beach exposed to bright sunlight. At a mean temperature of 28 °C there is a change in behaviour and the crabs move voluntarily into air and display responses discussed in the next section.

7.4.9   Facultative air-breathing in crustaceans

When a typical fish is removed from water, its secondary lamellae collapse and stick together so that, despite the relative abundance of oxygen in air (Table 7.1), the animal becomes internally hypoxic and metabolizes anaerobically. Heart rate falls and on replacement in water there is a lactate 'wash-out' from the muscles. In a sense, the fish could be said to be diving into air.

In many decapodan crustaceans the response is entirely different; they may move voluntarily from hypoxic water into air to become facultative air breathers for short periods. As you can see from Figure 7.26, the shore crab ventilates the gills actively in air and shows no reduction in heart rate; it also metabolizes aerobically at a rate of oxygen consumption that is the same as that in water (with no accumulation of lactate). So, perhaps surprisingly, the shore crab is also well adapted for aerial respiration.

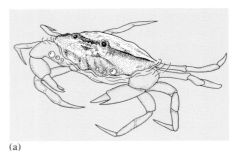

(a)

(b)

Figure 7.24   A shore crab (a) during emersion into air from hypoxic seawater. Streams of bubbles are appearing from the openings at the base of the chelipeds. (b) The crab, just submerged following a period of emersion, has resumed forward ventilation of the branchial chambers. A stream of bubbles is leaving the exhalent openings around the mouth.

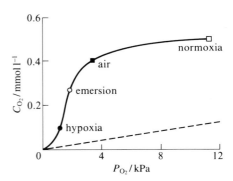

Figure 7.25   Oxygen dissociation curve for haemolymph at pH 7.8 from the shore crab. The points on the curve refer to post-branchial haemolymph values for P_{O_2} and C_{O_2} from crabs submerged in normoxic water, hypoxic water, following emersion from hypoxic water (emersion), and on exposure to air (air). The dashed line shows how much dissolved oxygen can be carried in the haemolymph.

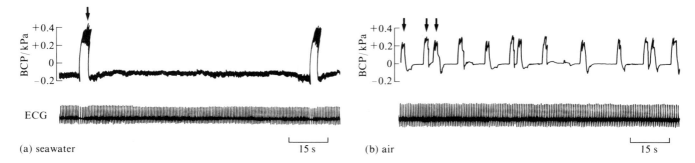

(a) seawater   15 s   (b) air   15 s

The gill lamellae in the shore crab have no secondary lamellae, are well spaced, and are covered by chitin rather than the layer of sticky mucus found on fish gills (Figure 7.20). They therefore resist clumping in air and retain their functional role in gas exchange; in this way a supposed disadvantage (i.e. chitin covering the gills) may be exploited as a positive advantage.

The changes that accompany long-term exposure to air are best known in the freshwater crayfish (Figure 7.27). This crustacean will voluntarily leave water in search of food or different bodies of water, and can survive for up to 72 hours in air. Crayfish posses filamentous gill lamellae which clump together when first exposed to air, resulting in a sustained internal hypoxia (Figure 7.27a) and hypercapnia (i.e. a rise in P_{aCO_2}, Figure 7.27d). On initial exposure to air the haemolymph has a very low pH_a (Figure 7.27e), the result of combined respiratory (carbon dioxide) and metabolic (lactic acid) acidosis. With time, this is compensated for by a reduction in circulating lactic acid (Figure 7.27g) and a rise in the concentration of HCO_3^- (Figure 7.27f), which buffers against the accumulated carbon dioxide. Some protons resulting from metabolism are

Figure 7.26   Pressures in the right branchial chamber (BCP) and heart beat (ECG) from (a) a crab submerged in normoxic seawater, and (b) following 1 hour exposure to air, at 15 °C. The major pressure fluctuations (see arrows) indicate that 'reversed' beating of the scaphognathite (the appendage responsible for ventilating water) is evident in both water and air, but is more frequent in air. This serves to ventilate the gills with air in either direction, alternating between forward and reversed ventilation. Note that heart rate is unaffected by exposure to air.

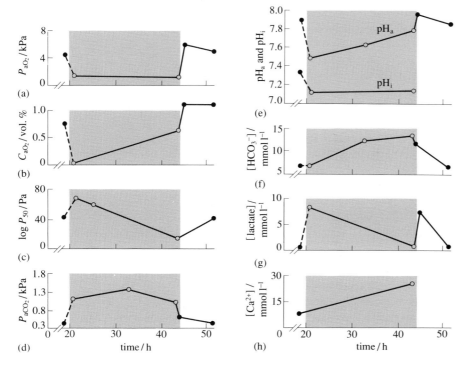

Figure 7.27   The effects of long-term air exposure on freshwater crayfish: changes in (a) the partial pressure of oxygen in the post-branchial haemolymph (P_{aO_2}), (b) the corresponding oxygen content (C_{aO_2}), and (c) relative oxygen affinity (P_{50}) of the respiratory pigment haemocyanin. (d)–(g) concern carbon dioxide transport and acid–base regulation in the post-branchial haemolymph and tissues: (d) the partial pressure of carbon dioxide (P_{aCO_2}), (e) the pH_a of the haemolymph, and the intracellular pH (pH_i) of muscle, and (f) the bicarbonate content [HCO_3^-] of the haemolymph. Finally, changes in (h) haemolymph lactate, and (i) calcium levels are illustrated. The grey shaded area indicates the period of air exposure.

sequestered in muscle which remains acidotic in air (Figure 7.27e), and the pH of the haemolymph returns towards the submerged level.

The compensation for the initial acidosis and re-establishment of a pH nearer 8.0 reverses a Bohr shift on the haemocyanin (Figure 7.27c). Oxygen affinity is further increased by elevated levels of lactate and calcium (Figure 7.27h). This restores the pigment's role in internal oxygen transport and elevates the post-branchial oxygen content to a level sufficient to maintain aerobic metabolism. The net effect of these changes is that, following an initial anaerobic period in air, the rate of oxygen consumption of crayfish is similar in air and water.

A similar set of physiological responses is observed in the European lobster (*Homarus gammarus*) on exposure to air. The response of this crustacean to aerial exposure is particularly interesting both to respiratory physiologists and to the shellfish industry. The lobster is marine and spends its entire life cycle under water, and can therefore be called a committed water-breather. However, lobsters are considered to be a luxury food item and have a high commercial value. As a result, these animals are deliberately removed from the sea and are found to survive long periods out of water during transport from distributor to market place. Lobsters survive the chronic internal hypoxia experienced on removal into air by mobilizing internal stores of $CaCO_3$, resulting in the elevation of HCO_3^- and Ca^{2+} in the haemolymph. The accumulation of these ions has a dual effect on the haemocyanin molecule, as in the freshwater crayfish. First of all, HCO_3^- ions buffer the progressive respiratory and metabolic acidosis accumulating in the haemolymph, restoring haemolymph pH levels and preventing an accumulating Bohr shift on the haemocyanin; second, Ca^{2+} ions have a direct modulating effect on haemocyanin, resulting in an increase in oxygen affinity. In addition, lack of oxygen supply to the tissues results in anaerobic metabolism and the production of lactate ions which also have an effect on haemocyanin oxygen affinity. Thus, the accumulation of Ca^{2+}, lactate and HCO_3^- ions serve to increase haemocyanin oxygen affinity during aerial exposure, causing an increase in oxygen delivery to the tissues, despite continuing systemic hypoxia. The lobster, therefore, despite its marine habitat, is well adapted for spending time on land, on the basis of its ability to compensate for internal hypoxia during aerial exposure. This ability to survive at least 24 hours out of water is exploited by the shellfish industry as these animals can be transported with relative ease by packing them in well ventilated boxes with damp packing material such as seaweed or newspaper soaked in seawater. The chances of survival are high if the transport temperatures are kept consistently low (less than 10 °C), and the lobsters are subjected to the minimum of disturbance, as excessive handling in air leads to an increase in oxygen demand and rapid accumulation of carbon dioxide and lactic acid in the haemolymph causing an acidosis which remains uncompensated, leading to death, probably by asphyxia.

Despite the ability to respire for a period in air, the decapodan crustaceans do not comprise an important group in terrestrial environments, where the arthropods are chiefly represented by the insects and arachnids. Land crabs are mostly limited to the fringes of the sea, or they live in burrows, though some species have evolved lung-like structures in their branchial chambers which function well in air. It is probable that the limitations set upon their invasion of land are only partially respiratory, and include water balance and ionic regulation, plus non-physiological factors such as the return to the sea for reproductive purposes, with many species having larval stages which are planktonic.

Summary of Section 7.4

Oxygen levels in aquatic environments are low and often variable, especially, for example, in rock-pools. Many aquatic animals can detect low levels of oxygen and respond behaviourally by moving to well-aerated water, and some bimodal air-breathers aerate the water around the gills with air (e.g. the shore crab).

The extent of respiratory gas exchange in fish is dependent upon rates of gill ventilation and perfusion, and on the gill's diffusive conductance. When fish are exposed to hypoxia, gill ventilation is increased. There is a reflex bradycardia (which is at least partly offset by an elevation of stroke volume) and an associated increase in pulse pressure: extra gill lamellae are thereby recruited, thus increasing T_{O_2}. Changes in ventilation rate, diffusive and circulatory conductance, and tissue oxygen utilization may accompany the elevation of circulating catecholamines in fish. Gill damage due to aquatic pollution may result in death due to circulatory failure, following disruption of ion and respiratory gas exchange over the gills.

In aquatic decapodan crustaceans, haemocyanin has a relatively high affinity for oxygen; the chitinous covering of the gills does not represent a substantial barrier to diffusion. Ventilation of the branchial chambers may be intermittent. When the freshwater crayfish is exposed to hypoxia, it exhibits hyperventilation, bradycardia, respiratory alkalosis and an increase in T_{O_2}, with the result that the rate of oxygen uptake is unchanged.

When taken into air, typical aquatic crustaceans initially become hypoxic and acidotic due to raised levels of carbon dioxide and lactate in the haemolymph. In the crayfish, HCO_3^- and Ca^{2+} levels are elevated by mobilization from an internal site; Ca^{2+}, together with lactate, increases the affinity of haemocyanin for oxygen, and HCO_3^- buffers the change in pH. Consequently, oxygen consumption is maintained in air. Such adaptations enable live lobsters to be transported to market in air.

7.5 Conclusion

When oxygen availability is limited, either by a reduction in supply (e.g. environmental hypoxia) or by systemic hypoxia (e.g. during diving), most animals show a range of adaptive responses in an attempt to maintain adequate levels of aerobic metabolism, with its high yield of ATP. The nature of these responses varies from behavioural via physiological to biochemical, with the overall response often including compensatory changes at all three levels. Furthermore, the type of response varies with the nature of the hypoxic problem and with the species and condition of the animal. For example, a lobster given time to settle in a respirometer maintains its oxygen consumption and heart rate at normoxic levels during moderate hypoxia. In contrast, disturbed animals at the same ambient partial pressure of oxygen show a marked bradycardia and a reduction in oxygen consumption. A pattern of responses typified in the laboratory, such as the 'diving-response' in air-breathing vertebrates, may occur only rarely in unrestricted animals in their natural habitat. Nevertheless, experimental manipulation in the laboratory has uncovered many of the physiological mechanisms that determine the overall response of the animal to hypoxia, and has revealed the sites and mode of action of central and peripheral chemoreceptors that initiate ventilatory and circulatory responses.

Oxygen supply to the tissues is limited by the rate of diffusion of oxygen across the respiratory surfaces in many aquatic gill-breathers. However, in typical lung-breathers oxygen supply is limited by perfusion, which is a product of the rate of blood flow ($\dot{V}_b$) and the transporting capacity of the blood ($C_{aO_2} - C_{vO_2}$). Ventilation rates of air or water are generally matched to rates of blood flow, according to their relative oxygen capacities. The 'typical' physiological response to hypoxia in both air and water breathers includes hyperventilation, which effectively presents more oxygen per unit time to the exchange surfaces than would be provided by ventilation rates typical of normoxia. It also removes carbon dioxide from the blood, resulting in a respiratory alkalosis and the possibility of a favourable reversed Bohr effect on the respiratory blood pigment, increasing its affinity for oxygen.

Hypoxia in air-breathing animals is often accompanied by a tachycardia, improving the rate of delivery of blood to the lungs and tissues. By contrast, in water-breathers hypoxia often involves a reflex bradycardia. Cardiac output is maintained, however, and the reduced heart rate may indicate redirection of blood through previously poorly perfused areas in the gills. Such changes, together with the distension of the epithelium and redirection of water (or air) flow may account for the increase in diffusive conductance of the exchange surface during hypoxia or exercise in a wide range of animals. An increase in T_{O_2} implies an increase in effective exchange area and/or a reduction in the effective diffusion distance.

This chapter has attempted a comparative account of the overall responses of animals to the problems of matching oxygen supply to demand. You should now appreciate the complex and flexible nature of the responses to hypoxia shown by a variety of different animals.

Objectives for Chapter 7

When you have completed this chapter you should be able to:

7.1   Define and use, or recognize definitions and applications of, each of the **bold** terms and indices of respiratory gas exchange.

7.2   Describe the 'classic' diving response of birds and mammals, and explain how this differs from the physiological changes observed during natural dives.

7.3   List the events that occur on exposure of fish to hypoxic conditions and describe how the responses contribute to the maintenance of gas exchange.

7.4   List the adaptive changes brought about by increased levels of circulating catecholamines during hypoxia, and relate these to the oxygen cascade in fish.

7.5   Describe the physiological responses of fish to toxic metal ions in the water and explain how these may limit aerobic activity and eventually prove fatal.

7.6   Interpret physiological data that refer to the events that follow (a) the exposure of the freshwater crayfish to hypoxia, and (b) the exposure of the crayfish to air.

7.7   Apply the principles and generalizations that relate to hypoxia by interpreting unfamiliar experimental data.

Questions for Chapter 7

(Answers to questions are at the end of the book.)

Question 7.1 (Objective 7.1)

The following mean values in Table 7.2 were obtained from experiments on dogfish in normoxic and hypoxic water. Using these values calculate the indices of oxygen uptake listed in Table 7.3. You will obtain different values for normoxic and hypoxic fish, which may give you some insight into the hypoxic responses.

Table 7.2   The mean values of the measured variables in intact dogfish during normoxia and hypoxia.

	Normoxia	Hypoxia
number of animals	10	10
mean mass / kg	0.75	0.75
P_{IO_2} / kPa	19.7	10.3
P_{EO_2} / kPa	14.8	7.9
P_{aO_2} / kPa	12.7	4.1
P_{vO_2} / kPa	3.1	1.5
C_{aO_2} / vol %	4.4	2.3
C_{vO_2} / vol %	1.6	0.36
$\dot{M}_{O_2}$ / μmol min^{-1} kg^{-1}	35.98	27.52
$\dot{V}_w$ / cm^3 min^{-1} kg^{-1}	760	1 180
$\dot{V}_b$ / cm^3 min^{-1} kg^{-1}	32.1	35.7

Calculate the missing values:

Table 7.3   For use with Question 7.1.

	Normoxia	Hypoxia
(a) $\dot{V}_w / \dot{V}_b$ =	–	–
(b) $P_{wO_2} - P_{bO_2}$ / kPa =	–	–
(c) T_{O_2} / μmol min^{-1} kPa^{-1} kg^{-1} =	–	–

Question 7.2 (Objective 7.2)

Provide an explanation in physiological terms for the following observations:

(a) Diving poikilotherms (amphibians and reptiles) can remain submerged for long periods, particularly at low temperatures.

(b) During the involuntary submersion of a seal there is a significant reduction in cardiac output, though the stroke volume of the seal's heart remains unchanged.

(c) During both involuntary submersion and natural dives, diving mammals can suspend breathing.

(d) In the Weddell seal, the heart rate during short voluntary dives is approximately twice that evident in dives of longer duration.

(e) In voluntary dives of long duration in the Weddell seal, the level of blood lactate at the surface during recovery increases as the duration of the dive is extended.

(f) Calculations of the oxygen store in the blood and tissues of a tufted duck give a value of approximately $30\,cm^3$. During voluntary submersion oxygen is used at a rate of $0.63\,cm^3\,s^{-1}$. The maximum duration of a natural dive recorded for this species is approximately 40 s.

(g) Ducks prevented from surfacing at the end of a natural dive subsequently show bradycardia.

Question 7.3 (Objective 7.3)

Briefly explain the following statements (a)–(f), referring to the responses of fish to hypoxia.

(a) Responses to hypoxia in fish are initiated by receptors sensitive to oxygen levels at various sites around the counter-current gas exchanger on the gills.

(b) In the dogfish, cardiac output is maintained during exposure to hypoxia, despite a marked bradycardia.

(c) In fish, an increase in pulse pressure in the ventral aorta on exposure to hypoxia may increase the effectiveness of oxygen transfer.

(d) The injection of atropine into the dogfish is likely to cause a reduction in T_{O_2} on exposure to hypoxia.

(e) In fish, the increased 'blow-off' of carbon dioxide that accompanies hypoxic hyperventilation may aid loading of oxygen by haemoglobin at the gills.

(f) During prolonged exposure to hypoxia, the concentration of organic phosphates in the red cells of eels decreases, increasing the affinity of the haemoglobin for oxygen.

Question 7.4 (Objective 7.4)

Describe, by means of a list, how an increase in circulating catecholamines in fish, on exposure to hypoxia, may improve the transfer of oxygen to the tissues: relate your answer to the oxygen cascade from water to mitochondria.

Question 7.5 (Objective 7.6)

(a) Describe, by means of a list, the progressive physiological changes recorded from fish exposed to toxic pollutants (refer to Figure 7.18).

(b) Explain how these changes may culminate in the death of the fish.

(c) What part may increased levels of circulating catecholamines play in these responses?

Amplify the following statements (a)–(e), describing the responses of the freshwater crayfish to progressive hypoxia (look at Figure 7.23).

(a) The rate of oxygen uptake by the animal showed an ambient P_c of 6.7 kPa.

(b) Branchial ventilation and heart rate varied.

(c) Carbon dioxide levels fell and pH was increased.

(d) The P_{O_2} in the pre- and post-branchial haemolymph decreased in response to progressive hypoxia but, despite this, the oxygen content of the haemolymph was maintained.

(e) Lactate levels increased in deep hypoxia.

Briefly, explain the ability of the lobster to survive commercial transport in air.

CHAPTER 8 EXERCISE, ALTITUDE AND DEPTH

Prepared for the Course Team by David Robinson

8.1 Introduction

The previous chapter described how animals respond to low oxygen concentrations in their environment. However, animals have a different type of hypoxic problem when their demand for oxygen outstrips their ability to supply the tissues, which consequently switch to anaerobic metabolism. The best example of this situation is vigorous exercise, a major physiological challenge since metabolism, for example, may increase by as much as ten times over BMR. This topic is discussed in relation to the problems that athletes face. This chapter describes some of the physiological problems related to exercise and training, and it uses exercise to explore the linking of physiological systems and to bring together some of the key physiological concepts from the earlier chapters in this book. The later sections deal with another challenge to homeostasis, the effect of adverse environments. In earlier chapters of this book the effects of extremes of temperature on animals were discussed in detail, but in this chapter we will examine the effects of changes in pressure. Such changes have obvious implications for the respiratory system, but there are thermal consequences as well. Most of the chapter deals with human examples but, where possible, there is comparison with data from animals.

The word 'exercise' has come to mean activity in relation to sport or healthy living, in human terms, but in physiological terms it is no different from other forms of muscular work. Animals like cheetahs that have explosive bursts of activity when hunting are undergoing the same types of physiological stress as human sprinters. Inevitably much of the research on muscular work has been done using human subjects and research tends to centre on endurance exercise under steady-state conditions, since it is then possible to compare both results between tests in one individual and from tests on several individuals.

8.2 Energy for exercise

Energy expenditure on different tasks has been measured in humans by methods that will be described in Section 8.3. The standard laboratory tasks require an energy expenditure of a few hundred joules. Over a complete day, energy expenditure is likely to range from around 6 MJ (~1 400 kcal) for a sedentary person to in excess of 30 MJ (~7 000 kcal) for someone in a job requiring prolonged hard physical work.

8.2.1 Sources of energy

In a mammal at the onset of a period of exercise, the ATP content of the muscle, which is normally very low, is quickly exhausted. A secondary source of ATP that is immediately available is the muscle phosphagen creatine phosphate, present in storage concentrations of about five times that of ATP. It is, however, relatively quickly exhausted in its turn, providing ATP for maximal levels of exercise for only about 1 minute. The muscles are then reliant upon ATP produced from intermediary metabolism: either aerobically (with the TCA cycle fuelled initially with lipid, and then a progressive switch to carbohydrate utilization), or anaerobically (with glycolysis converting muscle glycogen to lactate, or in some animals, alternative metabolites such as octopine).

When ATP production is aerobic, exercise necessitates increased activity in the cardiovascular and respiratory systems to provide additional oxygen and nutrients to the active muscle cells and to remove carbon dioxide, other nutrients, and the heat generated by muscle contraction. Approximately 20% of the energy released by the hydrolysis of ATP in contracting muscle provides the mechanical energy for movement, with the remaining 80% of the energy being liberated as heat. These changes in activity may in themselves increase energy demand. Light exercise or long-term activity requiring endurance (e.g. marathon running, fish swimming at cruising-speeds, animal migrations, etc.) are normally fuelled aerobically but the ability of the respiratory and cardiovascular systems to provide sufficient oxygen for maximal levels of exercise (e.g. sprinting, fish swimming at burst speeds, flight from predators, etc.) may be limited when $\dot{V}_{O_2}$ reaches a maximum (the **maximum oxygen intake**, the $\dot{V}_{O_2max}$) which is a measure of the animal's aerobic capacity for activity. The difference between the maximum aerobic capacity and the basal or resting rate of metabolism is often referred to as the **aerobic metabolic scope** or more simply, aerobic scope.

In a man, light exercise requires an energy expenditure of approximately three times his resting requirements, whereas high levels of exertion may require an increase of up to ten times resting levels. These demands are matched by similar increases in the rate of oxygen consumption. During sustained swimming in fish, $\dot{V}_{O_2}$ may increase by 12–15 times the resting level, with 93% of this increase directed to the swimming muscles, and the rest to the heart and ventilatory muscles. At higher levels of activity the muscles metabolize anaerobically.

Poikilothermic animals generally have lower metabolic rates than homeotherms, which limits their aerobic scope for activity. A tenfold rise in $\dot{V}_{O_2}$ above resting levels will merely approach the resting $\dot{V}_{O_2}$ of a homeotherm of similar mass. As the costs of locomotion are similar, birds and mammals thus are more capable of sustained, aerobically-supported, endurance activity than poikilotherms. Poikilotherms more often rely on anaerobic metabolism to fuel activity, as it is independent of oxygen delivery and can supply energy quickly. When the turtle *Pseudemys scripta* was stimulated into intense activity, estimates of whole body lactate concentration indicated that glycolysis had provided 60–75% of the energy used during the period of stimulation.

8.2.2 Reserves of substrates

A considerable quantity of glycogen (around 100 g) is stored in the liver in humans. This store, when oxidized, amounts to about 2 MJ, about one-third of the daily requirement for a sedentary person: during exercise it can be released at a rate of 1 g min^{-1}. However, during exercise, gluconeogenesis from lactate and other substrates takes place, so the liver stores are not the sole source of glucose.

■   What is the immediate source of the glucose reserve for exercise?

The muscles have localized stores of glycogen that are typically 1–2% of the total mass of the muscle, the extent of these stores varying with both the type of muscle and diet. It is possible to do a rough estimate of the total available energy available from muscle glycogen stores, since the combustion of 1 g of glucose yields 16 kJ of energy. In an adult human, with a total muscle store of 300 g (a typical figure), the energy available from the muscle glycogen reserve would be 300 × 16 kJ, or 4.8 MJ. This energy would last for about 2 hours of strenuous activity.

■   What other sources of energy could be utilized during exercise?

The lipid in adipose depots around the body provides a substantial reserve of energy, 20 kg typically yielding 200–300 MJ in a human. However, this resource can only provide energy from aerobic metabolism, unlike glucose. Protein can be used as an energy source, but as this depletes the muscles themselves, protein metabolism is the final resort. In terms of energy supply, protein can provide about the same amount of energy as carbohydrate, weight for weight.

8.2.3 Limits of gas transport

Increased rates of aerobic metabolism during exercise obviously increases oxygen demand in all animals and we can now consider briefly how oxygen supply may be increased during exercise and, in Section 8.7, following a period of training. We will consider oxygen transfer down the oxygen cascade from the environment to the metabolizing tissues — chiefly, in this case, the locomotory muscles.

Anaerobic respiration alone can provide energy for only a short period, typically 30 seconds in humans, which is long enough for a sprinter to complete a 100-metre race without the need of oxygen. For runners over a longer distance, lactate has built up to such a level after 30 seconds that they are obliged to switch to aerobic respiration. As the intensity of exercise increases, the production of lactate rises. If the concentration of lactate is plotted against the intensity of workload (Figure 8.1a) a point is reached where the slope of the curve increases sharply. This point, which occurs at a value of work load approaching half that which can be attained by aerobic metabolism, is called the anaerobic transition (AT). Figure 8.1 shows that for an untrained person (black line) the value of AT is lower than for an endurance-trained person (blue line) and the untrained person has a lower $\dot{V}_{O_2max}$.

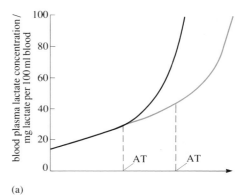

(a)

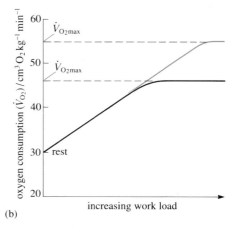

(b)

Figure 8.1   Changes in (a) the concentration of lactic acid in blood plasma, and (b) oxygen uptake, during an increasing work load of exercise. The black curves are for an untrained person and the blue curves are for a person trained for endurance exercise. The anaerobic transition (AT) and $\dot{V}_{O_2max}$ are shown for each person.

When the switch to aerobic respiration is made, the rate of supply of oxygen to the muscles and the rate of removal of carbon dioxide could become limiting. The total pressure *gradient* from air in the lungs to gas at the tissues is different for each gas, being 20 kPa for oxygen and 10 kPa for carbon dioxide.

■   How do you explain the difference in the two pressure gradients?

The gases have different solubilities, with carbon dioxide being five times more soluble than oxygen. There is some evidence that carbon dioxide levels could rise during excessive exercise to the point where the clearance rate for carbon dioxide became the limiting factor in exercise. However, analysis of gases in the blood in muscle capillaries of subjects during vigorous exercise have shown that the partial pressure of oxygen is close to zero. These measurements suggest that the limiting factor in exercise is the rate of supply of oxygen to the tissues, and that the limitations on performance in an individual come from the cardiovascular system or the respiratory system. These two systems will be examined further in Sections 8.5 and 8.6, respectively. The next section discusses both laboratory and field measurements of activity and the limitations of different methods.

8.3 Activity measurements in laboratory and field

Activity measurements on humans in the laboratory have largely been based on standard tasks. Although there have been many variations, the majority fall into three groups:

(1) cycling,

(2) stepping, and

(3) walking on a treadmill.

Measuring activity provides an indication of work output, but it also can give information about the factors limiting exercise, such as cardiac output or oxygen uptake.

8.3.1 Cycling

Cycles provide an experimenter with the opportunity to make measurements under standard conditions, and to vary the muscular effort required by loading the cycle. The subject pedals the stationary cycle against resistance provided by either a belt, an electromagnet or a dynamo. In a typical mechanical set-up, a belt goes around a flywheel. Knowing the diameter of the flywheel, the pedal speed and the force (belt loading) on the flywheel, it is then possible to calculate the power output of the subject.

$$\text{Work done (J)} = \text{force (N)} \times \text{distance moved (m)} \tag{1}$$

$$\text{Power output (W)} = \text{work (J)} \times \text{speed (s}^{-1}\text{)} \tag{2}$$

■   What major source of uncertainty can you identify in the final figure for power output?

The rate of working ignores the frictional losses due to the pedal mechanics and the friction between the belt and the flywheel. These causes of energy dissipation may give an uncertainty of 5–10% in the final figure for power output. An additional source of uncertainty when comparing individuals arises from the fact that power output varies with pedalling speed. Although the mean comfortable pedalling speed for an individual is around one revolution a second, experienced cyclists may use a faster speed. The limiting factor for subjects is usually muscle fatigue, which means that they have to stop exercising *before* they have reached any limits imposed by cardiovascular or respiratory efficiency, which is a disadvantage as one of the measures that is of interest in assessing a subject is the the $\dot{V}_{O_2max}$. The treadmill and stepping tests provide a better estimate of $\dot{V}_{O_2max}$.

8.3.2 Stepping

Stepping on and off a platform of standard height provides a cheap and uncomplicated method of measuring power output. A step height of 40 cm allows most subjects to reach their maximum oxygen intake, and provides a measure of power output with an uncertainty of about 6%. Power output is calculated from the body mass, the height of the step, and the number of ascents per second (see Question 8.1).

8.3.3 The treadmill

A treadmill is an endless belt, which can be inclined, and is driven by a motor. The subject on a treadmill walks or runs such that they remain in the same place. The speed of walking or running is under the control of the experimenter who can control the speed of movement of the belt. By measuring the oxygen consumption of a subject, the gross energy costs of walking and running at different speeds can be compared: rates from such an experiment are shown in Figure 8.2. The results show that, at low speeds of the treadmill, walking is more efficient than running but, as the speed increases, a cross-over point is reached where running becomes more efficient than walking. As the speed of the treadmill is increased even more, the running curve begins to level out, at the point at which the maximum oxygen intake and cardiac output of the subject have been reached.

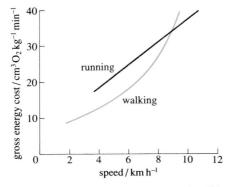

Figure 8.2   A comparison of the gross energy costs of walking and running. The data are derived from treadmill measurements.

8.3.4 Field measurements

Recording data from subjects during their daily life is more difficult than making laboratory measurements, but it has the virtue of being data from realistic tasks. A number of methods are available: a diary of diet and activity can be kept by a subject over a long period, or alternatively, an observer can record over several days. This latter method has worked well with soldiers and postal delivery workers. However, there are limitations in both these methods since they depend on making estimates of the speed and duration of activities to calculate energy expenditure. More accurate figures can come from attaching instruments to the subject.

Heart rate can be monitored by attaching electrodes and a small amplifier to a subject and then recording the heart rate on tape. Although heart rates are used to provide a measure of activity, the relationship between heart rate and oxygen consumption is not linear.

■ What other reason might there be for heart rate not being a perfect measure of activity?

The cardiac output is heart rate multiplied by stroke volume. It is possible for the heart rate to increase, perhaps in anticipation of something that might require strenuous activity, without cardiac output or oxygen consumption increasing. However, for vigorous exercise, heart rate is a reasonable indicator of oxygen consumption, with an error of 10–15%. Figure 8.3 shows how heart rate varies during a working day for three categories of worker.

As an alternative to measuring heart rate, it is possible to fit subjects with a portable respirometer, weighing a couple of kilograms. This provides accurate figures for oxygen consumption, and hence accurate figures for energy usage.

■ There are a couple of new areas of uncertainty introduced by this technique. What are they?

The weight of the respirometer adds to the work done by the subject, so figures for oxygen consumption for any particular task are likely to be greater than the true ones. Also, of course, the subject would be wearing a mask for breathing, which might distort their normal patterns of activity.

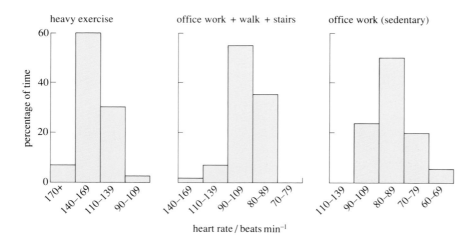

Figure 8.3 The heart rates of three different categories of worker during a working day.

■   Bearing in mind the ways of measuring metabolism in animals described in Chapter 1, what other methods might be used to measure activity in humans in the field?

The new method of using doubly-labelled water has been applied to human subjects, and is likely to yield results in the near future.

Summary of Section 8.3

Physiological measurements can be made on humans in the laboratory with comparative ease, since it is possible to devise standard exercise regimes. Such regimes may have limits to their absolute accuracy, but they can provide good comparative data. To relate the laboratory observations to conditions in the real world is more difficult, although miniature recorders that subjects can wear throughout a normal working day are beginning to give useful information. Heart rate is relatively easy to monitor, but respirometry measurements are still limited in accuracy because of the additional weight of the respirometer that the subject has to carry around. Before considering the limitations on performance imposed by these systems, we will discuss the function of the muscles themselves, in the context of exercise, in the next section.

8.4   Nerves, muscles and exercise

The muscles together form the largest organ system of the human body — about 40% by mass in a slim young adult. The blood supply is highly adaptable, and the variable demand for blood from the muscles produces the greatest changes in the cardiovascular system. This system is, in economic jargon, 'demand-led', and it is the muscles that generate the greatest demand. A good indication of the degree of influence of the muscles is the fact that the heart may pump around 5 litres min^{-1} in a resting human but 25 litres min^{-1} during heavy exercise. This increase represents a 100-fold difference in flow rate through the exercising muscle between rest and maximum rates of exercise.

8.4.1   Muscle fibres

The muscle fibres can be classified into a number of functional types. Of particular interest in the context of exercise are the differences between red and white muscle fibres. This distinction, based on the colour of the muscle, is an old one, and it has subsequently been refined. Red muscle fibres are rich in blood capillaries and myoglobin (hence the colour), and characteristically have substantial amounts of mitochondrial enzymes for aerobic respiration and low activities of the glycolytic enzymes. They develop their maximum tension relatively slowly and are known as slow twitch fibres (Table 8.1, *overleaf*). White muscle fibres, on the other hand, have high levels of glycolytic enzymes and few mitochondria (which gives them an anaerobic capacity) and they develop tension more rapidly than red fibres. There are also fibres of an intermediate type that have a fast twitch but both aerobic and anaerobic capability.

Table 8.1 Some properties of the three main muscle fibre types.

	Type I red, slow twitch slow oxidative	Type IIa intermediate fast oxidative	Type IIb white, fast twitch fast glycolytic
contraction velocity	slow	medium	fast
fibre size	small	medium	large
myoglobin content	high	medium	low
lipid content	high	medium	low
glycolytic enzyme content	low	medium	high
ATPase content	low	medium	high
mitochondrial enzyme content	high	medium	low
glycogen content	low	high	medium
size of motor unit	540 fibres	440 fibres	750 fibres

Skeletal muscle fibres are organized as motor units, a unit being a group of fibres attached to a single motor neuron. All the fibres of a motor unit are of the same type. A muscle usually has motor units of all three types of fibre, but the proportion of the types will vary in different muscles. For example, the locomotory muscles of ungulates that are capable of sustained activity have a high proportion of fast oxidative fibres (Type IIa). Lions, on the other hand, which are predators that rely on a brief burst of speed, have a high percentage of fast glycolytic fibres (Type IIb). In general, endurance athletes have a high proportion of Type I fibres in their muscles, while burst performance athletes will have more Type II fibres. For these burst athletes, the more Type IIa fibres present the more successful they are and there is some evidence that training can convert Type IIb fibres to Type IIa. However, there is no evidence that inter-conversion between Type I and Type II can occur, so it would appear that innate muscle structure predisposes a person to excel at either endurance or burst sports.

8.4.2 Testing muscle function

The measurement of the properties of isolated muscles has been carried out on a wide range of muscles from different animals. The force developed by isolated muscles, and the power output can be measured precisely, but the measurement of force generated or power output in the whole animal is a much more difficult task. It is known from studies of isolated muscles that the force developed is related to the cross-sectional area of the muscle. Studies in both Africa and Canada have shown that a straightforward measure of body mass can largely provide a good correlation with muscle strength, because body mass is influenced by size (and hence cross-sectional area) of muscles.

■ Under what conditions might this correlation break down in humans?

This correlation would be less good in individuals whose weight was excessive for their height, as the additional mass would be largely a consequence of increased fat deposits.

There are many mechanical means of estimating the force developed by human muscles. Measurements involving jumping can be used to calculate force developed and power output. The subject stands on a take-off platform that has strain gauges attached to it. As the subject jumps off the plate, the force necessary to lift off has an equal and opposite force against the platform, which moves the platform downwards slightly. The force is measured by the strain gauges. The mean force exerted on the platform by a young woman has been measured as 1.3 kN (1.7 kN for a man of similar build and age), and from this it is possible to calculate the power output.

■ What additional measurements would be needed?

In order to calculate the power output you would need to measure the time over which the force was exerted on the platform and the distance that the platform moved. The mean power output figure for the young woman was 2.4 kW.

The objective of such measurements is not only to obtain initial data, but also to develop methods that can be used to assess the performance of individuals and the success (or otherwise) of training. One test is of the maximum work performed over a brief period. If the subject is asked to cycle as fast as possible on a machine for 30 seconds, the power output over the first 5 seconds gives a measure of anaerobic power while the power output at 30 seconds gives a measure of anaerobic capacity. At this point, accumulation of metabolites such as lactate should be causing a switch to aerobic metabolism. The point at which that switch takes place would give an idea of the subject's capacity for aerobic metabolism in their muscles.

Summary of Section 8.4

The flow rate of blood through the muscles during exercise can increase by 100 times over the resting rate. The type of activity that muscles can sustain is, in part, a property of their fibre types, as muscle fibres can be oxidative or glycolytic. A muscle with a large proportion of glycolytic fibres is associated with bursts of energy, whereas sustained activity is due mainly to muscles with a high proportion of oxidative fibres. The force developed by a muscle is a function of its cross-sectional area, but there is also a good correlation between total body mass and muscle mass.

8.5 Exercise and the cardiovascular system

Cardiac output rises during exercise roughly in proportion to the increase in $\dot{V}_{O_2}$. This rise is to be expected, as blood flow is responsible for delivery of oxygen to the active tissues, but the increase may not be directly proportional. A period of moderate to heavy exercise in humans, resulting in a tenfold increase in $\dot{V}_{O_2}$, caused only a sixfold rise in cardiac output above the resting level. This rise is because oxygen delivery is the product of blood flow and arterio-venous oxygen content difference, which may be expressed as the **oxygen pulse** (cardiac stroke volume $\times (C_{aO_2} - C_{vO_2})$). The increase in cardiac output is achieved partly by a rise in heart rate, plus an increase in cardiac stroke volume, as the heart obeys Starling's law; the constriction of the great veins and the action of the locomotory muscles combine to improve venous return to the heart. This effect may be augmented by circulating catecholamines, which have a positive inotropic effect on the heart, increasing contractility. Trained athletes have larger hearts with higher resting stroke volumes and lower resting heart rates than non-athletic but healthy individuals of similar age. During exercise, heart rate may be lower in trained individuals and recovery after exercise is more rapid. Rats exercised regularly on a treadmill for 16 weeks experienced a 16% increase in $\dot{V}_{O_2max}$ and a 38% increase in the activity of the oxidative enzymes in skeletal muscle. During exercise, the trained rats had lower heart rates but a higher cardiac stroke volume and a greater arterio-venous difference in the oxygen content of the blood, so that oxygen delivery was increased due to an improved oxygen pulse, resulting in a rise in their maximum attainable aerobic running speed.

The increase in cardiac output during strenuous exercise causes an increase in blood pressure of up to 50% in a trained athlete despite a reduction in total peripheral resistance to 25% of resting levels. This reduction in resistance is due to improved perfusion of capillary beds in the exercising muscles and in the lungs, where lung capillary volume may increase by 50% in a non-athlete and by threefold in a highly trained athlete. The increased blood perfusion serves to improve the transfer of oxygen and carbon dioxide between the active tissues and the lungs. The dilation of capillaries in these tissues is accompanied by vasoconstriction in other tissues, particularly those that supply the gut. Blood supply to the brain and kidneys is maintained constant because their functioning is dependent on a constant blood pressure; blood flow and perfusion of the skin may increase during exercise because it is an important site of heat exchange, which can be used to cool the blood during exercise. These changes are illustrated in Table 8.2.

This redistribution of blood flow during exercise in humans may be even more selective than Table 8.2 implies. There is evidence that blood flow may be directed preferentially towards those types of muscle fibre that have a greater aerobic potential. This evidence comes from experiments in which radiolabelled microspheres were injected into the blood supply and then the muscles were assayed for radioactivity levels. The concentration in a muscle was directly proportional to blood flow. During periods of intense muscle contraction, blood

Table 8.2   Distribution of blood flow during rest and exercise in a well-trained athlete.

| Area | Rest / cm^3 min^{-1} | Exercise | |
		Light / cm^3 min^{-1}	Heavy / cm^3 min^{-1}
skeletal muscle	1 200 (21%)	4 500 (46%)	22 000 (85%)
heart	250 (4%)	350 (4%)	1 000 (4%)
skin	500 (9%)	1 500 (15%)	600 (2%)
brain	750 (13%)	750 (8%)	750 (3%)
kidneys	1 100 (19%)	1 100 (12%)	900 (4%)
viscera, etc.	2 000 (34%)	1 500 (15%)	400 (2%)
cardiac output	5 800 (100%)	9 700 (100%)	25 650 (100%)

flow to the highly aerobic fast red muscle fibres was $240\,cm^3\,min^{-1}$ per $100\,g$ of muscle fibre, to slow red muscle fibres $140\,cm^3\,min^{-1}$ per $100\,g$ of muscle fibre, and to the anaerobic fast white muscle fibres $70\,cm^3\,min^{-1}$ per $100\,g$ of muscle fibre. These differences in blood flow are proportional to the relative oxidative capacity of the different fibre types as measured by the concentration and activity of oxidative enzyme systems, such as the cytochromes. Training increases the aerobic capacity of white muscle, a change accompanied by a 50% improvement in its blood supply. So an increase in overall aerobic scope of approximately 10% is matched by additional blood flow to the trained muscles.

The cardiac responses to exercise in fish are variable. Some show a reduction in heart rate (bradycardia) during brief swimming excursions, whereas others show an acceleration (tachycardia) due to reduced activity in the vagus nerve. Although the elasmobranch heart lacks sympathetic innervation, in common with the heart in teleost fish, it has β-adrenergic receptors and shows a positive inotropic response to catecholamines. Circulating catecholamines increase during vigorous exercise in fish and may be involved in supplementing the increase in cardiac stroke volume that accompanies an improvement in venous return to the heart due to the action of the locomotory muscles.

The control of the cardiovascular changes during exercise in mammals is complex. The increase in cardiac output is due to a combination of:

(1)   a reduction in vagal, cholinergic activity

(2)   an increase in sympathetic, adrenergic activity

   (both (1) and (2) lead to cardio-acceleration)

(3)   an increase in cardiac stroke volume.

The increase in cardiac stroke volume arises from improved venous return, augmented by circulating catecholamines produced by the adrenal glands. Adrenalin is released following a massive discharge in sympathetic nervous supply, which occurs just before vigorous exercise as part of the 'fight-or-flight' syndrome. Similar influences affect peripheral vasomotor activity in sympathetic vasoconstrictor or vasodilator fibres, causing selective vasomotor effects in the various capillary beds mentioned earlier (Table 8.2). These effects are mimicked by circulating catecholamines. The capillary beds in tissues are also controlled by autoregulation (Section 7.3.2), a process attributed to the contraction of smooth muscle cells in response to distension caused by increased blood pressure and flow.

There is also evidence that blood flow through tissue is controlled locally in response to an accumulation of metabolites, variously identified as adenosine, phosphate, potassium or lactate ions. This effect is most marked in the heart and brain, which are highly oxidative tissues. It is less marked in muscle, though the effect is observed during exercise and may function to improve local blood flow, and is lower still in the less active gut and skin. The effect is lowest in the liver, which has a low dependency on oxidative metabolism. This local effect of metabolites seems to serve to improve blood flow, by vasodilation, to oxidative tissues and may be an important factor in the control of the differential distribution of blood flow to the various organs described in Table 8.2.

8.5.1   Diffusion into muscle

The vasodilation in exercising muscles is matched by blood flow to the muscles so that the velocity of the blood through the capillaries, and the consequent diffusion time for the exchange of oxygen and metabolites, does not change. The increase in surface area of the perfused capillaries, following recruitment of previously unperfused routes, increases the overall permeability of the capillary bed and gives a greater area for gas exchange. Diffusive conductance is also improved by a shortening of the mean diffusion distance from blood to mitochondria, as a result of the perfusion of more capillaries in exercising muscle.

The degree of vascularization of muscle differs with fibre type: slow, red (oxidative) muscle have a much higher capillary density than fast, white (glycolytic) muscle. In mixed muscles containing both fibre types the capillaries may be twice as dense around red fibres. After 8 weeks of endurance training by human subjects, the number of mitochondria (a good measure of aerobic capacity) increase in slow muscle fibres and there is a proportionate increase in capillary density in the muscle. The change in aerobic capacity of the muscle fibres (i.e. the increase in numbers of mitochondria) normally precedes the increase in vascularization. The stimulus for capillary growth may be tissue hypoxia or the accumulation of a similar list of metabolites to that believed to cause autoregulation of the capillary beds.

Trained athletes are characterized by a faster rise of $\dot{V}_{O_2}$ at the onset of exercise (see Figure 8.4). Responsiveness is normally measured as the time taken to reach 50% of the maximum $\dot{V}_{O_2}$, and you can see that this figure is significantly shorter in trained individuals. There is a consequent reduction in lactic acid accumulation compared with untrained athletes, suggesting that the oxygen transfer system adjusts to the increased oxygen demand more rapidly and effectively in trained muscles, possibly because of changes in the blood–tissue oxygen diffusion barrier. Clearly, the biochemical and physiological events occurring in skeletal muscle at the onset of exercise are complex.

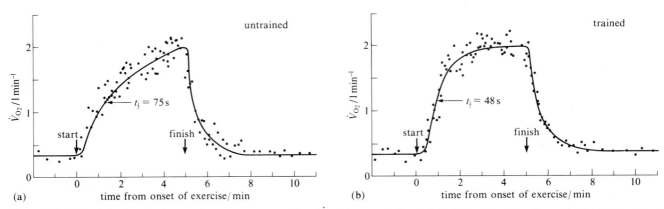

Figure 8.4   Breath-by-breath changes in oxygen consumption ($\dot{V}_{O_2}$) in an untrained subject (a) and a trained canoeist (b). Both subjects perform arm cranking movements lying down on their backs. The rate of increase in oxygen consumption is much faster for the trained canoeist (half the response ($t_{\frac{1}{2}}$) is attained in 48 s rather than 75 s) but the return to normal levels occurs at about the same rate in each.

Summary of Section 8.5

Cardiac output and $\dot{V}_{O_2}$ rise roughly in proportion during exercise. Training produces a lower resting heart rate and a larger stroke volume. In addition, trained individuals may have a lower heart rate during exercise and recover from exercise more rapidly than an untrained person. Blood pressure also rises during exercise, despite the drop in peripheral resistance to flow. There is a redistribution of blood flow during exercise, with the muscles and lungs receiving a proportionately greater flow than under resting conditions. There is evidence that flow is directed towards the muscles that have a greater capacity for aerobic work, and is partly explained by the fact that the degree of vascularization varies with muscle fibre type. There is a much higher density of capillaries in red, oxidative muscle.

8.6 Exercise and the respiratory system

During severe, short-term exercise, lung ventilation may increase, in human males, from 5 litres min^{-1} at rest up to 150 litres min^{-1}. This rise is accomplished by a fourfold increase in ventilation frequency (f_R) and a sixfold increase in ventilatory stroke volume (V_T) also sometimes referred to as tidal volume. The metabolic cost of ventilation rises 100-fold above its resting level because of greater inspiratory effort and a switch from passive to active expiration, using abdominal and internal intercostal muscles. (However, even in this circumstance the cost of respiration represents only 5% of the total metabolic rate.) The resistance of the airways is reduced by breathing through the mouth. The increase in ventilation with exercise is directly reflected in rates of oxygen consumption ($\dot{V}_{O_2}$) and carbon dioxide elimination ($\dot{V}_{CO_2}$), as shown in Figure 8.5. Notice that at all ventilation volumes athletes exhibit greater rates of gas exchange than untrained subjects. In addition, trained athletes have lower airway resistance, greater lung volume and greater compliance of the chest wall and lung. As a result, their breathing movements generate greater volume changes in the lungs per unit change in lung pressure.

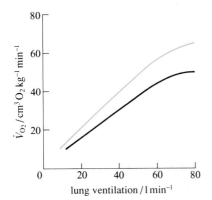

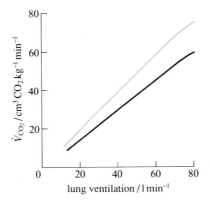

Figure 8.5 The rates of (a) oxygen consumption, and (b) carbon dioxide release, plotted as a function of lung ventilation per minute in untrained individuals (black) and in athletes (blue). The athletes exhibit greater rates of gas exchange at all ventilation rates.

In fish, water flow over the gills increases in proportion to oxygen uptake and the $\dot{V}_w : \dot{V}_b$ ratio may increase from 10:1 towards 30:1, which reduces the **residence time** of water at the gill lamellae and thus shortens the diffusion time for oxygen and carbon dioxide. The increased rate of flow may, however, become turbulent, reducing the boundary layer of water between the secondary lamellae and improving gas exchange so that the percentage extraction of oxygen from the water stream may not change during exercise, despite the increase in $\dot{V}_w$. At very high swimming speeds some fish switch to **ram ventilation**, swimming with the mouth and operculum held open to allow water to stream over the gills. This adaptation saves the metabolic work expanded by the ventilatory muscles, which can be considerable in water-breathers.

The control of ventilation in mammals during exercise is complex. The interaction between medullary inspiratory and expiratory neurons, pulmonary stretch receptors, and central and peripheral chemoreceptors cannot account for the high levels of hyperventilation observed during vigorous exercise. The change in P_{aCO_2} and P_{aO_2} may be relatively small, either because of effective gas exchange over the lungs or due to reliance on anaerobic metabolism, and yet respiratory 'drive' is clearly high.

There is some evidence that, in lung breathers, the sensitivity of the chemoreceptors in the medulla to increases in P_{CO_2} may rise during exercise. This may be partly due to the increase in body temperature, both directly and by stimulation of thermoregulatory centres in the hypothalamus, which may induce hyperventilation (panting). When exercising humans switched to breathing 100% oxygen for four to five breaths, they experienced a 16% reduction in ventilation rate after 20 seconds, indicating that a reflex hypoxic drive, possibly involving peripheral oxygen chemoreceptors, contributed to development of increased ventilation during exercise. In exercising trout there is no increase in P_{CO_2} or body temperature: the increase in gill water flow may relate to the utilization of the venous reserve of oxygen, resulting in stimulation of venous P_{O_2} receptors, or to changes in arterial blood oxygen content, which suggests that an oxygen receptor monitors arterial blood oxygen content and can increase ventilation on exercise.

The relatively rapid increase in ventilation after the onset of exercise in mammals suggests that neural control is exerted from centres higher in the CNS. In addition, stimulation of peripheral mechanoreceptors on the joints and in the muscles may influence ventilation: movement of the limb of a restrained animal evoked an increased ventilation in direct proportion to the number of joints moved.

As well as the fast component, i.e. a rapid increase in ventilation on the onset of exercise, there are increases that develop more slowly and reinforce the initial increase during long bouts of exercise, and there is evidence that these changes are hormonally controlled. The levels of circulating catecholamines like adrenalin and noradrenalin increase during exercise and injection of adrenalin can increase ventilation in a resting human.

8.6.1   Diffusion over lungs or gills

During exercise, the diffusive conductance for oxygen and carbon dioxide across the alveoli of the lungs of humans may increase to 3.5 times their resting level. This improvement is achieved by changes in the gradient for oxygen and carbon dioxide due to: (1) hyperventilation which reduces P_{ACO_2} and increases P_{AO_2}, and (2) greater consumption of oxygen by the tissues (utilizing the venous reserve of oxygen), which reduces the partial pressure of oxygen in the blood reaching the lungs (P_{vO_2}). As a consequence, the driving pressure for oxygen exchange ($P_{AO_2} - P_{vO_2}$) is greatly increased. In addition, a greater area of the lung becomes available for respiratory gas exchange because capillaries towards the apex of the lung, which are poorly perfused at rest, are fully perfused by the increase in pulmonary blood flow and pressure during exercise. In the next section we consider how training for exercise improves performance.

8.7   Exercise and training

Exercise may be defined as work done on the environment, primarily by the locomotory muscles, which results in an increase in the rate of energy production above the resting state. The provision of this energy (as ATP) may be aerobic, in which case exercise implies an increased oxygen demand, or anaerobic, utilizing substrate level phosphorylation. In Section 8.4 you read about muscle fibre types and the measurement of the force developed by muscles. In this section we shall consider the concept of fitness and the ways in which training can improve performance.

8.7.1   Fitness

The term 'fitness' has a particular biological meaning. It refers to the extent to which an organism is adapted to the surroundings. Fitness is generally used as a comparative term, since there is no absolute value for the fitness of an organism. One animal may have a greater fitness for a particular environment than another because it has a better chance of surviving and producing offspring. However, in human terms fitness need not have an evolutionary meaning. The term fitness is usually used to mean 'physical fitness'. A Sumo wrestler may be fit for his sport, but would not be regarded as fit in the sense of being an optimal weight for his height! So, physiologists have looked for measures of fitness that have a general applicability to, for example sport or operating machinery. In sport, measures of fitness may help to optimize training routines or identify potential athletes. Along with physiological tests would go psychological tests, of course, and it is important to realize that psychological factors may have quite an impact on physiological measurements. Indeed, in some sports a stable temperament may be far more important than physiological attributes.

8.7.2   Aerobic and anaerobic power

The maximum oxygen intake during exercise provides a measure of fitness, for at $\dot{V}_{O_2max}$ the subject will be producing the maximum aerobic power (Section 8.2.1). The maximum anaerobic power can be measured when a subject jumps vertically (as described in Section 8.4.2).

The principal factor influencing anaerobic power is the rate at which energy can be transferred from creatine phosphate to ATP. ATP is required for muscle contraction as it is essential to the interaction between actin and myosin filaments.

$$\text{creatine phosphate} + \text{ADP} \xrightarrow[phosphotransferase]{} \text{creatine} + \text{ATP}$$

This reaction has a time-lag of around 0.5 seconds, presumably as enzyme activation occurs. This time-lag has lead physiologists to measure anaerobic power after at least a second of activity, on the assumption that maximum power takes time to develop. As an alternative to jumping, subjects are asked to run up a flight of stairs as fast as they can and the time taken to travel from the 4th to the 6th step is measured, which can then be used to calculate power output. How long can that power output be sustained?

In Section 8.3.3 you read that accumulation of lactate forces a switch to aerobic respiration after about 30 seconds in exercising individuals. If a subject is asked to exercise at *maximum* effort, then the time at which exhaustion sets in and force an end to exercise is the **anaerobic capacity**. At this point, blood lactate levels are 10–15 mmol per litre.

■   What are the levels of lactate in the muscle likely to be?

The level of lactate in the muscles are likely to be substantially higher, maybe as much as 30 mmol per litre. After the subject has stopped exercising, blood samples taken at regular intervals will show the rate at which lactate is being metabolized, giving figures for the recovery oxygen (the oxygen debt). By plotting the log of the recovery oxygen against time it is possible to estimate the half-time for the recovery oxygen due to lactate and use this figure as a measure of anaerobic capacity (Figure 8.6).

Measurements of $\dot{V}_{O_2max}$ can be obtained from standardized exercise tasks but, as you read in Section 8.2.3, the best estimate comes from treadmill experiments. Figure 8.7 shows a typical curve of oxygen consumption against power output for a person on a treadmill. The slope of the treadmill is gradually increased during the test until the person is exhausted. The maximum oxygen uptake is the plateau value for oxygen consumption. Although there have been a number of attempts to devise a test that would provide a prediction of $\dot{V}_{O_2max}$ without testing to exhaustion, the treadmill test remains the best measure of aerobic power.

8.7.3   Prolonged exercise

There has been much discussion about whether blood glucose levels are the limiting factor in prolonged exercise. Certainly, when the blood glucose level of an exhausted subject is assayed at the end of a cycling task, the blood glucose level may be below the resting minimum of 3.9 mmol per litre. However, measurements of blood glucose levels in marathon runners at the end of a run have shown that the value for glucose is close to the normal non-exercising level. Blood glucose levels have been observed to fall during some team sports as muscle glycogen is exhausted, and poor teamwork and scoring ability late on in matches has been attributed to a lowering of blood glucose supplies to the brain.

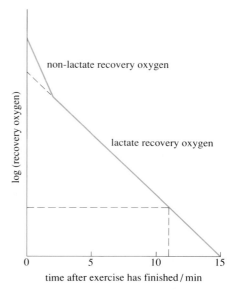

Figure 8.6   A graph of the log of recovery oxygen against time for the recovery period of a human subject who has exercised maximally to exhaustion.

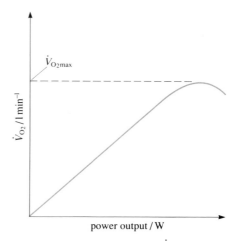

Figure 8.7   Measurement of $\dot{V}_{O_2max}$ in a human subject on a treadmill, by plotting oxygen uptake during an increasing workload of exercise.

There is a correlation between performance and muscle glycogen levels. A run that takes 2 hours for a subject with a starting muscle glycogen level of 2.2 g per 100 g of muscle, takes over 2 hours and 10 minutes for a subject with only 1.1 g per 100 g of muscle at the start. Figures of this sort have led athletes to attempt to boost glycogen stores before endurance races.

8.7.4   Training

Training of human athletes improves their work efficiency as they develop better coordination of limb movements, allowing maximum work output from muscle contraction. Rigorous training of a swimmer may result in a sixfold increase in their swimming efficiency. Exercising animals regularly for long periods similarly improves their performance. Other changes are more directly biochemical or physiological.

Regular exercise of a mammal causes an increase in muscle dimensions due to increased fibre size and improved vascularization. Biochemical changes in the muscles during long-term exercise improves their ability to metabolize aerobically, and changes in lung function, cardiac output and blood flow through the peripheral circulation all combine to improve oxygen delivery and increase aerobic scope. An untrained man exercising maximally can increase his $\dot{V}_{O_2}$ by eight- to twelvefold, whereas a trained athlete has a $\dot{V}_{O_2max}$ that is 16–20 times the oxygen consumption at rest; in a superior athlete, $\dot{V}_{O_2}$ can increase 25-fold (see Figure 8.4b). The type of training also influences performance. When eight international athletes who had trained for sports requiring great endurance (blue lines) were compared with another group who had trained for explosive, sprint activity (black lines), their response to a work test that induced $\dot{V}_{O_2max}$ levels of oxygen consumption differed (Figure 8.8). The endurance trained athletes showed:

(1)   a high percentage of oxygen extraction (Figure 8.8a),

(2)   a continuously high $\dot{V}_{O_2}$;

(3)   relatively modest increases in lactate levels, and then only towards the end of the test period (Figure 8.8b)

(4)   a drop in P_{aO_2} and a rise in P_{CO_2} levels (Figures 8.8c and d).

All these changes are indicative of a high level of sustained aerobic metabolism. The athletes trained for burst exercise showed a progressive reduction in percentage of oxygen extraction, and a substantial rise in lactate levels. Blood oxygen and carbon dioxide partial pressures were unchanged (Figures 8.8c and d), indicating a greater reliance on anaerobic metabolism. The maximum obtainable oxygen recovery (i.e. the anaerobic scope) may be increased by explosive training.

8.7.5   The endocrine system

Exercise has an effect on a number of hormones, generally increasing the rate of secretion. Growth hormone (GH) is one of the hormones that is secreted in greater quantities during exercise, which is of interest as it is thought to promote growth of muscle and bone tissue as well as metabolism of fats. Thus it may be that GH has a role in the improvement of muscle performance as a result of training. As you might expect, secretion of hormones such as insulin and glucagon increases as part of the response to greater glucose utilization. With prolonged exercise, insulin levels start to decline.

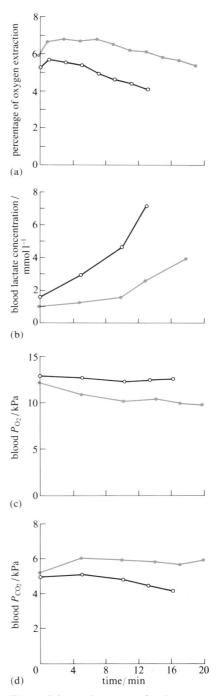

Figure 8.8   Performance of endurance (blue lines) and explosive athletes (black lines) during a steady increase in work. (a) shows the percentage oxygen extraction from the inhaled air. (b) shows lactate production, measured from arterial samples. (c) and (d) show blood gas values from blood samples taken from the ear lobe. Values are given for both P_{O_2} and P_{CO_2}.

■   What explanation can you offer for this decline in insulin levels?

The subsequent decline in insulin secretion as exercise is prolonged reflects the switch to fatty acid metabolism as glucose reserves are depleted. Catecholamine concentrations also increase, inducing lipolysis and glycogenolysis. During exercise there is, in addition, an increase in prolactin secretion that has an inhibitory effect on the ovaries; female athletes who undertake substantial amounts of exercise often experience a delay in the onset of menstruation and may experience reduced or absent menstrual flow.

Summary of Section 8.7

Training is often associated with an increase in fitness, but fitness is an ill-defined concept. A measure of the ability of an individual to engage in strenuous exercise can be made from their maximum oxygen intake ($\dot{V}_{O_2max}$), known as the maximum aerobic power. $\dot{V}_{O_2max}$ is best measured using a treadmill technique. The limitations on prolonged exercise are not certain, but a limitation in some individuals may be the concentration of glucose in the blood plasma, and glycogen in the muscles. Training can improve efficiency of performance by promoting physiological and biochemical changes in the muscles, and the effect can be seen as an increase in the $\dot{V}_{O_2max}$ of the individual.

8.8   Effects of pressure changes

In 1860, the French physiologist Paul Bert showed that the primary limit on survival at high altitudes is the reduction in the partial pressure of oxygen that results from the reduced barometric pressure: hypobaric-hypoxia.

An animal breathing air at sea-level has the advantage of a considerable head of pressure (approximately 20 kPa) driving oxygen from the atmosphere to its mitochondria (Figure 7.1). Animals ascending to high altitude, either by climbing or flying, must compensate for a reduction in this driving pressure because as barometric pressure decreases the P_{O_2} falls in direct proportion to the decrease, falling below 7 kPa above 8 000 m. Lower barometric pressure reduces the driving pressure for oxygen towards a level that is insufficient to support the requirements of aerobically metabolizing tissues, and ultimately may limit the ability of animals to be active or even survive at high altitudes.

Despite these constraints, animals are able to survive at high altitude. Some humans live permanently in settlements at 5 000 m and can climb for short periods to above 8 000 m. Even Mount Everest in the Himalayas (8 900 m) has been climbed in recent years without recourse to pressurized air or oxygen.

8.8.1   Oxygen transfer

The exchange of respiratory gases obeys the laws of physical diffusion and, if the oxygen requirements of deep body tissues are to be provided by the environment, a diffusion gradient must be maintained. This gradient is known as the oxygen cascade, and was described in Section 7.1: it is separable into steps that describe gradients of diffusive and convective conductance (Section 7.2).

The rate of oxygen transfer down the cascade may be limited by the relative conductances of any of these steps. The factors that determine oxygen levels and rates of exchange at each step of the cascade are fundamentally the same for air and water-breathing animals. In Section 7.2.2 you read about oxygen transfer in water-breathing animals. In this section we confine our interest to humans and consider the mechanisms allowing compensation for hypobaric-hypoxia.

In humans, tidal volume is only about 15% of total lung volume. The alveolar gas space is, therefore, relatively stagnant. As oxygen diffuses through the alveolar walls to the pulmonary capillaries and carbon dioxide diffuses out into the alveolar space, the mixture of gases in contact with the exchange surfaces at the alveoli has a P_{O_2} (approximately 13 kPa) that is lower than inspired air, and carbon dioxide accumulates to a relatively high level (approximately 5 kPa). The rate and depth of ventilation affect the composition of the alveolar gas; both are under the control of spontaneously active neurons in the medulla. These neurons show oscillatory activity which drives the ventilatory muscles. The neurons respond to a variety of afferent inputs from:

(1) central receptors in the ventral region of the medulla which monitor pH;

(2) receptors in the lungs sensitive to distension of the bronchioles in mammals (and to changes in carbon dioxide levels in the lungs of birds);

(3) peripheral chemoreceptors in the major arteries (the carotid and aortic chemoreceptors), which monitor P_{aO_2} and P_{aCO_2}.

Lung ventilation is adjusted to maintain a relatively constant level of carbon dioxide in the alveolar gas-space, so that increased activity (e.g. exercise), which generates carbon dioxide, is accompanied by a compensatory increase in ventilation. Mixed venous blood supplied to the lungs by the pulmonary arteries contains a variable venous reserve of oxygen with a P_{O_2} of approximately 5 kPa. The driving pressure for oxygen transfer over the lung of a resting human at sea-level is, therefore, $13.5 - 5 = 8.5$ kPa.

The rate of ventilation of the alveolar gas volume in the lung ($\dot{V}_A$) is approximately 5.25 litres min^{-1} and is almost exactly matched by the rate of blood flow through the capillaries in the lung ($\dot{V}_b$). Thus, the ratio of air flow:blood flow or the ventilation:perfusion ratio ($\dot{V}_A:\dot{V}_b$) is approximately unity. The flows are matched according to their almost equal capacity to carry oxygen, with air containing 210 cm^3 O$_2$ per litre and human blood, when saturated with oxygen, having a similar oxygen content. The rate of delivery of oxygen to the tissues is determined by the rate of blood flow in the systemic circulation and by the difference in oxygen partial pressure between arterial and venous blood. In humans resting at sea-level, the respiratory blood pigment haemoglobin is completely saturated with oxygen on leaving the lung because the partial pressure of oxygen that ensures complete saturation of haemoglobin is roughly equal to the partial pressure of oxygen in the alveolar gas space (P_{AO_2}), both at about 13 kPa. The problem with exposure to hypobaric-hypoxia is that the reduced environmental partial pressure of oxygen fails to saturate the haemoglobin. Delivery of sufficient oxygen to the tissues can be sustained only by a series of compensatory responses, which occur at each step of the oxygen cascade and result in the modest driving pressure of oxygen satisfying the demand of the mitochondria.

A complete description of these responses is necessarily complex because they occur at each step of the oxygen cascade and are interactive. An additional complication is that, even in humans, the nature of the response varies according to the duration of exposure to high altitude. The initial reactions to acute exposure in a climber, termed compensations, are distinct from the longer term adjustments of a lowlander chronically exposed to high altitude, and from the processes of natural acclimatization or adaptation seen in native highlanders.

8.8.2 Lung ventilation

When first exposed to high altitude, lowlanders immediately begin to hyperventilate (i.e. convective conductance rises). The rate of lung ventilation increases over the first week of exposure until it is up to 50% above the rate at sea-level. Rates of lung ventilation are elevated to a lesser extent in native highlanders such as the Quechua Indians of the Peruvian Andes. The increase is accomplished by deeper breathing at moderate altitude, with increases in the frequency of ventilation occurring above 6 000 m. Hyperventilation serves to increase the P_{AO_2} and also 'blows-off' carbon dioxide so that P_{ACO_2} is markedly reduced to about 4.5 kPa. This reduction in P_{ACO_2} is an essential part of the response, as it effectively raises the proportion of the total gas mixture in the alveolar gas space that is oxygen. The blood passing through the lungs virtually equilibrates with the alveolar gas space and the reduction in P_{aCO_2} levels causes an initial *respiratory alkalosis*, which is corrected by excretion of excess bicarbonate by the kidney, thus restoring blood pH to normal levels.

At sea-level, ventilation is controlled largely by the level of carbon dioxide but the extent of the ventilatory response to carbon dioxide is influenced by the prevailing oxygen levels. The key point is that, at altitude, sensitivity of the respiratory centres to carbon dioxide is greatly increased and thus hyperventilation can be sustained despite the reduction in P_{aCO_2}. The respiratory sensitivity to carbon dioxide increases in less than a day at high altitude and then continues to increase to the eighth day. In contrast to this heightened sensitivity to carbon dioxide, highlanders show a reduced or 'blunted' response to hypoxia alone.

The carotid bodies monitor the partial pressure of oxygen in systemic arterial blood; exposure to chronic hypoxia causes disturbances of the form and function of these bodies in mountain dwellers. There is a progressive increase in the weight of these chemoreceptors with age at high altitude, so that the carotid bodies of the Quechua Indians are larger, heavier and less sensitive to oxygen compared to those of natives living on the coast. The carotid bodies of guinea-pigs, cattle, rabbits and dogs are also significantly larger in animals living in the Andes than those reared in lowlands. This increase in size is partially an increase in vascularization but includes changes in cell number and degeneration of ultrastructural features, including the vesicles that are thought to be involved in the formation and release of neurotransmitters as part of the receptor mechanism.

8.8.3   Alveolar/arterial oxygen transfer

The diffusive conductance of the lungs with respect to oxygen does not appear to change during acquired acclimatization and the transfer of oxygen at high altitude is therefore limited by the reduced diffusion gradient at the lung surface. Hyperventilation increases P_{AO_2} and so more oxygen may be transferred to the blood during its passage through the lungs by virtue of the blood's increased oxygen capacity following acclimatization.

For a typical acclimatized mountaineer resting near the summit of a mountain such as Everest, there is a marked limitation of oxygen transfer by diffusion which prevents complete equilibration of gases over the lung surface: the arterial blood may leave the lung with a P_{aO_2} only 50% of the P_{AO_2}, in great contrast to the sea-level resident, where overall the blood passing through the lungs comes into almost complete equilibrium with the alveolar gas (i.e. the P_{aO_2} is virtually identical to the P_{AO_2}).

In native highlanders there may be important adaptive changes in lung anatomy and ventilation, including an increase in the amount of air contained in the dilated alveoli following expiration. This effect, together with a permanent dilation of the capillary bed, contributes to a marked increase in the maximal diffusive conductance of the lungs. Highlanders also display a considerable increase (50%) in the ventilation:perfusion ratio ($\dot{V}_A : \dot{V}_b$) because of sustained hyperventilation. These changes may virtually eliminate the P_{O_2} gradient between alveolar air and the blood leaving the lungs (i.e. P_{aO_2} approximates to P_{AO_2} as in the normal subject at sea-level).

8.8.4   Blood capillary/tissue oxygen transfer

Although the partial pressure of oxygen in capillary blood and mixed venous blood ($P_{\bar{v}O_2}$) is reduced at high altitude, it is maintained at a level sufficient to ensure some diffusive flux of oxygen to the mitochondria, where oxygen levels are very low (around 0.1 kPa).

Initially the oxygen supply to the tissues may be maintained by an increase in cardiac output. This increase is reinforced by an increase in the number of circulating red cells (polycythaemia) because, if tissue oxygen consumption is maintained at the same rate and the rate of blood flow returns to normal, then the supply to the tissues is sustained by the increased oxygen capacity of the blood.

After about a week at high altitude, the initial increase in heart rate reduces, corresponding with a progressive increase in capillary density in the tissues. Such an increase can be identified morphologically after prolonged exposure to altitudes above 4 000 m. The number of muscle fibres is unchanged so that the ratio of capillaries to fibres is substantially elevated. A 50% increase in capillary number occurs after 3 weeks exposure to an equivalent altitude of 5 600 m, and this is associated with a doubling in tissue diffusive conductance due to shortening of the diffusion path for oxygen from capillary to mitochondrion. Without this response, the gradient for oxygen diffusion from the hypoxic blood would be insufficient to supply the most distal sites and a large proportion of the tissue would become anaerobic.

Biopsy samples of muscle from subjects acclimatized to high altitude have elevated levels of myoglobin, which could result in a more effective transfer of oxygen to the metabolizing muscles because myoglobin has a higher affinity for oxygen than the circulating haemoglobin. So, at a P_{O_2} of 1.3 kPa, myoglobin may be 70% saturated while haemoglobin is only 10% saturated. It is equally possible that the rate of oxygen diffusion through the muscle may be increased by facilitated diffusion, which appears to involve movement or reorientation of myoglobin molecules after association with oxygen, and can increase the rate of oxygen diffusion through muscle sixfold.

8.8.5 Mitochondrial phosphorylation

Heart muscle sampled from cattle born and raised at 4 250 m shows a 40% increase in the number of mitochondria compared with animals from sea-level. The probability of molecular oxygen contacting a mitochondrion as it diffuses through the tissues is thereby increased, which in turn increases the oxygen diffusive conductance of the tissue for oxygen.

The *in vitro* rate of oxygen consumption and the overall activity of oxidative enzymes per gram wet weight of tissue also increases at high altitude. More specifically, the concentration of enzymes, such as NADH-oxidase, succinate oxidase and cytochrome oxidase, increase inside the mitochondria, thus increasing the rate at which they oxidize substrate. This increase in the maximum aerobic capacity in the tissues of animals at high altitude may serve to maintain their rate of oxygen utilization relatively constant during systemic hypoxia at high altitude. Thus, aerobic metabolism with its high phosphorylation yield is retained during hypoxia, which may be particularly important during exercise.

8.8.6 Responses to high pressure

Humans can only experience higher than normal pressures by diving under water, and physiological problems can occur even in shallow water. Pressure increases with depth and the effect on gas in the lungs is to increase the partial pressure, thus increasing the steepness of the oxygen cascade (Figure 7.1). Chapter 7 described the physiological adaptations to diving in animals; in this section we give brief consideration to the physiological problems faced by humans.

Free-diving humans do not normally go to great depths. The lungs are filled with air at the surface and there is a progressive decrease in oxygen content as the dive proceeds. The rising levels of carbon dioxide in the blood are mirrored in the cerebrospinal fluid, the consequent pH change being detected by chemoreceptors in the brain, and the urgent signals from the respiratory centres force the diver to surface. However, there are circumstances under which when these signals are delayed.

■   Under what circumstances might the signals of a rising carbon dioxide level not give warning of the need to breath?

There is a temptation to breathe deeply (hyperventilate) before a dive in order to load oxygen. This action depresses carbon dioxide levels in the alveoli and so the carbon dioxide level in the blood may rise too slowly. Under these circumstances the symptoms of oxygen shortage would appear first, euphoria followed quickly by declining mental abilities. Even if the diver started the ascent the falling partial pressure of the remaining oxygen in the lungs, as a consequence of reducing pressure, would reduce oxygen transfer from the lungs to the blood. This situation is potentially lethal.

Most sports and commercial divers use pressurised gas to breathe underwater. SCUBA divers can use bottles of compressed air which are open circuit, with exhaled air bubbling out into the sea. However, diving times can be substantially increased by breathing from a closed-circuit system in which the gas is recirculated after carbon dioxide has been removed by a soda-lime canister. Pure oxygen can be used, but oxygen becomes highly toxic at depth as the partial pressure increases, so usually oxygen is mixed with another gas. Some gases exert narcotic effects, the severity of which is related to their lipid solubility (Table 8.3).

Table 8.3 Lipid solubility of gas and the relationship to narcotic effects, expressed relative to the values for nitrogen.

Gas	Narcotic effect	Lipid solubility
xenon	25.0	25.4
krypton	7.1	6.4
argon	2.3	2.1
nitrogen	1.0	1.0
hydrogen	0.55	0.54
neon	0.28	0.28
helium	0.23	0.22

Helium, with its low lipid solubility, is favoured for gas mixtures breathed at depths greater than 30 metres. The increase in partial pressure of oxygen as a consequence of the increased pressure means that only a small proportion of inhaled gas need be oxygen for sufficient to be delivered to the tissues, perhaps 2% oxygen to 98% helium. Indeed, if the oxygen concentration were higher, too much oxygen would reach the tissue and there would be a real risk of oxygen narcosis.

A consequence of breathing a gas containing so much helium is that there is a greater loss of heat from the lungs. Helium conducts heat more effectively than air. As water is also a better conductor of heat than air there is a very substantial heat loss from a diver with a consequent risk of hypothermia. The response to excessive heat loss is peripheral vasoconstriction, which increases central blood volume, although an effect of pressure is to force blood from the peripheral tissue anyway. Helium also alters the resonance properties of the vocal cords, so speech is distorted.

The problems of decompression in divers are well known as the occurrence of the 'bends' or decompression sickness, a result of supersaturation of the tissues with inert gas at depth, particularly nitrogen. As the diver returns to the surface and the pressure is reduced, the gas starts to form bubbles which can cause blockages in blood vessels and circulatory failure. To prevent this the gas must be allowed to release slowly from the blood, and divers must gradually decompress. Decompression times can be long, so for divers who have to work at depth a technique called saturation diving has been developed. The divers live the whole of a working shift of 3 weeks at a pressure equivalent to their working pressure, for example that of 300 m. They move between pressurised living quarters on the surface and their work at depth in a pressurised diving bell. Thus the long period of decompression required after diving to that depth need only be carried out periodically. For divers returning from 300 m, the decompression time may be more than a week.

8.8.7 Exercising at low pressure

You read about the general effects of low pressure on animals and humans in earlier sections. In this section, we consider the particular problems of exercise at altitude.

The shape of the oxygen dissociation curve (Figure 8.9) means that low and moderate altitudes pose little physiological problem for humans. However, above 5 000 m the oxygen partial pressure in the atmosphere is about half the sea-level value and oxygen intake is reduced (Figure 8.10). For people exercising at altitude, such as athletes and climbers, there is a reduction in aerobic power and endurance performance. This reduction may be offset in certain sports by the effect of the reduced air resistance and the cooler environment, but such gains are small.

The reduction in anaerobic power is largely a consequence of the fall in arterial oxygen, but there is another contributory factor. Heart rate declines at altitude and the maximum heart rate, which may be close to 200 beats min^{-1} at sea-level, has been shown to reduce in climbers to as low as 135 beats min^{-1} near the top of Everest. Of course, most sports are carried out at under 4 000 m, where the effects of altitude are not so marked, but altitude sickness is still a possibility at such heights.

On arriving at high altitude from sea-level, the initial obvious response is a breakdown of the normal even breathing pattern, and short periods of hyperventilation alternate with periods of hypoventilation. The buffering capacity of the cerebrospinal fluid reduces during the first day, restoring the pH levels around the medulla and restoring central control of the respiratory rhythm. Over a period of weeks the buffering capacity of the arterial blood also falls, leading to a decreased ability to transport carbon dioxide that is only partly offset by the increased haemoglobin content of the blood. As time progresses, resting heart rate and cardiac output revert to their sea-level values but during exercise both stroke volume and maximum heart rate remain depressed below their sea-level values.

For athletes who need to acclimatize to high altitude, an acclimatization period of weeks would seem to be needed, but such long periods are not actually necessary. Over a period of weeks the athlete's training schedule would be disrupted, of course, but a long period of acclimatization is not necessary because of a gradual reduction in the fluid content of the blood, and a decrease in stroke volume. The optimum period of acclimatization is 3 days, which is long enough for the acid–base balance to be restored and for recovery from mountain sickness.

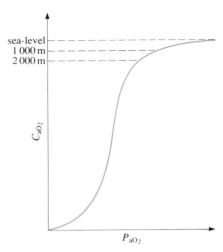

Figure 8.9 The oxygen dissociation curve for human blood, showing the effect on oxygen content of a small change in altitude from sea-level.

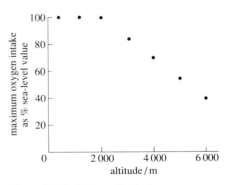

Figure 8.10 Effect of altitude on maximum oxygen intake.

Mountain sickness can afflict people above 3 000 m, or athletes undergoing vigorous training at lower altitudes. The low oxygen and carbon dioxide partial pressures disturb tissue oxygen supply and may cause sodium pump failure in cell membranes as a result of tissue anoxia. The effect on sodium pumps means that there is an imbalance in fluid regulation in the tissues, which may add to an additional problem that altitude causes, that of dehydration. Water loss is greater at reduced atmospheric pressure and increases even more due to hyperventilation. Normally, mountain sickness reaches a peak at 48 hours after arrival at high altitude and then recovery is relatively swift, as acclimatization takes place.

8.9 Thermoregulation and exercise

As you read in Section 8.5, a period of moderate exercise in a human can produce a tenfold increase in $\dot{V}_{O_2}$ and a sixfold increase in cardiac output. The increase in metabolism represents a substantial change in the body's heat output. It is possible to measure the temperature at different sites in an actively exercising human to get a picture of core temperature and peripheral temperature, and relate these to muscle temperature. In Figure 8.11, results are shown from three thermistors implanted in an exercising human subject. The muscle temperature rises sharply at the onset of exercise, as you would expect, but the skin temperature falls at first.

■ What reasons can you suggest for this fall in skin temperature?

There is an initial vasoconstriction at the skin, caused by the sympathetic system.

■ As the core temperature rises what are the physiological responses?

The central temperature receptors detect the rise in temperature and stimulate peripheral vasodilation and sweating, which is seen as a gradual rise in skin temperature.

■ What can you deduce from the rise in core temperature?

You should recall from Chapter 6 that there is a set-point in the hypothalamic temperature regulation system. The rise in core temperature suggests that the set-point is reset to a higher level.

■ Can you suggest why the set-point might be raised?

An increase in temperature produces an increase in the rate of chemical reactions, which is particularly important in the exercising muscles. There is also an increase in the delivery of oxygen to the tissues because the oxygen dissociation curve for haemoglobin is temperature-sensitive and the curve is shifted to the right.

The core temperature cannot rise much above 41 °C without causing serious damage to the tissues. If the ability to lose heat at the skin surface is reduced, for example by heavy clothing or high humidity (Section 3.3.2), the homeostatic mechanisms will be unable to operate correctly, and heat stroke or death may occur.

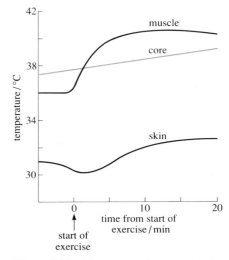

Figure 8.11 The changes in core, muscle and skin temperatures in a human subject exercising at a constant work load.

8.10 Conclusion

Exercise is often regarded as activity that increases fitness or improves sporting performance. However, exercise is not fundamentally different, in a physiological sense, from any activity that involves increased muscular work. Exercise physiologists are interested in two particular areas — the long term adaptations that are a consequence of training, and the short-term changes that accompany sudden exercise.

Measuring activity in humans can be done in the laboratory using standard tasks. The cycle ergometer and the treadmill are basic tools used to produce such tasks. Field measurements are also possible, as equipment can now be made more compact.

Muscle contraction during exercise alters the metabolism of the muscles involved. ATP and creatine phosphate together only provide sufficient energy for under a minute of exercise. Anaerobic metabolism can provide energy for around 30 seconds of exercise, so aerobic metabolism is the primary source of energy for muscular activity. However, increased aerobic metabolism requires a greater supply of oxygen to the muscles, the rate at which it can be supplied being limited by the rate at which blood flows through the muscles. The maximum oxygen usage is $\dot{V}_{O_2max}$, which is often used as a measure of performance. Following exercise, the accumulated lactate in the blood has to be oxidized: the extra oxygen required to do this is referred to as the recovery oxygen.

Exercise has effects on the endocrine system, and the increase of growth hormone during exercise may be linked with the changes in muscle fibres associated with the effect of training.

In addition to studying exercise under normal conditions, it is possible to do similar measurements on people at altitude. The primary effect of altitude is on the respiratory system, as the partial pressures of oxygen and carbon dioxide in the blood are reduced as altitude increases. The resulting homeostatic changes in the respiratory control system are part of the normal suite of responses to hypoxia.

Breathing at depth is an abnormal situation for a human. Certain mammals do dive to great depths, but rely on air taken in at the surface, and hence at atmospheric pressure. Human divers breathing gas under pressure are in a situation for which there are no evolutionary precedents and are not biologically adapted for such diving.

Objectives for Chapter 8

When you have completed this chapter you should be able to:

8.1 Define and use, or recognize definitions and applications of, each of the **bold** terms.

8.2 Explain how activity measurements are made, both in the laboratory and under field conditions.

8.3 Distinguish between aerobic and anaerobic power.

8.4 Describe the physiological changes associated with training.

8.5 Describe the responses of the cardiovascular system and the respiratory system to exercise.

8.6 Outline the physiological changes that occur when a human moves from sea-level to altitudes above 4 000 m.

8.7 Analyse the physiological problems faced by human divers, and make comparisons with other diving mammals.

8.8 Discuss the problems of athletics at high altitudes.

Questions for Chapter 8

(Answers to questions are at the end of the book.)

Question 8.1 (Objective 8.2)

In an experiment, a woman of mass 66.0 kg climbs on and off a 0.40-m high step, once every 3 seconds. What is her power output?

Question 8.2 (Objectives 8.2, 8.3 and 8.4)

What techniques are used to make measurements of

(a) anaerobic power;

(b) maximum aerobic power;

(c) the distribution of blood flow during exercise.

Question 8.3 (Objectives 8.4 and 8.5)

For each of (a)–(g) decide whether there is an increase, a decrease or no change during exercise:

(a) heart rate;

(b) cardiac output;

(c) blood flow to muscles;

(d) plasma glucose;

(e) lipolysis;

(f) prolactin secretion;

(g) $\dot{V}_{O_2max}$.

For a person who normally lives close to sea-level, exercising at an altitude of 4 000 m produces rapid fatigue. What physical and physiological factors account for this fatigue?

(a) What are the immediate responses of humans to hypobaric-hypoxia ?

(b) Which of the physiological responses to shortage of oxygen at high altitude:

(i)   is associated with the development of respiratory alkalosis?

(ii)   results in an elevation of P_{aO_2} relative to inspired P_{O_2}.

(iii)   is the result of an increased sensitivity of the central chemoreceptors to carbon dioxide?

(iv)   results in an improved unloading of oxygen at the tissues but an impaired uptake of oxygen at the lung?

(v)   is responsible for an improvement in the rate of delivery of oxygen from the blood to the mitochondria?

(vi)   results in an increased capacity of the animal to metabolize oxygen?

In what ways would the adjustments to hypoxia displayed by a mountaineer after 3 weeks acclimatization to high altitude differ from those of an indigenous native in the Peruvian Andes?

GENERAL FURTHER READING

General

Eckert, R., Randall, D. and Augustine, G. (1988) *Animal Physiology*, W. H. Freeman. A useful older source book. Chapter 10 on muscle and movement and Chapter 16 on energetics provide useful background material.

Hill, R. W. and Wyse, G. A. (1989) *Animal Physiology*, Harper and Row. Contains good chapters on thermal relations, energetics, metabolism and diving.

Louw, G. N. (1993) *Physiological Animal Ecology*, Longman Scientific. An excellent and up-to-date account of temperature and thermoregulation, water relations, nutrition and energetics and reproduction.

Stanier, M. W. and Forsling, M. L. (1990) *Physiological Processes—An Introduction to Mammalian Physiology*, McGraw-Hill Book Company.

Withers, P. C. (1992) *Comparative Animal Physiology*, Saunders College Publishing. A good comparative text. Chapters 1–5 on temperature and energetics, Chapter 10 on locomotion. and Chapters 12 and 13 on respiration are particularly relevant.

For specifically human physiology there is a large number of medical books available. Of particular interest are:

Lamb, J. F., Ingram, C. G., Johnston, I. A. and Pitman, R. M. (1991) *Essentials of Physiology*, Blackwell. A very good physiological text. Chapter 16 on exercise provides useful support for Chapter 8 of this book.

Solomon, E. P., Schmidt, R. R. and Adragna, P. J. (1990) *Human Anatomy and Physiology* (2nd edn), Saunders College Publishing. A well illustrated account of human physiology that includes a number of test questions at the end of each major section.

Specific subjects and original papers

Alexander, R. McNeill (1989) *The Dynamics of Dinosaurs and Other Extinct Giants*, Columbia University Press.

Avery, R. A. (1979) *Lizards—A Study in Thermoregulation*, Edward Arnold.

Bakker, R. T. (1986) *The Dinosaur Heresies*, Morrow.

Benedict, F. G. and Lee, R. C. (1938) *Hibernation and Marmot Physiology*, Carnegie Institute, Washington, Publication 497.

Crockett, E. L. and Sidell, B. D. (1990) Some pathways of energy metabolism are cold adapted in antarctic fish, *Physiological Zoology,* **63**, pp. 472–488.

Davenport, J. (1992) The precarious life of high-latitude marine fish, *Biologist*, **39**, pp. 218–221.

Davis, L. S. and Darby, J. T. (1990) *Penguin Biology*, Academic Press.

Dawe, A. R. and Spurrier, W. A. (1969) *Science*, **163**, pp. 298-299.

Derocher, A. E., Nelson, R. A., Stirling, I. and Ramsay, M. A. (1990) Effects of fasting and feeding in serum urea and serum creatinine levels in polar bears, *Marine Mammal Science,* **6**, pp. 196–203.

Fowler, P. A. (1988) Thermoregulation in the female hedghog, *Journal of Reproduction and Fertility*, **82**, pp. 285–292.

Gauthier-Pilters, H. and Dagg, A. I. (1981) *The Camel*, University of Chicago Press.

Girardier, L. and Stock, M. J. (1983) *Mammalian Thermogenesis*, Chapman and Hall.

Groscolas, R. (1986) Changes in body mass, temperature and plasma fuel levels during the natural breeding fast in male and female emperor penguins *Aptenodytes forsteri*, *Journal of Comparative Physiology*, **156B**, pp. 521–527.

Johnston, I. A. (1989) Antarctic fish muscles — structure, function and physiology. *Antarctic Science*, **1**, pp. 97–108.

Klir, J. J. and Heath, J. E. (1992) An infrared thermogenic study of surface temperature in relation to external thermal stress in three species of foxes: the red fox (*Vulpes vulpes*), arctic fox (*Alopex lagopus*), and kit fox (*Vulpes macrotis*), *Physiological Zoology*, **65**, pp. 1011–1021.

Larsen, T. S., Nilsson, N. Ö. and Blix, A. S. (1985) Seasonal changes in lipogenesis and lipolysis in isolated adipocytes from Svalbard and Norwegian reindeer, *Acta Physiologica Scandinavica*, **123**, pp. 97–104.

Lindgård, K. and Stokkan, K.-A. (1989) Daylength control of food intake and body weight in Svalbard ptarmigan *Lagopus mutus hyperboreus*, *Ornis Scandinavica*, **20**, pp. 176–180.

Mrosovsky, N. (1990) *Rheostasis: The Physiology of Change*, Oxford University Press.

Nelson, R. A. (1980) Protein and fat metabolism in hibernating bears, *Federation Proceedings*, **39**, pp. 2955–2958.

Pond, C. M. and Mattacks, C. A. (1985) Body mass and natural diet as determinants of the number and volume of adipocytes in eutherian mammals, *Journal of Morphology*, **185**, pp. 183–193.

Pond, C. M. and Ramsay, M. A. (1992) Allometry of the distribution of adipose tissue in Carnivora, *Canadian Journal of Zoology*, **70**, pp. 342–347.

Ramsay, M. A., Nelson, R. A. and Stirling, I. (1991) Seasonal changes in the ratio of serum urea to creatinine in feeding and fasting polar bears, *Canadian Journal of Zoology*, **69**, pp. 298–302.

Shephard, R. J. (1987) *Exercise Physiology*, B C Decker Inc.

Stokkan, K.-A., Sharp, P. J. and Unander, S. (1986) The annual breeding cycle of the high-arctic Svalbard ptarmigan (*Lagopus mutus hyperboreus*), *General and Comparative Endocrinology*, **61**, pp. 446–451.

Twente, J. W. and Twente, J. A. (1965) Regulation of hibernating periods by temperature, *Proceedings of the National Academy of Sciences USA*, **54**, pp. 1054–1061.

Wang, L. (1987) Mammalian hibernation, in Groot, B. W. W. and Morris, G. J. (eds) *Effects of Low Temperatures on Biological Systems*, Edward Arnold, London.

Widdicombe, J. and Davies, A. (1983) *Respiratory Physiology*, Edward Arnold.

ANSWERS TO QUESTIONS

The design points that you would need to consider in preparing to attach a radiotransmitter to a seal would be the mass that the seal could be expected to carry, where you would fix the radio so that the seal could not rub it off or reach it with its flippers, and how you would attach an aerial. You might also have thought about the fact that radio waves are not transmitted through water, so the radio could only transmit at the surface or when the animal was on land.

The doubly-labelled water technique for measuring metabolic rate uses two isotopes because the measure of metabolism is the rate of carbon dioxide production. This can be measured by monitoring the rate of disappearance of labelled oxygen from the blood, providing it is possible to separate out the loss in water from the loss in carbon dioxide. By labelling hydrogen, the rate of loss of hydrogen from the blood can be monitored. The difference in loss between the two labels allows the carbon dioxide loss to be calculated.

The differences between the two animals are substantially greater than the differences between the tissues of each animal. The lower surface area of mitochondrial membrane suggests that the tissues of animal A are much less active metabolically than those of animal B. The lower levels of the metabolic enzyme activity seen in animal A are consistent with this. Animal A would appear to be bradymetabolic (a reptile), whereas animal B is tachymetabolic (a mammal).

In terms of body temperature and evolutionary position the following are the most likely answers:

A, cat; B, opossum; C or D, platypus; E, lizard.

(a) The explorer (an endotherm) in the frozen meat store is acclimating to low temperature. Temperature is a single variable and hence acclimation, rather than acclimatization, is the correct term. However, we have no information about the lighting inside the meat store, so it is just possible that the explorer would be acclimatizing to a different light/dark cycle at the same time.

(b) *Sceloporus* is an ectotherm. Each group is acclimated to a different temperature. The difference in mean oxygen consumption of the two groups at the *same* temperature is an example of temperature compensation.

Question 2.2

(a) The effect of a sudden immersion in seawater on the T_b of the iguana would be a rapid cooling. The seawater is below the temperature a lizard could attain by basking, but since the iguana feeds under water, it can tolerate changes in temperature and remain active. We would classify this animal as a thermal generalist.

(b) (i) The advantage of hysteresis in the heat gain or loss curves for an animal with a high preferred body temperature (often called mean selected body temperature or MST) is that the selected temperature is conserved, and the maximum time is spent close to that temperature. (ii) Of the physiological mechanisms that could be used to control heat gain and loss, the ones that you might suggest are changes in body colour, as in the gecko, or a change in blood flow to the skin. In fact, experiments have shown that the heart rate is reduced on entering the water, so less warm blood reaches the body surface, and T_b falls more slowly. When the iguana returns to the shore to bask, the heart beats faster, and heat absorbed at the surface is transferred rapidly to the deep body (see Figure 2.18).

Question 2.3

The final graph that you should have is shown in Figure 2.19. Neither the point at which H_{ev} rises on your graph nor its slope may be identical to those on the figure, but the point of inflection should lie within the thermoneutral zone. Below the critical temperature, T_b is dependent upon the production of extra metabolic heat by thermogenesis. Above the critical temperature, physiological mechanisms enhance heat loss.

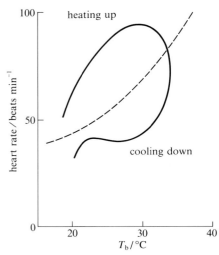

Figure 2.18 The relationship between heat rate and body temperature in *Amblyrhynchus*. As the iguana heats up, the heart rate follows a different line from that followed when it cools down, *over the same temperature range*. (The dashed line represents the division between heating up and cooling down.) Thus the plot of heart rate against temperature is direction dependent, and the curve is said to show hysteresis.

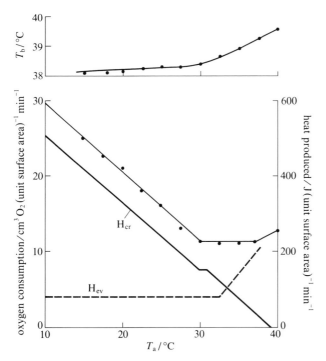

Figure 2.19 The curve plotted from the data in Table 2.1 (Section 2.4) and in Question 2.4.

Vasodilation increases heat loss through the skin (the plateau in H_{cr}) until the maximum is reached. Then as H_{cr} falls again the body temperature starts to rise and the level of sweating increases sharply. When body temperature and ambient temperature are equal, net heat loss by conduction and radiation should be zero. Thus the curve H_{cr} should cut the x-axis at T_b.

Question 2.4

You can see from Figure 2.20 that population P (○) regulates T_b much more than population Q (●). The line $T_b = T_a$ is almost the same as the line plotted for Q. Thus Q is probably a thermal generalist living in a varied environment such as a forest. P is likely to be a population in a less varied environment, e.g. open country. In fact the data refer to two populations of the same species of lizard, *Anolis cristatellus*. The slope of each line provides an index of the energy expended on thermoregulation.

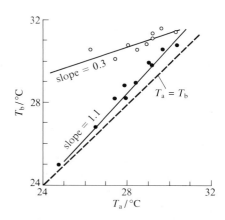

Figure 2.20 The completed version of Figure 2.17.

Question 3.1

(a) True. This statement is the definition of critical temperature (see also Chapter 2).

(b) True. Because homeotherms (by definition) normally remain in heat balance, increased heat loss to the cold environment can be offset by increased metabolic heat generation.

(c) True. In Figure 3.1, A–C represents the thermoneutral zone, but within this range, thermal conductivity may change by virtue of alterations in peripheral blood flow. As ambient temperature falls, peripheral blood flow decreases, so increasing insulation (i.e. decreasing thermal conductivity).

(d) True. As explained in (c), the decrease in thermal conductivity that results is immediately advantageous in the cold because it tends to reduce the rate of heat loss.

(e) False. As shown in Figure 3.2, rats become hypothermic on exposure to cold, unless previously cold-acclimated. During acclimation to the cold, the rats' ability to generate heat by NST is enhanced.

Question 3.2

An important point mentioned at the end of Section 3.2.2 is that shivering is reduced or even eliminated by exercise (because muscles involved in coordinated movement cannot produce heat simultaneously by high-frequency contractions). However, NST can be maintained during exercise. If you relate these comments to the rats, you can see that warm-acclimated individuals would generate heat in the cold by shivering, which is much reduced during forced exercise. Their ability to thermoregulate in the cold is therefore limited. By contrast, cold-acclimated rats use NST in the cold. This form of heat production is not affected by exercise, so body temperatures are maintained over a wide range of ambient temperatures.

Question 3.3

(a) X. In this animal the BMR is displayed over a wider range of ambient temperatures.

(b) X. Here, BMR is increased at a lower ambient temperature.

(c) On the evidence in Figure 3.23, animal X. This animal does not have to increase its metabolic rate until the ambient temperature falls considerably, which is likely to be an advantage in energetic terms.

(d) Y. Remember from Chapter 2 that smaller animals have a higher surface-to-weight ratio than large ones, so at a particular environmental temperature, small animals tend to lose more heat per unit body weight than do larger ones, and consequently need to generate more metabolic heat in cold conditions. Thus, the metabolic rate tends to increase more steeply below the critical temperature in small species than in larger ones.

(e) Y. Animals that lose much of their metabolic heat through poor insulation have to generate extra heat in compensation in cold conditions, so metabolism has to increase more steeply as ambient temperature falls.

From this question you should note that the critical temperature and the slope of the line of increasing metabolism provide a useful clue as to the effectiveness of adaptations to the cold. As a general rule, animals adapted to the cold have lower critical temperatures. The slope of each of the lines in Figure 3.23 is approximately equivalent to that animal's thermal conductivity. Usually, tropical animals have a high thermal conductivity. Rather as in neonates, small drops in ambient temperature cause significant increases in metabolism, because conductance is so high. In contrast, mammals native to cold climates show a less marked increase in metabolism and have low conductivities (high insulation).

Question 3.4

(a) False. This procedure is likely to be useful in an emergency, but it is unlikely to be efficient, because when the saliva evaporates it may carry away little *body* heat. Remember that the evaporating surface is insulated from the skin by fur. Much of the heat that is involved in the vaporization may therefore be from the environment and not the animal itself.

(b) True. Both panting and gular flutter involve evaporation 'within' the body and only water vapour is dissipated (unlike the situation in sweating, in which salts are lost).

(c) False. Under normal conditions, the rate of ventilation is matched to the rate of metabolic carbon dioxide production, which means that carbon dioxide levels in the blood are kept stable. During panting, there is a risk of excessive loss of carbon dioxide and a consequent increase in pH (alkalosis), but many panting animals avoid hyperventilating the respiratory exchange membranes by taking frequent *shallow* breaths (see Figure 3.14). However, animals that pant heavily can become alkalotic in second-phase panting.

(d) True. Taking advantage of the natural elastic properties of the thoracic cavity means that the extra internal heat load generated by panting is lessened.

(e) True. Note that this flow of air avoids the problem of heat recovery in the nasal passages that would occur if flow through the nose was two-way. With two-way flow the temporal heat exchanger operates; on inhalation, heat is removed from the wall of the nasal passageways, but at exhalation, because air flows in the opposite direction over cooler surfaces, heat is returned to the wall.

(f) False. Over a wide range of conditions, panting occurs at a constant resonant frequency (see (d)), and you know already that changing the depth of breathing would have serious consequences for gas exchange. Therefore heat loss appears to be modulated by changing the route taken by the air through the nose and mouth, and by switching panting on and off. However, in some species, in second-phase panting, alveolar ventilation is increased and the animal may become alkalotic, as mentioned in (c). The data in Figure 3.14 are consistent with this mechanism, because alveolar ventilation eventually increases if the heat load is high enough.

Question 3.5

(a) False. Most small desert animals avoid rather than endure heat stress, but it is true that some species, including birds, can tolerate body temperatures of 4 °C above normal (it is unlikely that such storage could be important in combating heat stress, because a small body absorbs relatively little heat per °C rise in body temperature). However, if a burrow-dwelling desert animal stores a small amount of heat in this way, it could be readily unloaded on return to a cool burrow, where conditions for heat loss by radiation and convection are favourable.

(b) True. In the absence of insulation, environmental heat onto the evaporating surface (the skin), would promote water loss. The coat insulates the skin from this influx of heat by reflecting solar radiation and in its absence, water loss is likely to increase. Note, however, that the coat must not be so thick as to impede the effective vaporization of water at the skin, and it is interesting in this context that many camels have rather a thin uneven coat (Figure 3.20b) with thicker fur on the back and less on the sides.

(c) False. In general, the tissues of desert-dwelling animals are not especially tolerant of hyperthermia. For example, the kangaroo rat is unable to tolerate a body temperature in excess of 40–41 °C for long.

(d) True. As explained in Section 3.5, the kidneys of sheep and goats are well adapted to produce a concentrated urine. Furthermore, on the evidence of Figure 3.20, sheep have moderately effective insulation. In addition, sheep and goats possess a very effective brain-cooling mechanism; so do cattle (but not horses). Finally, goats and sheep are probably more tolerant of dehydration.

(e) False. Larger mammals tend to rely more on sweating than on panting, but panting is evident in some reptiles and is important in most birds.

(f) False. Reptiles have sophisticated autonomic responses and also rely extensively on behaviour. Birds and mammals also respond to heat stress where possible by behavioural means, which probably have the advantage of being cheaper in energetic terms. In all these animals, there are both behavioural and autonomic responses and, as mentioned in Section 3.1, the distinction between them is imprecise.

Question 3.6

(i) (a) and (f) and possibly (b). Note that the radiation temperature of a clear blue sky is a good deal lower than air temperature (Figure 3.19) and so heat loss by radiation from the warm ears can be substantial. The urine is concentrated (b), but not to the same degree as in the kangaroo rat. In a relatively small animal, the insulation (c) cannot be a very effective barrier, nor can the heat storage effect (e) be very marked.

(ii) On the evidence presented in Chapter 2, (a) only, although our knowledge of the physiological basis of thermoregulation in desert reptiles is rather incomplete. However, (c), (e) and (f) are most unlikely. Many reptiles appear to lose heat by panting and do not sweat (d).

(iii) (a) and (b). Again, a small animal is unlikely to rely on (c) and (e) and this animal cannot sweat (d). Recall that the species is nocturnal, living in burrows during the day.

(iv) (b) (c), (d) and (e). Behavioural strategies in the camel are certainly important (e.g. movement to the shade) but burrowing is unlikely! Most camels have a substantial coat, so (f) is unlikely (but see Figure 3.20b).

Question 3.7

(a) Such behaviour minimizes the surface area exposed directly to solar radiation and so reduces heat loading.

(b) The most likely explanation is that the bird is *increasing* the insulation value of its plumage, which might help to protect the body from the enormous heat loads.

(c) This strategy seems wasteful of water but is less costly in energetic terms than panting or gular flutter. As the urine evaporates, it cools the blood flowing just beneath the skin of the naked legs and feet, the uric acid and salts forming a white deposit.

(d) The presence of one parent is important in such species, because the chicks have to be shielded from solar radiation.

Question 3.8

(a) (i) Figure 3.21 clearly implies that all these birds can cool exhaled air to a considerable extent (evidently much more so than the human, but less so that the kangaroo rat, which has a nasal heat exchanger that is so efficient that exhaled air is cooled to a temperature below that of the ambient air). It is noticeable that the budgerigar is almost indistinguishable in this respect from the house sparrow.

(ii) The key point is that the structure of the nasal passages determines the extent to which heat exchange occurs. Cross-sections of the nose of the kangaroo rat show an extremely narrow convoluted passage with a large surface area, which is the best arrangement for the exchange of heat between the air and nasal tissues. In birds, the passages are shorter and of a wider bore, so the surface area is smaller and conditions for heat exchange less favourable. In the domestic duck, the nasal heat exchanger is much less effective, doubtless because the nasal passages are wider.

(b) There are good theoretical reasons why a relatively low BMR might be an advantage in the heat. If metabolic rate is comparatively low, the amount of heat generated internally by metabolism is lessened, which reduces the total heat load in a stressful environment. For example, in birds, the poor-will has a BMR that is half of what would be expected on the basis of body size. A bird in dry air can get rid of heat by gular flutter at three times the rate of heat production by metabolism. As a consequence, a substantial extra heat load from the environment can be dissipated. However, we should say that the adaptive value of a low

BMR is unproven. Many desert-dwelling species of birds and rodents have a normal BMR, and those desert species that do display low BMRs have close relatives that are temperate species with low BMRs.

Question 3.9

(a) In both species, pumping air into the nasal passages would increase the rate of evaporation from the nasal mucosa, which would decrease the temperature of the venous blood flowing from the nose. In the sheep, the cooled blood passes close to the arterial blood *en route* for the brain and in this species the disposition of the blood vessels is favourable to heat exchange. So, the arterial blood supplying the brain would be cooled. However, in the rabbit, in which there is little opportunity for heat exchange, the cooled blood from the nose passes directly back to the heart (via the jugular vein) and this chills the arterial blood leaving the heart *before* the temperature of the brain is affected.

(b) It is interesting that the full potential for brain cooling seems to be evident in dogs that are generating an internal heat load because of exercise. It may be that this response is linked to 'second-phase' panting, mentioned in Section 3.3. The increased ventilation evident during exercise has the primary function of delivering more oxygen, and such intense panting promotes evaporation, both in the nasal passages and the mouth. Venous blood draining these areas is therefore cooled, which in turn cools the brain by heat exchange. It may be that only rapid shallow breathing, with unidirectional flow of air out of the mouth, is evident when the dogs are placed in hot conditions. Perhaps in these circumstances evaporation from the respiratory mucosa is more limited and the extent of brain cooling is therefore less marked. Blood supply to the mucosa is also increased significantly during exercise, which may explain the enhanced cooling of the brain.

Question 4.1

All energy temporarily stored as ATP appears ultimately as heat, e.g. when a fetus kicks, energy from the conversion of ATP to ADP appears as heat (the usual 'inefficiency') and as kinetic energy. The latter is dissipated as heat in stretching membranes and muscles, moving fluid, etc. However, the ATP involved in effecting biosynthesis passes some of its stored chemical energy on to the chemical energy in the biosynthesized molecules, e.g. protein. In a period of rapid cell division and cell growth, such energy usage may be quantitatively significant. Note, however, the data in Section 4.5: only 13% of ATP energy is conserved in a newly formed peptide bond and 87% appears as heat! Thus, assumption (4) in Section 4.2 may not be unreasonable.

Question 4.2

(a) False. The placenta exports heat to the emerging baby until the umbilical cord is severed.

(b) False. Shivering plays no part! Human neonates do not shiver as they have neither the sufficient muscular development nor adequate motor maturity in the brain. Arguably, too, human neonates are not truly homeothermic: they certainly are not without parental help.

(c) True. Although it is true that metabolic heat generation is not possible until the fetal blood is sufficiently oxygenated, NST happens rapidly after breathing begins.

(d) True or false depending on your view of the question! From a species point of view, it is false—as it also is for all neonatal mammals born in a nest in which the parents remain. Reduction of heat loss by providing clothing and warm shelter is critically important in many human environments. For the unaided baby, the statement is true: a baby can do nothing that is behaviourally useful (regarding thermoregulation) except cry.

(e) False. Though human neonates do resemble those of pigs, sheep and horses in terms of surface area:volume ratio, their thermobiology is much more like that of rat and rabbit neonates. Other big neonates shiver and rely less or not at all on NST (whereas human newborn do not shiver and depend on thermogenesis via BAT).

Question 4.3

(a) W + B, though more usually just W. B is more usually characterized by multilocular adipocytes.

(b) W + B. Triacylglycerol (formerly known as triglyceride) is neutral fat and is *the* storage molecule of both WAT and BAT.

(c) W + B. All cells, including BAT, need ATP. However, much less of the energy liberated by BAT cells is channeled into ATP production, and most appears directly as heat without associated ATP synthesis. This is because BAT mitochondria are partially or fully uncoupled.

(d) B. All experiments suggest that UCP is *the* characterizing component of BAT.

(e) B. This, too, is typical of only BAT. In contrast, fatty acids and fat droplets are exported from WAT to other tissues in need of oxidizable fuel.

(f) B. Both the vascularization and innervation by the sympathetic nerves are essential features of the thermogenic mechanism in BAT.

(g) B. The presence of uncoupled mitochondria is the basis of the thermogenic mechanism in BAT.

(h) N. Propranolol is an antagonist of noradrenalin: it has no effect on WAT and *decreases* BAT thermogenesis.

Question 4.4

In BAT that has been activated by noradrenalin released from sympathetic nerve endings, brown adipocyte mitochondria are largely uncoupled. As a consequence, all energy released by fatty acid oxidation appears as heat and almost none as ATP. A further consequence of uncoupling is that fatty acid oxidation proceeds much faster than in the coupled state; oxygen consumption and heat production are therefore much greater. In contrast, mitochondria are coupled in skeletal muscle, with the consequence that less heat is released and the overall metabolic rate is much less (illustrated in Figures 4.7a and b).

Question 4.5

In the cold-acclimated rat (a) the proportion of UCP would be greater, (b) the diameter of the fat vesicles would be less, (c) the mass of BAT would be greater, (d) the proportion of preadipocytes would be greater, and (e) sympathetic activity would be greater (see Tables 4.1 and 4.2, and associated text).

Only (e) is correct.

In general, the climate is harsher in Antarctica than in the Arctic. There are plenty of fish in the Arctic Ocean (although they are of different species from those in the Southern Ocean). Polar bears eat seals, not birds (although they might eat a penguin if the species ever met). Leopard seals are common in coastal waters of the southern oceans and penguins are their principal prey, but the two species have coexisted successfully for millions of years. Many migratory birds breed in the Arctic and a few, notably ptarmigan, are resident. With bears, reindeer, arctic foxes, birds, walruses and numerous fish, as well as seals, the Arctic has more species of vertebrates than Antarctica, which is without any fully terrestrial vertebrates.

Svalbard and Norwegian reindeer ate different amounts even when they had unlimited access to food and were exposed to the same environmental conditions, so the appetites of the two subspecies must be at least partially under endogenous control (see Figure 5.2).

The effects of exposure to continuous light on food intake and body mass depends upon the season at which the treatment is started. At very high latitudes, there is continuous light or continuous darkness for several months (see Figure 5.1), so daylength would not by itself be a sufficiently precise clue to seasonal breeding that must be accurately timed to favourable weather and food supply, e.g. for ptarmigan (see Figure 5.4).

Only (b) is generally true. It would be impossible to sustain permanently more animals than the food supply could support. At the beginning of fasting, bears are both fat and lethargic, but the one does not cause the other: male penguins are least active during incubation, and walk briskly back to the open sea at the end of the fast when they are thin. Bears and penguins, like large animals everywhere, have few predators, but smaller birds, lemmings and fish have plenty of predators. Since many fish and terrestrial animals are fat while in arctic regions, it cannot be true that the available food is less nutritious. There is no clear evidence for (g): BMR actually falls below normal for weeks at a time in bears and penguins and is less in winter- than summer-acclimatized foxes (Figure 5.3).

(a) Body temperature is a crude and somewhat indirect measure of activity. In both bears and penguins, body temperature falls slightly at the start of fasting (see Figure 5.8). Since there is no evidence that the body insulation has changed, the rate of production of heat (i.e. BMR) must have decreased. Body temperature rises abruptly during egg-laying in female penguins; the synthesis of components of the relatively large egg and the effort of laying would raise BMR.

(b) RER provides information about the chemical composition of the fuel broken down by respiration. An RER close to 1 indicates that carbohydrates are being used; a lower RER mean that proteins and/or lipids are being used.

(c) Chemical analysis of blood plasma provides detailed information about the concentrations of different fuels available to cells (e.g. fatty acids, glucose, β-hydroxybutyrate) and about the rates of formation and accumulation of breakdown products of metabolism (e.g. urea, creatinine, β-hydroxybutyrate).

Question 5.5

Only (d), (g) and (h) are true. Many arctic mammals have subcutaneous adipose tissue for part of the year, because many are large and they naturally become obese because the food supply is seasonal. However, in mammals, having subcutaneous adipose tissue is not an essential or unique feature of living in an arctic climate. Penguins, particularly the large species, have subcutaneous adipose tissue. In Carnivora, including bears, the partitioning of adipose tissue is related to body size, not to habits or habitat. In any one animal, the adipocytes enlarge with increasing fatness, but the total adipocyte complement, and hence the relationship between mean adipocyte size and fatness, differs from individual to individual.

Question 5.6

(a) Without haemoglobin in red blood cells, oxygen is carried in solution in the blood, but the solubility of oxygen in water increases with decreasing temperature. The enormous reduction in density of cells in the blood offsets the increase in its viscosity at low temperatures, so the blood flows faster for the same work of pumping by the heart. These factors mean that at −1.5 °C, the muscles of an icefish receive nearly as much oxygen as those of a fish with haemoglobin, but such fish would be unable to swim efficiently in warm water.

(b) The salt concentration of the body fluids of fish is less than that of seawater so their supercooled body fluids are at risk from freezing if they come into contact with ice crystals. Because ice is less dense than water, it floats at the surface. The salt concentration of the body fluids of most invertebrates is similar to that of seawater, so they are not vulnerable to freezing until the seawater itself freezes. There are also more diving birds such as penguins and skuas, and marine mammals in surface waters, all of which eat fish.

Question 6.1

(d) and (g) are not hibernators, although for (g) there is some evidence for mild torpor in food-deprived individuals. (b) is not a deep hibernator but shows shallow torpor (dormancy) on a seasonal basis. (c) is a deep hibernator with unbroken period of torpor, (e) is a deep hibernator on a seasonal basis, (a) and (f) show shallow daily torpor, and (h) shows daily torpor.

Question 6.2

The fact that the ability to hibernate is scattered throughout both similar and dissimilar species of mammals and birds, and is not apparently a primitive feature, supports this argument, as well as the fact that very different cues are used to trigger hibernation in different species.

Question 6.3

(c) and (e) are true.

(a) is false. The increased activity in the gonads in the ground squirrel occurs very early in the year and in a situation in which photoperiod may not be perceived.

(b) is false. Many animals lay down fat on a seasonal basis (e.g. migrating species), and some hihernators store food as well as fat.

(d) is false. Atropine, which blocks parasympathetic activity, has no effect on the long period of asystole.

Question 6.4

- If there is a fall in peripheral resistance, there are compensatory increase in heart rate and cardiac output.
- A rise in the level of carbon dioxide stimulates an increase in respiratory rate, and the period of apnoea becomes shorter.
- An undue fall in T_b leads to increased thermogenesis.
- Alarm arousal can take place following appropriate stimuli.

(You could, of course, also have given the example of thermoregulatory surveillance.)

Question 6.5

(a) True. There seems to be a very clear relationship between T_b and metabolic rate — much as you would expect from such a small, and therefore vulnerable animal.

(b) False. Although we can only infer T_b since here we are looking at metabolic rate by measuring oxygen consumption, T_b probably varies with T_a between 18 °C and 30 °C; below 18 °C the linear rise in oxygen consumption suggests homeothermy, though of course at a lower T_b than when active.

(c) False. There is no indication of arousal — if there were, you would expect to see oxygen consumption rise suddenly to at least the corresponding 'active' level, and probably much higher.

(d) True. T_b is allowed to fall with T_a until a certain point, at which thermogenesis increases as T_a falls further, thus maintaining the animal's T_b but without resulting in arousal.

Question 6.6

Although many hibernators have considerable quantities of BAT, its role in thermogenesis during arousal is important but not necessarily essential. In bats, BAT plays a significant part in raising T_b. In other mammals, in which interscapular BAT pads are absent, the major sources of heat are probably the heart and muscles.

Question 6.7

One type of explanation suggests that periodic arousals are triggered for repair or restoration (e.g. to counter a fall in blood plasma glucose or to excrete a metabolite that has risen to high levels). Another type of explanation suggests that periodic arousals are pre-programmed and do not need a circulatory signal. They may be viewed simply as periods of wakefulness in an altered sleep–activity cycle.

Question 6.8

- Cooling the hypothalamus alone raises the metabolic rate in a hibernator.
- Heating the hypothalamus locally lowers metabolic rate even though T_a may fall below the lower threshold value.
- The metabolic response to lowering the T_b is the same in both euthermic and hibernating individuals, and is proportional to the difference between T_b and the T_{hy} threshold.

Question 6.9

On entrance into hibernation, threshold T_{hy} values can be determined by measuring the metabolic response to lowered T_{hy}. The value of threshold T_{hy} drops with time and this governs the rate of entrance into hibernation.

Question 6.10

(a) False. Freeze tolerance, as defined, does not exist in any mammal.

(b) False. Cryoprotectants have only a very small effect on lowering the freezing point of the blood; their action is to keep the ice-crystals very small.

(c) True. Both ice-nucleating proteins and cryoprotectants act to produce the effect in (b) above.

(d) False. Glucose secretion begins only as soon as the first ice-crystals form in the skin of the wood frog.

Question 6.11

Only a minority of ectotherms regularly hibernate under circumstances where the T_a will fall below the freezing point of their body fluids ($-0.5\,°C$) for sustained periods, where they will come into contact with ice crystals. The majority can choose locations where the T_a remains higher (e.g. deep burrows, the bottom of ponds and lakes, etc.).

Question 7.1

Table 7.4   Answer to Question 7.1.

	Normoxia	Hypoxia
(a)	23.7	33.1
(b)	9.4	6.3
(c)	3.8	4.4

These indices show that hypoxia reduces the oxygen gradient over the gills ($P_{wO_2} - P_{bO_2}$). The dogfish responds by increasing $\dot{V}_w/\dot{V}_b$ and T_{O_2}.

Question 7.2

(a) They are poikilotherms so that their body temperatures vary with the environment. At low temperatures their oxygen demand will be low so that oxygen reserves in the blood and tissues will last for long periods. In addition, both can exchange some gases over the skin, which is an excellent route for carbon dioxide excretion into water. This is particularly true of amphibians, which typically have a well vascularized skin.

(b) The reduction in cardiac output is attributable solely to the bradycardia typical of forced dives.

(c) The cessation of breathing during a dive is probably attributable to some form of reflex inhibition of respiration, originating from a receptor responsive to water and/or cold. Activity in the central respiratory neurons may also be reduced. It is now thought unlikely that the respiratory drive (the urge to breathe) is dimished in diving animals because of reduced sensitivity to carbon dioxide of central and/or peripheral chemoreceptors, though such an explanation has been forwarded in the past.

(d) Evidence suggests that cardiovascular adjustments are more typical of dives of longer duration (or involuntary dives) when there may be substantial bradycardia together with vasoconstriction of peripheral vessels and a switch to anaerobic metabolism.

(e) As the answer to (d) implies, anaerobic mechanisms become more prevalent as the duration of the dive extends. (After a dive of 60 minutes, the blood lactate level can be as high as 25 μmol l^{-1}, compared to a resting level of less than 1 μmol l^{-1}).

(f) These figures suggest that the tufted duck could remain submerged for 47 seconds utilizing the entire oxygen store in the blood and lungs. The observation that natural dives are normally of a shorter duration than this implies that dives are normally aerobic, with little lactate production or major cardiovascular readjustment.

(g) This is evidence that the classic diving response in ducks may be used only as an 'alarm' response, when return to the surface has to be delayed. There are two interesting implications here: (i) that bradycardia displayed by seals (and perhaps ducks) during involuntary dives might be abolished by prolonged training as the animals became 'used' to the conditions (there is some experimental evidence to support this), and (ii) during diving the cardiovascular adjustments that are made result from the opposing influences of exercise (maintaining peripheral blood flow and heart rate) and the classic diving response (bradycardia and peripheral vasoconstriction).

Question 7.3

(a) There is experimental evidence for oxygen receptors sited peripherally on the gills, in the arterial vessels (oxygenated blood), and in the venous system (deoxygenated blood) of fish. In addition, the fish brain is sensitive to hypoxia but not to increased carbon dioxide or reduced pH.

(b) Cardiac slowing in the dogfish is accompanied by increased diastolic filling time and increased stroke volume which maintains cardiac output. In addition, the release of catecholamines during hypoxia may increase cardiac contractility.

(c) There is evidence that increased pulsatility of blood flow opens up previously poorly perfused areas in the gill lamellae, increasing the effective area for gas exchange, leading to an increase in T_{O_2}.

(d) Atropine blocks muscarinic cholinoceptors on the heart, abolishing inhibitory control exerted by the parasympathetic vagus nerve. Consequently, heart rate will be unchanged during hypoxia and the absence of the increase in blood pressure accompanying bradycardia will reduce T_{O_2} (see answer to (c) above).

(e) Hyperventilation during hypoxia reduces carbon dioxide levels in the blood, causing respiratory alkalosis. This in turn causes a left-ward Bohr shift on the haemoglobin, increasing its affinity for oxygen. Thus increased rates of ventilation have a double benefit, improving oxygen supply externally to the gills and improving oxygen delivery by the circulation.

(f) Hypoxia reduces the levels of GTP in red blood cells of eels. This reduces the allosteric effects of GTP on haemoglobin, directly increasing its oxygen affinity. In addition a reduced number of protons are held in the red blood cell and the intracellular pH rises, causing a left-ward Bohr shift.

Question 7.4

Circulating catecholamines increase oxygen transfer at all levels of the oxygen cascade from environment to tissues as follows: (i) ventilation rate increases, (ii) the diffusive conductance of the gills increases, (iii) cardiac contractility and blood pressure may rise, improving tissue and gill perfusion, (iv) haematocrit increases and red blood cell pH_i is maintained, improving oxygen capacity of the blood. In addition, rates of glycolysis in skeletal muscle are increased, fuelling higher rates of exercise.

Question 7.5

(a) (i) Ion regulation breaks down, resulting in a fall in the blood plasma concentration of Na^+ and Cl^-, and a rise in the concentrations of Ca^{2+} and K^+.

(ii) Consequent gill damage results in the failure of gas exchange. Oxygen levels fall, and carbon dioxide and ammonia accumulate.

(iii) The fish metabolizes anaerobically, and lactic acid accumulates in the blood.

(iv) A combined respiratory (carbon dioxide) and metabolic (lactic acid) acidosis causes plasma pH to fall.

(v) Haematocrit increases.

(vi) Heart rate and blood pressure rise.

(b) The rise in haematocrit increases the apparent viscosity of the blood (the resistance of capillary beds to the passage of red cells). The increased heart rate and blood pressure, accompanied by tissue hypoxia and acidosis, then lead to death from heart failure.

(c) The increase in haematocrit, heart rate and blood pressure all resemble the physiological responses triggered in fish by increased levels of circulating catecholamines (see Answer to Question 7.4).

Question 7.6

(a) Oxygen uptake in the crayfish was independant of ambient P_{O_2} down to a P_c of 6.7 kPa (i.e. it was regulated). Below this level the oxygen uptake varied in proportion to the reduced P_{O_2} (i.e. it conformed to P_{O_2}).

(b) Progressive hypoxia caused a marked increase in ventilation rate and a bradycardia.

(c) Hyperventilation reduced haemolymph P_{CO_2}, causing a respiratory alkalosis.

(d) The alkalosis during hypoxia increased the oxygen affinity of haemocyanin so that its percentage saturation stayed high, maintaining the oxygen content of the haemolymph in moderately hypoxic water.

(e) In deep hypoxia, oxygen transport failed and the crayfish switched to anaerobic metabolism, accumulating lactic acid.

Question 7.7

When taken from water the lobster is both hypoxic and hypercapnic and accumulates lactic acid. However, it mobilizes $CaCO_3$ to buffer the potential acidosis. Calcium and lactate ions increase the oxygen affinity of its haemocyanin, and oxygen transport is sustained. Consequently, so long as it is kept cool and not disturbed it will survive in air during commercial transport over long distances.

Question 8.1

The power output is calculated using Equations 1 and 2 in Section 8.2.1.

$$\text{Work done} = \text{force} \times \text{distance} = \text{mass} \times g \times \text{distance}$$
$$= 66.0 \times g \times 0.40 = 258.98 \text{ joules}$$

$$\text{Power output} = \text{work} \times \text{speed} = 258.98 \times (\tfrac{1}{3}) = 86.33 \text{ watts}$$

Question 8.2

(a) Anaerobic power is measured by asking the subject to run up stairs, and timing them as they pass from the 4th step to the 6th step. This time can be used to calculate power output.

(b) Aerobic power is generally taken to be equivalent to oxygen intake. This can be measured using a subject on a treadmill or a cycle ergometer. When $\dot{V}_{O_2max}$ is reached, the subject is delivering the maximum aerobic power.

(c) The distribution of blood flow during exercise can be measured by using radiolabelled microspheres and assaying the activity level in muscle.

Question 8.3

There is an increase in heart rate (a), cardiac output (b), blood flow to the muscles (c), lipolysis (e), and prolactin secretion (f). There is a decrease in plasma glucose (d), and $\dot{V}_{O_2max}$ (g) is unaffected.

Question 8.4

From Figure 8.10, we can see that the maximum oxygen intake is about 70% of that at sea-level, and from Figure 8.9, that the arterial haemoglobin is not fully saturated. Also, if acclimatization has not occurred, the reduced plasma P_{CO_2} will not yet be fully compensated for, and so the respiratory drive from the central receptors will be depressed. The reduced oxygen delivery to the muscles causes fatigue.

Question 8.5

(a) The immediate human responses to hypoxia at high altitudes are hyperventilation (which develops within a few hours and is sustained) and an increased blood flow, associated with tachycardia, which is transient and costly in energetic terms. Note, however, that cardiac output may not increase due to a reduced stroke volume (probably because hypoxia directly depresses the contractility of the cardiac muscle).

(b) (i) Hyperventilation. Increased removal of carbon dioxide from the blood elevates blood pH; excess bicarbonate is excreted and thus restores normal H^+ concentration readjustment.

(ii) Hyperventilation, by replacing a higher proportion of the alveolar air with freshly inspired air.

(iii) Hyperventilation. It is now thought that the initial increased ventilation on exposure to high altitude is probably produced by low levels of oxygen in the blood. However, sustained hyperventilation is achieved because the central chemoreceptors develop an increased sensitivity to carbon dioxide, a response that occurs within 15 hours of exposure.

(iv) A right-ward shift of the dissociation curve. As you know already, a decrease in the affinity of haemoglobin for oxygen probably increases unloading of oxygen at the tissues and maintains a high tissue P_{O_2} but at the expense of oxygen loading in the lungs. Note also that the Böhr effect is greater in some native highlanders, which means that for a given reduction in pH at the tissues, the resultant decrease in the affinity of haemoglobin for oxygen is significantly greater than in sea-level residents.

(v) An increase in capillary density, an elevation of tissue myoglobin, and an increase in the numbers of mitochondria.

(vi) An increase in the number of mitochondria and in the activities of key mitochondrial enzymes, which may contribute towards an elevation of the aerobic capacity of high-altitude animals.

Question 8.6

Both the native highlander, whose carotid bodies may be enlarged, and the acclimatized mountaineer, would be hyperventilating — though this would be more marked in the mountaineer. Lung capacity is often proportionately greater in the native highlander. Pulmonary diffusive conductance is enhanced only in the native (Section 8.8.4), probably because in such subjects there is an increase in blood pressure in the pulmonary circuit (pulmonary hypertension), which may distend previously unopened capillaries. In both individuals, polycythaemia would be evident and a right-ward shift of the dissociation curve may be apparent, depending on altitude. Some highlanders, such as Sherpas, seem to display a left-ward shift of the dissociation curve, which probably favours survival at extreme altitudes. Capillary density may also be raised in both individuals, though evidence is inconclusive, as is also true of any changes in mitochondrial function.

ACKNOWLEDGEMENTS

The present course team gratefully acknowledges the work of those involved in the chapters who are not also listed as authors in this book.

Grateful acknowledgement is made to the following sources for permission to reproduce material in this book:

Figures

Figures 1.1, 2.11: Adapted from Withers, P. C. (1992) *Comparative Animal Physiology*, Copyright © 1992 by Saunders College Publishing, reproduced by permission of the publisher; *Figure 1.4*: William, S. von Arx (1962) *An Introduction To Physical Oceanography*, pp. 119, 126 and 131, © 1962 by Addison-Wesley Publishing Company, Inc. Reprinted by permission of the publisher; *Figure 1.5*: Fowler, P. A. (1988) Thermoregulation in the female hedgehog, *Journal of Reproduction and Fertility*, **82**, pp. 285–292; *Figure 1.11*: Eckert, R., Randall, D. and Augustine, G. (1988) *Animal Physiology*, Copyright © 1988 by W. H. Freeman and Co. Reprinted with permission; *Figure 1.12*: Louw, G. N. (1993) *Physiological Ecology*, Longman Group UK Ltd; *Figure 2.2*: Hull, D. and Smales, O. R. C. (1978) *Temperature Regulation and Energy Metabolism in the Newborn*, Grune & Stratton Inc.; *Figure 2.16*: Rieck A. F. *et al.* (1960) Oxygen consumption of whole animal and tissues in acclimated amphibians, *Proceedings of the Society of Experimental Biology and Medicine*, **103**, Company of Biologists Ltd; *Figure 2.17*: Huey, R. B. (1974) Behavioural thermoregulation in lizards, *Science*, **184**, pp. 1001–1003, © American Association for the Advancement of Science; *Figure 2.18*: Reprinted from Himms-Hagen, J. (1970) *Advances in Enzyme Regulation*, Copyright © 1970, pp. 131–151, with kind permission from Elsevier Science Ltd, The Boulevard, Langford Lane, Kidlington, OX5 1GB, UK; *Figure 2.19*: Reprinted from Bartholemew, G. A. and Lasifioski, R. C. (1965) *Comparative Biochemistry and Physiology*, Copyright © 1965, pp. 573–582, with kind permission from Elsevier Science Ltd, The Boulevard, Langford Lane, Kidlington, OX5 1GB, UK; *Figures 3.2, 3.19*: Based on Folk, G. E. (1974) *Textbook of Environmental Physiology* (2nd edn), Lea and Febiger; *Figure 3.3*: Heldmaier, G. (1971) Zitterfreie warmebildung und Korpergrosse bei Saugetieren, *Zeitschrift fur Vergleichende Physiologie*, **73**, Springer-Verlag GmbH & Co KG; *Figures 3.4, 3.5*: Scholander, Walters, Hock, Johnson and Irving (1950) Body insulation of some arctic and tropical mammals and birds, *Biological Bulletin*; *Figures 3.6, 3.20*: Dill, P. B. and Irving, L. (1964) *Handbook of Physiology*, American Physiological Society; *Figures 3.7, 3.10*: Richards, S. A. (1973) *Temperature Regulation*, Wykeham Science Series, Taylor & Francis; *Figure 3.8*: Ingram, D. L. and Mount, L. E. (1975) *Man and Animals in Hot Environments*, Springer-Verlag GmbH & Co KG; *Figure 3.11*: Reprinted with permission, Ingram, D. C. (1965) Evaporative cooling in the pig, *Nature*, **207**, p. 416, Copyright © 1965, Macmillan Magazines Ltd; *Figures 3.13, 3.15*: Taylor, C. R. (1977) Exercise and environmental heat loads, *International Review of Physiology: Environmental Physiology II*, **15**, University Park Press; *Figure 3.14*: Hales, J. R. S. (1967) The partition of respiratory ventilation of the panting ox, *Journal of Physiology*, **188**, The Physiological Society; *Figure 3.16*: Menaum, B. and Richards, S. A. (1975) Observation on the sites of respiratory evaporation in the fowl during thermal panting, *Respiratory Physiology*, **25**, Elsevier Biomedical Press; *Figure 4.1*: Abrams, R. M. (1974) Energy exchange in utero, in Moghissi, K. S. and Harfez, E. S. (eds) *The Placenta: Biological and Chemical Aspects*, Charles C. Thomas; *Figure 4.12*: Edson, J. L., Hull, D. and Elphick, M. C. (1981) The development of cold-induced thermogenesis in hamsters, *Journal of Developmental Physiology*, **3**, Oxford University Press; *Figure 4.13*: Lean, M. E. J. (1989) Brown adipose tissue in humans, *Proceedings of the Nutrition Society*, **48**, p. 247; *Figures 4.14–4.18*: Bukowieka *et al.* (1982) Brown adipose tissue hyperplasia, *American Journal of Physiology*, **242**, The American Physiological Society; *Figure 4.23*: Hull, D. (1965) Oxygen consumption and body temperature, *Journal of Physiology*, **177**, The Physiological Society; *Figure 4.24*: Reprinted with permission, Perkins, M. N. (1981) *Nature*, **289**, pp. 401–402, Copyright © 1981 Macmillan Magazines Ltd; *Figure 4.28*: Kurosawa, M. (1991) *Journal of the Autonomic Nervous System*, **33**, Elsevier Science Publishers BV; *Figure 5.13*: Dill, P. B. and Irving, L. (1964) *Handbook of Physiology*, The American Physiological Society; *Figures 6.4, 6.8*: Strumwasser, F. (1960) Some physiological principles governing hibernation, *Bulletin of the Museum of Comparative Zoology*, **124**, Harvard University; *Figures 6.5, 6.13*: Lyman, C. P. and O'Brien, R. C. (1960) Circulatory changes in the thirteen-lined ground squirrel during the hibernating cycle, *Bulletin of the Museum of Comparative Zoology*, **124**, Harvard University; *Figure 6.9*: Musacchia, X. J. and Volkert, W. A. (1971) *American Journal of Physiology*, **221**, The American Physiological Society; *Figure 6.10a*: Fisher, K. (1964) *Annals of the Academy of Sciences of Finland, Series A, IV*; *Figure 6.11*: Lyman, C. P. (1948) The oxygen consumption and temperature regulation of hibernating hamsters, *Journal of Experimental Zoology*, **109**, Wiley; *Figure 6.14*: Hayward, J. and Lyman, C. P. (1967) in Fisher, K. *et al.* (eds) *Mammalian Hibernation III*, Oliver and Boyd; *Figure 6.16*: Reprinted from Heller, H. C. and Hammer, H. (1972) *Comparative Biochemistry and Physiology*, Copyright 1972, with kind permission from Elsevier Science Ltd, The Boulevard, Langford Lane, Kidlington, OX5 1GB, UK; *Figure 6.20*: Heller, H. C. and Colliver, G. W. (1974) *American Journal of Physiology*, **227**, The American Physiological Society; *Figure 6.22*: Heller, H. C. (1977) *Pflugers Archiv*, **369**, Springer-Verlag GmbH & Co KG; *Figure 7.1*: Heath, D. and Williams, D. R. (1981) *Man At High Altitude*, Churchill Livingstone; *Figure 7.4*: Scholander, P. F. (1940) Experimental investigations on the respiratory function in diving mammals and birds, *Hvalradets Skrifter* No. 22, Det Norske Videnskaps Akademi; *Figure 7.5*: Butler, P. J. and Jones, D. R. (1982) The comparative physiology of diving in vertebrates, *Advances in Comparative Physiology and Biochemistry*, **8**, Academic Press Inc.; *Figure 7.6*: Butler, P. J. and Woakes, A. J. (1982) Telemetry of physiological variables from diving and flying birds, *Symposium of the Zoological Society, London*, No. 49, The Zoological Society of London; *Figure 7.7*: Butler, P. J. and Woakes, A. J. (1976) Changes in heart rate and respiratory frequency with natural submersion in ducks, *Journal of Physiology*, **256**, The Physiological Society; *Figure 7.9*: Truchot, J. P. and Duhamel-Jouve, A. (1980) The marine intertidal environment, *Respiration Physiology*, **39**(1), Elsevier North-Holland; *Figure 7.13*: Reprinted with permission, Wood, S. C. and Johansen, K. (1972) Adaption to hypoxia by increased HbO_2 affinity and decreased red cell ATP concentration, *Nature*, **237**, p. 278, Copyright 1972 Macmillan Magazines Ltd; *Figure 7.19*: Wilson, R. W.

and Taylor, E. W. (1993) The physiological responses of freshwater rainbow trout, *Oncorhynchus mykiss*, during acutely lethal copper exposure, *Journal of Comparative Physiology B*, **163**, pp. 38–47, figures 7 and 8 courtesy of Dr Rod Wilson; *Figure 8.3*: Shepherd, R. J. (1987) *Exercise Physiology*, B. C. Decker; *Figure 8.4*: Cerretelli, P. *et al.* (1979) *Journal of Applied Physiology*, **47**(4), American Physiological Society; *Figure 8.5*: Selkurt, E. E. (1984) *Physiology*, 5th edn. This copy has been produced by permission of Little Brown & Company (Inc.), further reproduction from this copy is prohibited; *Figure 8.8*: Emery, T. M. *et al.* (1983) *Journal of Physiology*, **336**, **343**, The Physiological Society.

Plates

Plates 2.1, 2.2: Courtesy of Dr Peter Davies; *Plate 5.1*: Courtesy of Dr Caroline M. Pond; *Plates 5.2, 5.3*: Courtesy of Dr Alison Ames; *Plate 6.1*: Courtesy of Frank Lane Picture Agency Ltd / S. Maslowski; *Plate 6.2*: Courtesy of Frank Lane Picture Agency Ltd / Dembinsky; *Plate 6.3*: Courtesy of Frank Lane Picture Agency Ltd / Mark Newman; *Plate 6.4*: Courtesy of J. Dunning/Vireo; *Plate 6.5*: Courtesy of C. H. Greenewalt/Vireo.

INDEX